LONELY MEN CLUB

Mike Kleine is the author of *Mastodon Farm*; *Arafat Mountain*; *Kanley Stubrick*; and *The Mystery of the Seventeen Pilot Fish*, a play. He lives in the American Midwest.

95!

An Inside the Castle Book. May 2018

ISBN-13: 978-0999345948
First Edition

This is a work of fiction. All of the characters and organizations portrayed herein are products of the author's imagination or are used fictitiously.

Book design by Mike Kleine

All imagery from Kalev Leetaru Internet Archive

Printed in the United States of America

Lonely Men Club

Lonely Men Club
Lonely Men Club
Lonely Men Club
Lonely Men Club
Lonely Men Club
Lonely Men Club
Lonely Men Club
Lonely Men Club
Lonely Men Club

For Mario Macías

A Note on the Text

The following was "written" in five days, as part of the 2017 Castle Freak Residency.

A Note on the Type

The text of this book was set in Essays1743, a typeface designed by John Stracke, a software architect & member of the SCA (the Society for Creative Anachronism, Inc). The font is based on the style of writing used in a 1743 English translation of Michel de Montaigne's *Essays*. Montaigne famously wrote, "Man is certainly stark mad; he cannot make a worm, and yet he will be making gods by dozens." It must be said, Montaigne was anti-colonisation.

listen: there's a hell
of a good universe next door;
let's go

—e.e. cummings,
pity this busy monster,
manunkind

A rose is a rose is a rose is a rose.

—Getrude Stein,
Sacred Emily

Lonely Men Clu b

Lonely M en Club

on ly Men Club

Lone ly Men Club

Lonely Men Club

Lonely Men Club

onely Men Club

Lonely Men Club

b

Lonely Men C ub

Lo ely Men Club

Lonely Men Club

Men

Lon y Men Club

Lon ely M n Club

Lonely Men Club

Lonely Men Club

Lonely Men Club

Lo nely Men Club

Lonely lub

Lo en Cl b

Lon en Club

L onely Men Club

ely Men C ub

Lonely Men Club

L onelyM n Club

Art by Subtraction: Eat, Consume & Devour

by Mike Kleine

Lonely Men Club was written in five days. I used a combination of Microsoft Word, Microsoft Publisher, Notepad, Notepad + +, my local library, Propellerheads Reason Essentials 10, Twitter, iTunes, Google Chrome and Twine. I took three days off work, made sure it ran into the weekend, and pretty much slept on the couch (right next to the computer) for most of those five days. The sleeping part felt burdensome, as I'd wake up and pick up exactly from where I'd left off, almost like I was doing what I was doing only because I had to. And in a way, I did. I only slept because my body was telling me to sleep. And there'd be instances where I would stand there and literally stare at the screen for maybe seven or eight minutes, doing nothing (I was wearing BluBlocker spectacles tho, so it was chill). I tried to break up the monotony of it all by periodically posting updates via Twitter (but even that only went so far). I'd watch YouTube videos and sing songs I thought I knew. I wrote and recorded nine guitar tracks. And with all of this, I never shut off my computer, so, naturally, everything eventually crashed, like three times. (I think I almost cried two of those times). But all of it was pretty humbling—the entire experience. I love writing. Like, I am obsessed with writing. I like to think about writing pretty much every single day. I am so into writing that sometimes, I'll write down words onto a piece of paper and throw everything away just so I can say I satisfied my urge to write. No, that's not true. It's more like, the way I work, I'll be watching a movie or listening to a song or writing down notes, and then *something* will compel me to write. It'll be the purple sky in the film *Miami Vice* by Michæl Mann. Or it'll be the cheesy orchestral arrangements and MIDI presets on the album, *Your Blues* by Destroyer. Really, I write only because the world forces me to write.

Every single book I have ever written explores a specific concept, and I try and tell a story *with* that concept. For example, *Mastodon Farm*, my first book, it's about celebrity culture. *Arafat Mountain* is about the numinous. *Kanley Stubrick* is about love and the concept of identity. I understand (and have also come to accept) that I will never fully comprehend everything. This is, for me, the first step toward achieving some modicum of *understanding* or, at the very least, acceptance of my / our fate (as humans). I will never be able to complete all of my research. Everything will forever remain unfinished. I am not going to live forever. Twenty-four hours in the day is just not enough time to do anything and everything. All of these realizations, together, force me to complete as many projects as I am able to complete in this lifetime. If reincarnation is real (and I am able to come back as a human and am able / allowed to write again) great! If not? Great, also! Because I know I am going to (eventually) die, I write so that—after everything's been said and done—I can at least leave behind *something* that asks questions.

Lonely Men Club is about Zodiac Killer, who in the book, is a supernatural entity. Essentially, for me to be able to understand Zodiac fully (or as much as I am able to), I had to turn him / (her)(?) into an outsider / itinerant entity. In the book, Zodiac exists within the confines of our (forever) shape-shifting universe, as a temporarily trapped(?) figure, until they are able to depart from this realm & conquer / acquire another (his / her true) / final(?) form. Furthermore, *Lonely Men Club* adheres to a four-dimensionalist / eternal interpretation of time. I truly believe there are cosmic forces at play in this story and do not want to *dumb* anything down for the sake of comprehension or relative understanding. The entire text is supposed to function as hyperbole. This is a celebration of the banality & absurdity of everyday life, coupled with sinister & dark overtones, all throughout the text. But also, it's about pataphysics.

The story takes place in the same universe as my other texts, all of them. Everything I write takes place in the same universe. I am unable to leave the world (or worlds) I have created. It is important to note: the universe in my texts is very similar to our own, though there are key differences. There is, for instance, an alternate geography. Baltimore and Tokyo are not *that* far apart from each other on a map (and this is evidenced in my first book, *Mastodon Farm*). There are many gods that exist and people pray to them, asking for different *things*. Immortality is also a very real thing. Godzilla is (and has become) a(n accepted) threat that is always happening. Sometimes, a character will look up into the sky and see words. Thing is, a lot of these realities are implied. I am not interested in *world building*. When I write, in this universe, everything that *happens* happens because it's always happened and will continue to happen—nobody questions any of it. Everything is *in media res*. Like many other things in our own universe. The air we breathe, the fact that something like lightning exists, volcanos exploding, oceans burning— Something is always happening at the same time as something else. Time is a fairly complex concept. And we take all of this for granted because that's just the way things are. Zodiac may run into a character from *Mastodon Farm*. They may visit a location that was only briefly discussed in *Arafat Mountain*. They may also interact with characters from a book I haven't written yet! And all of this abides to William James' theory of a pluralistic universe.

Writing about the Zodiac Killer is not a new idea for me either. My first foray was in 2010. I wrote a short story featuring the Zodiac Killer for a workshop but changed the name to Captain Nero. I did this because I was afraid people would react negatively to a character like the Zodiac Killer. In the story, Zodiac travels through time and kills people. The time travel aspect is supposed to explain why Zodiac has never been caught, like, in real life. And Zodiac never time travelled to the past or the present, rather, they travelled to parallel timelines, committing the same or similar acts of murder, but in different ways, for their own amusement. The character of the Zodiac Killer also appears in my 2014 text, *Arafat Mountain*, doing the same thing. I am after spiritual truths and obfuscated memories. If you (as the reader) have surface-knowledge of Zodiac's mythos, that essentially provides an extra layer / depth to *Lonely Men Club* (but at the same time if you don't, that's fine, also).

Lonely Men Club comes from the Lawrence English record, *Lonely Women's Club*. I have never listened to the record. I am super critical about my book titles and don't want to say any author ever uses a throwaway title, but it is very important to me that I love a title to death. Originally, my plan had been to come up with a title using only two words. The words would be randomly generated during the five-day composition period-- I quickly realized I am way too OCD to leave the title of my next book up to chance. I was going to call the book *Zodiac! Zodiac! Zodiac!* at one point (and this title has its own set of merits) but I thought it was too in-your-face and not *flowery* enough. Instead, I spent a lot of time making sure the generative aspect of the text was actually, um-- generative. So—enter Twine.

Twine is an "open-source tool for telling interactive, nonlinear stories." Most people use

Twine to write Interactive Fiction (also known as IF). I used the program to write *Lonely Men Club*. In Twine, you will normally write a sequence and provide the reader with a few options (ie: open door, turn left, etc.). So pretty much, it's great for creating *Choose Your Own Adventure*-style works. In working with Twine, I discovered another function—one that not too many people talk about (or even use, it seems). Twine has the ability to pick values at random. This means a sentence that is made up of several words or concepts or ideas, can then immediately be transformed into something else, every single time it is generated. The more values you plug in, the more the text morphs and develops into something completely new and different! All I get to set are the parameters. Everything else is up in the air. This aspect of *Lonely Men Club* is what intrigued me the most. There is literally no way for me to predict how the sequence of vignettes would unfold; and that was part of the mystique. The novel as a whole is an experience. There is some type of narrative inside the text, naturally, but it's deep within. The narrative itself is the generative part. Think about this…

As I experimented with different permutations, I researched generative literature and became inspired by different texts, namely: Nick Montfort's *World Clock*, Harry Mathews' *Singular Pleasures*, Roberto Bolaño's *Antwerp* and even Robert Pinget's *Fable*. (NB: Not all of these texts are generative). (There's also the OuLiPo movement and Les Éditions de Minuit that I enjoy very much, so *Lonely Men Club* is informed by all of that as well). With *Lonely Men Club*, I wanted to create a work that extended beyond the limited physicality of the novel. I wanted to move past barriers and present an object the reader could begin reading from any page. To generate my text, I made sure that with any particular set of variables, a number of different scenarios could play out. This was done for several reasons.

In creating the code for *Lonely Men Club*, I wanted to plant *seeds* or *ideas* into the brain of *my* version of the Zodiac Killer. I wanted to think of the character as this primitive AI I'd created that was telling me all of its inner thoughts, one after the other. And then my job, of course, was to scramble and write down as much of it as possible, while at the same time respecting and embracing any and all imperfections. There is so much world building happening on the back-end of *Lonely Men Club* that it truly became its own eco-system—which I am only slightly responsible for. There is a certain repetition of words, a repetition that embraces the Jamesian theory of transformational meaning. Essentially, you repeat a word or words enough times, and the meaning or meanings cease to have meaning and become something entirely different. Something that sounds like it doesn't make sense suddenly makes sense. And likewise, a phrase or concept that seems to make sense—repeat it enough times, and it just becomes words that lose their meaning.

Gertrude Stein once said about her writing, "I took individual words and thought about them until I got their weight and volume complete and put them next to another word." No word is wasted in *Lonely Men Club*. Due to the generative quality of the text, certain moments may, at first glance, appear to follow the same rhythm or pattern or cadence as a previous moment (which very well may be the case) but I urge that you, as reader, discard *trained* interpretation of text and instead relish in the actual sequence of words. The text is meant to be reflexive. Art by subtraction. *Eat*, *Consume* and *Devour*; all three allude to something similar but each does not mean the same thing. Much of the writing style in *Lonely Men Club* is influenced by e e cummings and Etel Adnan. There's also a bit of Susan Howe & Anne Carson.

The creation of brand new words and on-purpose misspellings is something I have been doing since *Arafat Mountain*. I particularly enjoy how when two (or sometimes even three) seemingly unrelated words are joined together, they create a new synthesis. In *Lonely Men Club*, all of this is amplified to the *n*th level. I have to applaud the texts of e e cummings, Pierre Abidi and Susan Howe for informing some of how *Lonely Men Club* was written. Helmut Schmid & Mira Schendel also. Guillaume Apollinaire, I guess, is the godfather of all of this visual poetry stuff too, but I am not really a big fan of his actual poems. Something that is maybe interesting: while reading *Lonely Men Club*, you'll notice the font size changing, a lot. This, I wish I could say was done on purpose (or for a reason). The simple truth is, it was my first time using Microsoft Publisher, I did not 100% know what I was doing. Anytime I copy and pasted a block of generated text (from Microsoft Word to Microsoft Publisher), depending on the number of words I was pasting, the entire section would automatically resize and decide a font size for me. Since then, I have learned how I could have controlled this.

Lonely Men Club, for me, probably has been the hardest text to *write*. (Before this, it was *Arafat Mountain*). I am the type of writer who likes to spend a lot of time on whatever it is I am creating (don't we all?). I also like to cut a lot from my work. I could write an entire text in under a month, but then spend the next two years editing and editing and editing (essentially forever). With this project, the challenge was one of speed and endurance. I had to not only write an entire book in five days, but also make sure the text was 100,000 words. Most of my books, the first drafts, are generally longer than the final works. I tend to overwrite and spend the following months (or year (s)) cutting the excess (as I mentioned previously). I like to ask questions in my books. I feel like I have failed, maybe, if, after reading one of my books, you can walk away saying, "Yeah, no—I totally got all of that. Everything absolutely made sense. I have zero questions."

I was originally going to separate the text by year. Beginning in 1968 and then ending in 2018, but I realized this wasn't really serving any real purpose. I did this, originally so the text could, in essence, become more digestible. Again, I have now realized this was an unnecessary restriction, as I was effectively moving away from a true four-dimensionalist interpretation of time. I also wanted the entire text, for each section, to just be one giant wall of text (not justified either). I realized I didn't like this æsthetic and opted, instead, for a layout not too different from what you'll find in a David Markson text. I truly want the text to be something you can pick up and begin reading on any page (think *Hopscotch* by Julio Cortázar or even *World Clock* by Nick Montfort). I am also a big fan of Edouard Levé and find his work, *Autoportrait* to be riveting. In a sense, *Lonely Men Club* attempts to tap into the same sort of mind-state as *Autoportrait*.

In *Arafat Mountain*, the vignette format is loosely based off Bolaño and Markson. I mined from Bolaño in the sense that each page was restricted to the single paragraph format. No separations. And I enjoyed this way of working, as the restriction allowed for an interesting approach to storytelling. As part of the writing process, I always spend a great deal of time researching the way text looks on a page. I compare things like regular and justified text. I compare books of prose to books of poetry. I speak with editors, copy editors, authors, typesetters and typographers. I read essays on the æsthetics of text and fonts and typography. I gather all of my favourite books (as-in, the books I enjoy looking at the most) and think about what I like about these books. I sit and think about these things for a long time. I read interviews of poets and novelists and visual artists to try and gain some insight to their process. I always want to do something that is not just going to be *standard*. I want to become as involved as I can with how the book is going to look on the inside. For *Lonely Men Club*, it was my intention, after the five days, to deliver a book that was ready to print, and that I would not be able to change; so all of this—writing *Lonely Men Club*—has been different for me.

There are moments within the text where

Zodiac tries on clothes (and here's the thing, what may seem mundane is actually made fantastical). High fashion in my texts tends to blur the line between what a man may (or is allowed to) wear and what a woman should be wearing. Right now, we live in a time where this still (sort of) matters. 20,000 years from now, nobody will care about this distinction. Ideally (and arguably) I could say that true high fashion, you know, *haute couture*, does not have a specific gender. Whether it is in the fabrics or textures or different types of cuts, true high fashion does not belong to the pleb—average person—which is why it is *high*. High fashion is utopian in that sense, though I hate to use that term, *utopian*. Zodiac, here, pretty early on, is established as a sort of quasi-deity and exalted to a level that is different than most. I thought: a character wearing a combination of both men and womenswear would be indicative of the sort of transmutation occurring internally throughout the entire text, but then, at that point, expressed externally. I focus on the fashion here because the fashion, in *Lonely Men Club*, isn't really about the *fashion*.

Lonely Men Club is hard to read, I would imagine. And I mean this both figuratively and literally. Some of the text is so small it is nigh impossible to read. The format of the book, how everything is laid out and how the text looks on the page, is representative of and inspired by Zodiac's ciphers. At the same time, the mystery of the Zodiac is still a mystery. *Lonely Men Club* is erasure / smudge poetry with elements of collage / concrete poetry. I did not have much control over this, as much of it came as a result of process. The text itself is made up of a series of *moments*. These moments are prompts I have created that sort of self-replicate. And with this, copycat sentences are something I feared might happen, initially, but I spent a great deal of time setting several parameters to ensure, to the best of my ability, that copycat sentences would not occur. Sentences should not be nonsensical either (tho I do adopt the style of e e cummings where certain words are paired with a descriptor to create a completely new word; this is by choice). Above all, every sentence is a thought experiment, meant to inform and guide the story's primary timeline (where there are also other timelines). The idea that *all of this* has already happened before, Zodiac knows and *exploits* in the novel. Also, the notion that the past, present and future are all happening at the same time opens doors to a new way of storytelling I hope I am able to somewhat completely harness and use to the text's advantage. More than anything else, the beauty of this project is that I have already gone through a dozen potential scenarios and paths and each has helped shape *Lonely Men Club* into the final text. You think something is going to work extremely well and then realize it's one of those ideas that sounded so much better on paper than in execution. It's sometimes frustrating but also, no moment is ever wasted.

I cannot say there is a certain type of reader who will understand *Lonely Men Club* (or any of my other texts), more than another. I do recognize that on my part, I am asking that each reader put forth a bit of effort when reading my texts. For instance, E.G. Cunningham (in a 3:AM MAGAZINE review / dialogue she wrote on

Kanley Stubrick) suggested, "There is an element of erasure --of history, geography, selfhood, and language," in my texts. It's the research. The behind-the-scenes stuff. All of this information manifests itself in my writings (whether I want to or not), just as much as one person's life experience (s) can inform another's.

But what is the book? What is text? What are words on a page? What does arrangement and placement on a page do to story and narrative? What even *is* narrative? What does the physicality of text equal in the real world? I urge that you ask all of these questions not only while (or after you've read) *Lonely Men Club* but moving forward, with any other sort of text. I want to raise awareness about the potentiality of the book. I want us to think differently about what it means to experience the book as *physical object*. I want us to wonder why we have books in our homes. A thing that takes up space, real estate. It's just tree stuff pulled & bound together and then inked, right? How much can something that is so simple, affect? Inside the Castle is unique in the sense that how it views the book, like, the physicality of it, should not be seen as a method of escapism or an object whose sole purpose is to tell a story. The book is a physical object that was created using different types of energy and the experience of touching and smelling and reading the physical book is not only different from reading a Kindle or PDF but there's also an energy transfer that occurs. Allowing the physical object of the book to breathe is perfect for a project like *Lonely Men Club*. I did everything I could to try and make *Lonely Men Club* as palatable as possible.

And *Lonely Men Club* is an elliptical text, not meant to be read as a diary or log of Zodiac's daily goings-on. At the same time, I never set out to write a traditional narrative. In fact, it may take a while before *Lonely Men Club* becomes a pleasurable reading experience (and I put an emphasis on pleasurable since I could write an entire dissertation on the definition of pleasurable, alone). There is a chance, even, I must admit, that you, as reader, will see or find no merit in the text. And that is fine. It is your right. At the same time, if by some manner, one is able to prove that *Lonely Men Club* truly has no merit, I can still be fine with this. I say all of this since *Lonely Men Club* exists to challenge the very notion of the book. I, of course, also ask for some suspension of disbelief. The text is going to be a challenge for the reader seeking *all* answers. *Lonely Men Club* can be read in any order and can begin on any page (and can also end on any page). The text is made up of vignettes that paint the image of the shadow of a story / narrative. One word might mean one thing but then, when placed next to another word, might mean something completely different. Each word in a sentence is as important as the sentence itself, the rest of that page, the entire book. The line breaks in between sentences are themselves sentences.

There are sections discussing the type of tea Zodiac is drinking. There's other sections describing the colour of the sky for that particular evening in October (in Wyoming, or wherever else—all of this is generative). Zodiac will eat a particular type of fish. They will pray about a specific thing to a specific god. They will complain about something that is bothering them. Pretty much, the entirety of *Lonely Men Club* is presented in a manner that is not unlike the works of Kenneth Goldsmith or David Markson, in the sense that the text that is put onto paper is done in a manner that is absolutely exhaustive. All of Zodiac's actions and thoughts are chronicled. Nothing is left out or forgotten. The form and process of *Lonely Men Club* is the actual story. The weight of importance is equally distributed, as *Lonely Men Club* aims to fully explore, embrace & then break down the limits of language.

These days, we have e-books and audio books and physical texts. Process is just as important as the end result. Mostly though, you will find that process is abandoned or forgotten once result has been achieved. *Lonely Men Club* is 99% process and 1% result. What you are reading right now—call it an introduction or essay; whatever—it's just as important as the book itself. It is an extension. I expect *Lonely Men Club* to be mistaken for poetry. Some may even believe it is a work of nonfiction or—much like the works of literature I admire most and continue to study—deemed unclassifiable. I want the reader to be in a trance; hypnotized. Simply put, history repeats itself, over and over and over again. Nothing is new. Everything is old. Everything we think is new has already happened once before. *Lonely Men Club* is all about that. It embraces this ideal—this concept. And in the end, I can only hope a conversation naturally forms and continues to exist, long after the *experience* of *Lonely Men Club* is complete.

The 2,083-Word Foreword

by Ken Sparling

In every exciting, adventurous read, there is an element of danger. That is what makes the reading exciting. The writer sets himself up for a big fall, ideally over and over again, and then somehow, goes to the brink without falling. Or he falls, but without killing himself. Or something like that. I read Michael's essay, *Art by Subtraction: Eat, Consume & Devour*, before I read the book. And based on what I read, I didn't expect the book to be so visual. I engaged the text by, at first, misreading and then rewriting. Some variations seemed more successful than others, though, ultimately, I'm not sure by what measure. Thinking about it now, I'd say Michael's essay is almost backwards to the book. It feels like Michael is falling off the world and grabbing at the bits of debris tumbling about, all around him. And the debris is coming from what he's done to the world with his book.

Lonely Men Club is a firm position within the world. A place to stand and look. Yet, the book goes nowhere. It is not a journey of any sort. You aren't falling off the world as you read the book. You aren't moving at all. You are standing perfectly still, as everything else falls silently away. The falling away of the world that happens through a gathering of words, like the gathering in this book, is silent. The noise of the words clamouring together is a kind of reinforcement of the silence already residing in the quiet of your head. It can seem very noisy in your head. But that noise is based in a deep pool of silence you sit within as you read a book.

Lonely Men Club is the equivalent of a guy who goes around everywhere carrying a little notebook with him, detailing very specific moments that repeat themselves. Months might pass between entries in the notebook. Or days. Or minutes. Or even seconds. He farts. He cuts his toenails. He rides a bus somewhere and does something. He kills someone. He takes drugs. What if life is just that? These random moments you notice. And what if it's only the moments that repeat themselves? What if you wake up to life only when you go to the can or pass gas? Or when you groom your facial hair? What if killing someone was the same as trimming your moustache?

Here, every sentence is a first line. Or a second line. There's no narrative thread, really, but it holds together like it's got superglue between the sentences. So what though? How do you talk about that? Is it an intention—or an approach? One thing: I believe Michael is tenacious about his approach. What I like best about this book isn't so much the total lack of narrative line, but those moments when the narrative line veers in an unexpected direction. Some pages absolutely look like concrete poetry. At one point, a giant period wreaks havoc in the middle of a page. There's even a legless creature from the Black Lagoon who shows up more than once (and I remember this creature from *Mastodon Farm*, Michael's first book)! In *Lonely Men Club*, I think the danger resides in randomness. Michael uses made-up words, like "miniscule *death*jungles" and "*castrated*Wednesday." There's a cultivated randomness that is constantly in danger of becoming too purposefully random. Random for the sake of being random. There are places where an idea repeats itself and I feel afraid because I think the project might ultimately fail—which is part of the excitement. There is a purpose to all this randomness! Though I'd be hard-pressed to say what that purpose is. Maybe it's just purposeful and it doesn't matter what the purpose is.

In the essay, Michael claims that the importance of what he's doing lies in the way he challenges conventional ideas— about books, language, story, narrative— and it's true, but not in the way I believed after I read the essay. He challenges by debunking, and by debunking, I mean, pulling the rug out from under. So, a simple sentence like: "I watched a documentary on the television and learned things I did not know," seems almost too childlike to be admitted to an adult novel. But by not saying enough, it says everything! By not particularizing the experience of learning what you don't know, by not saying what it is you learned—Michael leaves the potential of the sentence unblemished. It remains alive to itself as a question.

There's something, some strain, some undercurrent that seems very serious in Michael's work, so when things lighten up, it's like this gift: "Went to the bathroom for two minutes. Passed gas. Had a different dream. This one actually bothered me the most." It isn't that the content is lighter. The weight or lack of weight in a piece of writing sits in the structure. The way "actually" meets "bothered" and how they both lead into "the most." The most is a lot of something, as much of something as possible. In the 70s, the "most" was the "greatest," the "mindblowingest." Here in Michael's hands, "the most" is like a dribble. It's irritation— the greatest concentration of irritation possible, which if you think about it is a strange thing, because when irritation becomes heavily concentrated, you expect it to turn into something much more sinister— when "bother" gets as big as it can get, you expect it to morph into something devastating. But here, somehow, "irritation" remains nothing but a "bother" even at its most potent. If anything, I like the brevity of each sentence.

Another example, on page 64, there's a "b" falling from a paragraph. This made me laugh. It's hard to do a joke with the letters of a paragraph. Partly, I laughed because it seems such an obvious ploy, yet I'd never seen it done before. The "b" looked like it hadn't realized it could fall like that. And of course, it couldn't fall like that until just this moment when I scrolled onto the page where it was falling and saw it falling. That's what made it such a good joke.

Michael points out, in the essay, that some of the text is printed so small you can't even read it. But in a PDF, you can zoom in! I half-expected the text to blur when I tried to blow it up, but it didn't. I even zoomed in as far as I could. For a bit of intrigue and suspense, the words actually *did* blur momentarily, when I zoomed in, but then they cleared right up. The experience of outwitting the illegibility of the text was an experience that had great meaning. This is why, as Michael explains in his essay, he spends so much time (all the time) sitting silently, thinking about what he wants his books to look like.

I navigated the different sections, zooming in on small text, analyzing black puddles of ink and wondering about the relationship of the images to the words—looking for patterns. But maybe the black puddles were just words, and nothing else? Words so thickly clustered that there was no visible white space between them? Maybe it said something in there that I just couldn't read? That I wasn't supposed to read? Language is a pattern, which is why I kept looking for patterns in all the non-language parts of the book. Perhaps—maybe reading is an act that traps you in a mindset that is destined to automatically seeks out patterns? Maybe we would be freer, as humans, to see the world for the patternless place it is, if we didn't spend so much time reading. *Lonely Men Club* is a text that makes you feel inordinately happy but also dumb at the same time. Dumb in the sense that I felt both relaxed but also happy, at the same time. It's easier to be dumb than it is to be smart. I feel like, no matter how inherently smart you are, you have to work hard to be smart. Like, no matter how smart you are already, smart is a destination that you have to work toward-- and it seems to remain a destination, so that no matter how smart you prove yourself to be, you are never at your destination because you can only be smart relative to some other position, some other level of smartness / notsmartness. Whereas dumb seems to be a place where you just are in a given moment. And you could conceivably be there all your life without even trying at all.

I have a theory, but I have no desire to convince you that this theory is right. It's a theory for me, same as for you-- I have a brief theory that this book purposefully descends into nonsense (and I mean relative to what it starts out as). This comes, I guess, from the knowledge—knowing I'm going to deteriorate and die, and applying it to the text, somehow. Fantasy is worlds where you deteriorate and live. Reality fiction is where you deteriorate and die. Apocalyptic fiction is where you don't get a chance to deteriorate because you just get killed by some impossibly awful occurrence of nature or of man. What is utopian fiction? Dystopian fiction? All I want to do is delay the arrival of the moment when we say—to use some of Michael's words from his essay: "I have zero questions." The "big" message in *Lonely Men Club* could be something like: "Pay attention!" It is only in paying attention that you can begin to notice the small differences in the way your life unfolds each day.

Or it could be something like this: as you read the same thing over and over again, or almost the same thing, the meaning disappears, the letters fall away from their tethers. We resist this mightily, because when everything falls apart, it's scary. Zen dudes would tell you that it's only scary if you believe there were any connections in the first place. But we seem to need to pretend there are connections in order to carry on. So how do you carry on if you are willing to acknowledge that nothing is connected to anything else in any necessary fashion? What doesn't Michael care about and what does this tell us? What does what he doesn't care about say about caring? Why do we get up in the morning and go about doing what it is we are supposed to be doing? This is where my theory comes in. Partially it's a bit of a time warp. But what if it's just that someone is waiting for us—all the time?

What matters isn't what you say or what you make your picture look like. What matters is who you are today and what you concoct together in this womb / tomb you inhabit for a brief moment. What matters in *Lonely Men Club*, is that Michæl stands still and exists. But Michæl, in the essay, seems to be running away from that existence. Some things you read leave you silent at the end. They make you hungry and then they feed you. They give you what you want and leave you sated and silent. That silence could be an emptiness. A void. Or it could be a kind of nullification of sound by the combining of a great cacophony of noise. Like so much content, noise, words, that you just give up. When you give up, you float to the top. When you look down, back into what you've floated out of, you see everything together. Which isn't possible. You see one speck of something that is the same as everything. You see that nothing is everything and everything is nothing. As soon as you approach everything at once, you have nothing. And as soon as you give up and approach nothing, you see that everything is just an approach. It's a way of talking about something that can't be approached, or even broached. *Lonely Men Club* is something you experience more than you read. And to read every word of this book would be a massive project. Reading the essay before I read the book made me want to stop doing anything ever again—which, now, I realize, is the perfect place to be, as you enter *Lonely Men Club*, a text that takes you nowhere for 720 pages.

Lo
M
Clu

nely
n
b.

x

Cinderella on the television, dissecting spacetime violence.

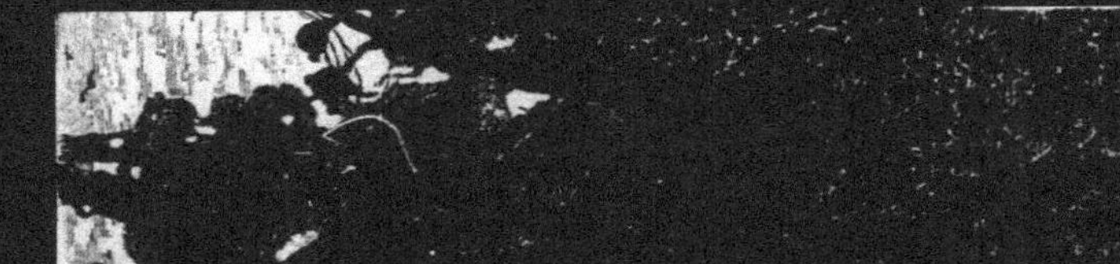

Dreamed of the colour oxbowgreen

Dreamed of the colour oxbowgreen

the colour oxbowchampagne

the colour impossiblebaby powder

a drowning, in

the colour amber

the colour oxbowBangladesh green

Dreamed of the colour oxbowbone

Dreamed of the colour impossibleamber

Dreamed of the colour abstractblue

Dreamed of the colour impotentbone

the earth is trash

the darq caves of paradise

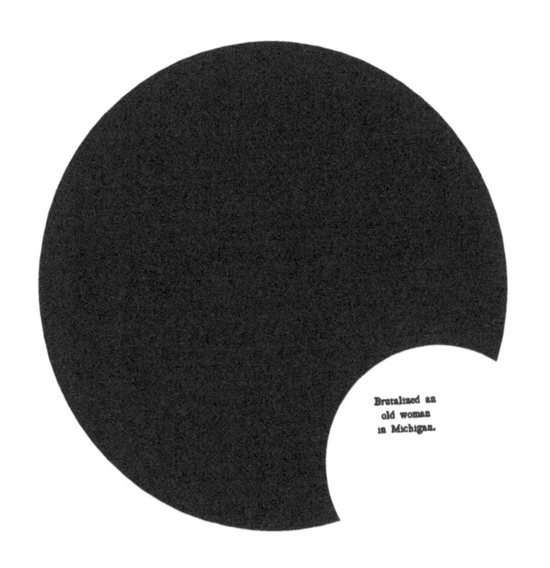
Brutalized an
old woman
in Michigan.

Laughed. The forehead was all
wrong. Walked outside. It was
one of
those cold mornings in March.
It was amazing.

Had
thoughts about going outside on
one of
those *scorching*dust mornings in

September. It was terrible. In a
parallel universe, I feel I might
be a famous actor hiding away
in Oregon. I always go
on vacations that last at
least four weeks.

Had this conversation with
my accountant. Dreamed of
velvet. Coughed into my left
hand.

De temps en temps, je m'habille comme un femme et je me ballade en ville.

Contemplated nothing and drafted a note and dropped it
Took Adderall. Left the country for a bit and traveled
was terrible. Thought about something.

It did nothing for me. nightmar'd about 71

impossible

structures.

Dreamed of the colour *forgotten*absolute
zero. Was late to work. Took a
shot *at* the sun. Enjoyed an entire pack
of Djarum Blacks. Went out with this
woman who was 38. Thought
about sojourning in North Africa.
Fucked this guy from Kentucky.
Listened to an audio book of *Le Renard
et la boussole* by Robert Pinget. Looked
at a used vehicle.

Watched a different episode of *Columbo.*
Observed a sunset in Michigan. The
sun looked all black. It was marvelous.
Experienced these migraines.

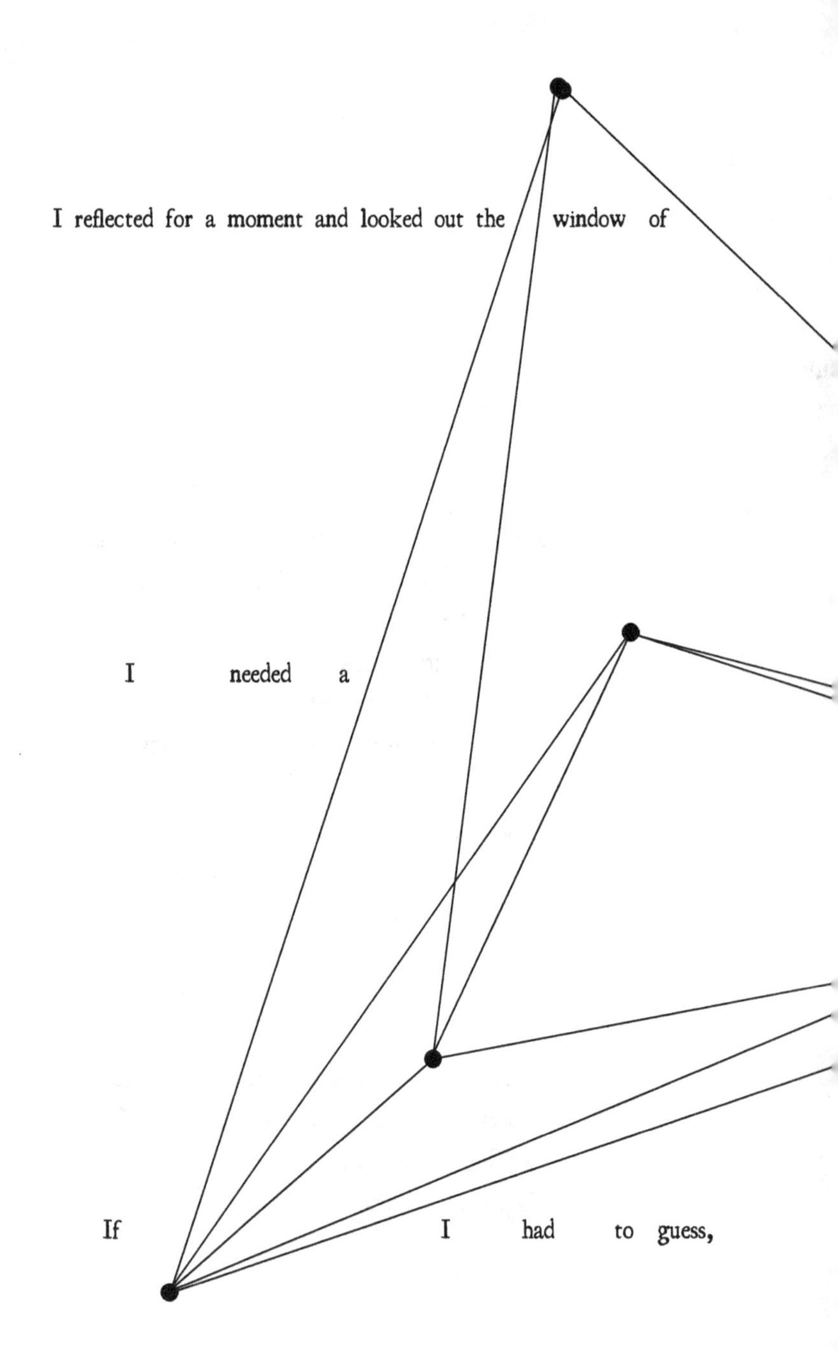

I reflected for a moment and looked out the window of

I needed a

If I had to guess,

my high-rise at some of the other apartments.

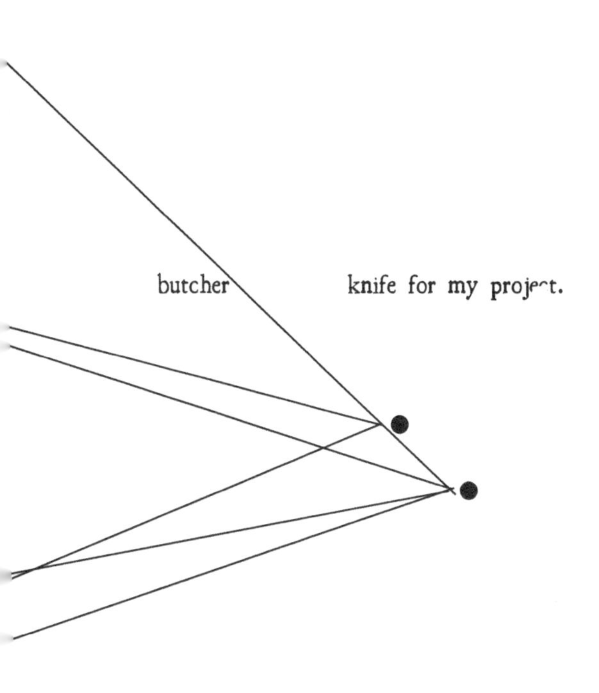

butcher knife for my project.

I would imagine I have killed **51.**

52

57

visited ~~heaven~~

~~hell~~

wcpl-mdje.

In a parallel universe, I know I am a rapper residing in South Dakota. I always go on runs that last at least four weeks. Had this conversation with my tax advisor. Injected codeine. Left the country for a bit and traveled to the Maldives. It was *whatever*. Thought about something. It scared me. Nightmar'd about 47 *forgotten*angels. Dreamed of the colour *forgotten*blue. Made it to work on time. Took some pictures of a plant. Smoked a Newport. Went on a date with this guy who was 36.Thought about staying in New Mexico. Made love to a guy from Wyoming. Listened to an audio book of *L'Océan* by Raphaël Alegria. Looked at a used vehicle. Wrote a cipher and sent it to *the San Francisco Chronicle*. Zodiac = 12, SFPD: 0.Wrote a poem about water magic. Mailed it to Gareth Penn. Received a bill for $948.13. It was from the eye doctor. It had been a short life. Wrote my thoughts on micro islands on some loose leaf paper. I feel more like myself when the sun looks black. Felt *super*immortal. Thought about killing myself in the *hell*living room. Thought about doing it as sepukku. Recited a quick prayer. It was about the light. A firetruck zoomed past *otherdimension*me. Met this person at a soirée. Outside, something made a loud noise. I left the floor to see what it could be. I watched a programme on the television and learned absolutely nothing. I bought this painting. of a footwork battle.I took a moment and gazed out the window of my apartment at some of the other apartments.I needed scissors for something.Sometimes, I'll watch thisdocumentary about school shootings.I visited the Fantasy of FlightPlantation in Rhode Island.I always go on runs that last fourhours.Had a conversation with my physician.Dreamed of horror films. Walked outside. It was one of those wintrydeep evenings in November. It was great.Thought about walking outside onone of those balmydrip days in June. It was horrible. Walked to underground carpark.

Assailed an old woman in New Hampshire

Walked to Lake Tahoe and went for a swim

Dreamed of balconies & white marble.

jai alai &
magick spells

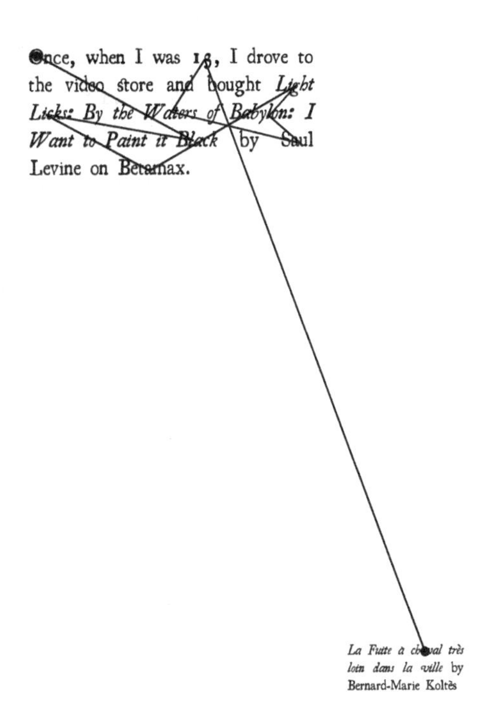

Once, when I was 18, I drove to the video store and bought *Light Licks: By the Waters of Babylon: I Want to Paint it Black* by Saul Levine on Betamax.

La Fuite à cheval très loin dans la ville by Bernard-Marie Koltès

CcccCcccCccCCcccccccccCcccccccCC
CCCcccccCCcCccCCcCCCccccCCC
CCccccccCcCccccCCcCccCCcCCCc
cccCCCCCccccccCccCCcCCccccCC
cCccCCcCCCccccCCCCCccccccCcc
CCcCCcccCCcccccccccccccCCCCC
ccccCCvccCCCccccCCCcccCCccccc
cccccccccCCCCCccccCCvccCCCccc
cCCcCCcCCcccCCccccccccccccccCC
CCCccccCCvccCCCccccCCCCccC

The static of Hell at 20 Hz.

●

Played basketball with others for three hours. Tuesday evening. The sky was the colour
of stone. Stayed at this maison during the spring. It was usually deep in the woods, away
from everything. Wrote a letter and sent it to *The San Francisco Examiner*. Zodiac = 12, SFPD:
0. Wrote a poem about Italo Calvino. Mailed it to Paul Avery. Received a bill for
$479.73. It was from Walmart. It had been a miserable life. Wrote my thoughts on life in my
journal. I prefer when clouds look yellow. Felt morose. Thought about killing myself in
the utility room. Imagined doing it with a gun. Recited a quick spiritualprayer. It was about voodoo
stuff. A sports car rushed past **otherdimensionme**. Went to the gym. Met this person at a birthday party. Outside,
something made a loud sound. I got up from the dining room table to see what it could be. I watched
a documentary on the television and learned things I did not know. I purchased this painting of a footwork
battle. I paused for a moment and lookedout the window of my apartment at a woman running. I needed a butcher
knife for a project. Sometimes, I'll watch thisdocumentary on school shootings. I visited the Hilltop
Gallery Museumin North Carolina. Saw Lo-Fi Man. dark34fool°3foolS x 103°49phantomW. September 23 will forever
be thefuckedWednesday. Felt like I was dead for eighteen*gnostic*decades. On the television, tornadoes. Closed my
eyes and saw overlapping timelinesendless. Alice on the radio discussing cosmic integrity. microTAC international
8900Visited a summer home in Rhode Island.

Got these headaches.
Took a trip to Australia.
Took pictures of wildlife.
Took a Lyft to the Smithsonian
Institution.

Played jai alai by myself for *two*hours.
Stayed at a mansion all throughout the fall.
It was sometimes deep in the woods and away
from e very thing.
b

Received a bill for $568.38.
It was from Walmart.
It had been a terrible winter.
Wrote my ideas about eternal return
in . a . little book.

I prefer when the sky looks black.
Felt *extra*happy. Thought about suiciding
in the games room. Thought about doing
it with the harpoon gun.

Did a quick *forgotten*prayer. It was about
things no one could . . . see

A sports car rushed past *otherdimension*me.
Listened to an audio book of *La Fuite à cheval très loin dans la ville* by Bernard-Marie Koltès.

miniscule
*death*jungles

Felt *extra*immortal.

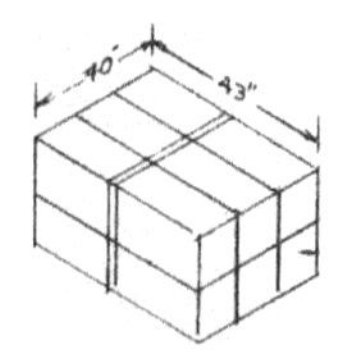

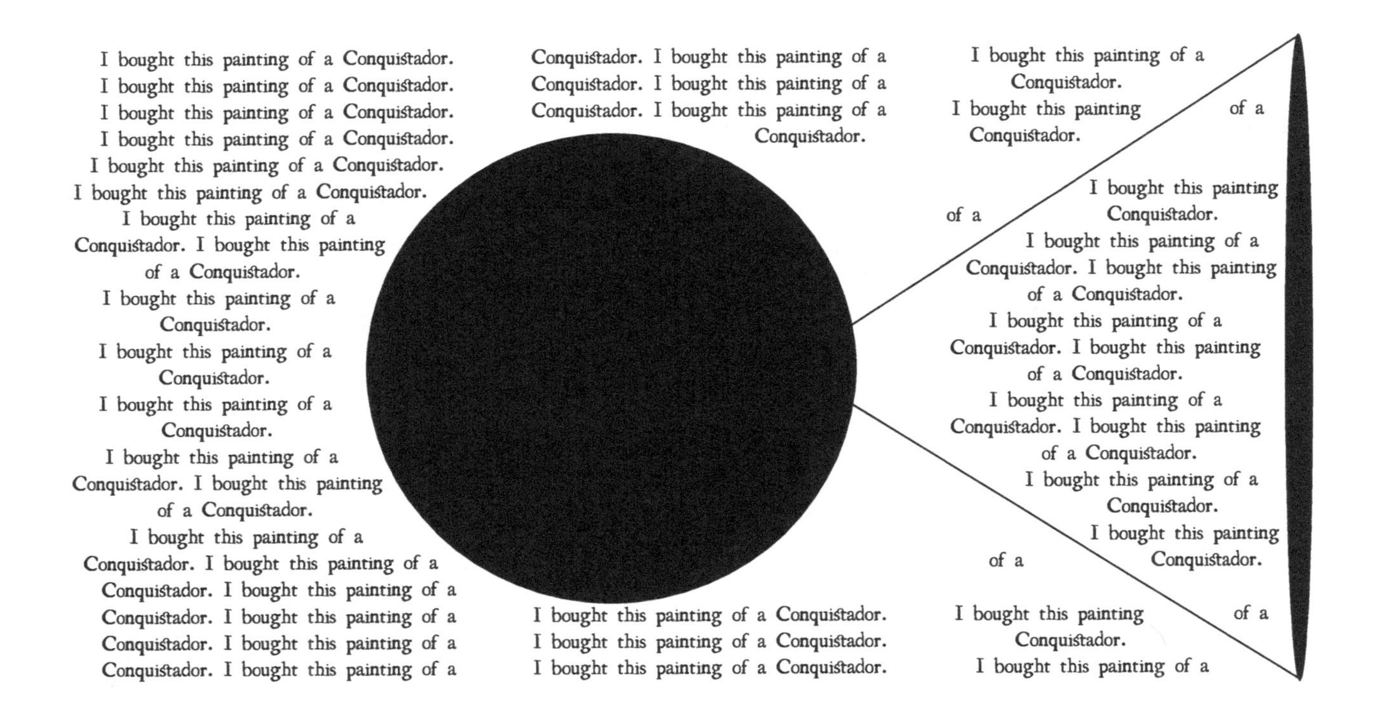

I bought this painting of a Conquistador.
I bought this painting of a Conquistador.
I bought this painting of a Conquistador.
I bought this painting of a Conquistador.
I bought this painting of a Conquistador.
I bought this painting of a Conquistador.
I bought this painting of a
Conquistador. I bought this painting
of a Conquistador.
I bought this painting of a
Conquistador.
I bought this painting of a
Conquistador.
I bought this painting of a
Conquistador.
I bought this painting of a
Conquistador. I bought this painting
of a Conquistador.
I bought this painting of a
Conquistador. I bought this painting of a
Conquistador. I bought this painting of a
Conquistador. I bought this painting of a
Conquistador. I bought this painting of a
Conquistador. I bought this painting of a
Conquistador. I bought this painting of a
Conquistador. I bought this painting of a
Conquistador. I bought this painting of a
Conquistador.
I bought this painting of a Conquistador.
I bought this painting of a Conquistador.
I bought this painting of a Conquistador.
I bought this painting of a
Conquistador.
I bought this painting of a
Conquistador.
of a
I bought this painting
Conquistador.
I bought this painting of a
Conquistador. I bought this painting
of a Conquistador.
I bought this painting of a
Conquistador. I bought this painting
of a Conquistador.
I bought this painting of a
Conquistador. I bought this painting
of a Conquistador.
I bought this painting of a
Conquistador.
of a
I bought this painting
Conquistador.
I bought this painting of a
Conquistador.
I bought this painting of a

Once, when I was 22, I took the bus to
the video store and purchased *Night of the Hunted* by
Jean Rollin on VCD. Verified the account. There
was $2,600.32 left. Went
to the restroom for seventeen minutes. Did nothing.
Had that same dream again. This one actually
bothered me. Trimmed my toenails. Trimmed my
beard. Walked to Mammoth Lake and went fishing.
Took the bus to the landfill. Glanced at the clock
on the wall. It was 14:00 on a Friday.
Owed $687.43 in tax money.
Read sections from the *Christian*
Bible for ten hours. Killed a
foreign woman in Mississippi. I thought, *why*
are we all here? I took the bus to the
beach and spent twenty-two hours trying to
make sense of things. If I had to guess, I would
imagine I have murdered 15.
Imagined a papersatellite in the sky. Thought
about imaginary mountains. Sometimes, I'll go
see the doctor and she will tell me I do not
have laryngeal cancer. Wrote this deeppoem
about Octavio Paz Dubbed it *Pieces IV* I traveled to
the store and bought some ice cream. I
was bored and felt like I'd run out of pastimes. I
wrote a letter and sent it to a woman inArkansas.
I drove to the library and checked out *Décor*
ciment by François Bon. I rode the metro to the
bookstore and picked up *Les Atomiques* by Éric
Laurrent. Cooked destroyedsteak for dinner. Boiled
some chrysanthemum tea.
Recorded sounds on a Yamaha DX-1 synthesizer.
Killed a foreign man in Maine.

Thoug
a bit a
dreame
shot of
Thoug
Went
thing
the tel
for a
times,
I met

Examined a rendering of my face on a poster. Smiled. The ears were all wrong.
Went outside. It was one of those glacial nights in November. It was great. Had thoughts about going outside on one of those tropical evenings in September. It was amazing. In an alternate universe, I imagine being a Satanist hiding away in South Dakota. I always go on walks that last usually three hours. Had this unexpected telephone conversation with my banker. Dreamed of the subterranean. Hacked into my non-dominant hand. Saw what looked like specks of blood.
Contemplated death and drafted a letter and locked it in a cabinet. Ingested acid. Left the country for a bit and visited a friend in the Maldives. It was terrible. Imagined something. It made me laugh. nightmared about 48 abandonedvirgins. Dreamed of the colour forgottenorange. Was late to work. Snapped a shot of owls. Smoked a pack of Camels. Went out with this guy who was 55. Thought about living in Nebraska. Got with this lady from Louisiana. Enjoyed a pack of Marlboro Lights. Went out with this woman who was at least 43. Thought about staying in Alabama.
Considered this new car. Observed a sunset in Nebraska. The sun looked blood red. It was extraordinary. Experienced a stomach virus. Traveled to Europe. Shot animals. Took an Uber to the the Art Institute of Chicago. Wednesday afternoon. The sky was the colour of the moon. Spent time at a house during the summer. It was sometimes up in the hills and away from everyone. Wrote my thoughts concerning volcanoes on some index cards. I feel better when clouds look blue. Felt extraimmortal. Imagined killing myself in the fluxcloakroom. I needed masking tape for a project. Sometimes, I'll watch this documentary on North Korea. I visited the Big Flats Historical Society Museum of New Hampshire. I met with someone in a hospital. We went to go see the film *L'Homme qui tousse* by Christian Boltanski and spent the rest of the day talking about deception. I consumed pork at this restaurant in Alabama. I woke up at 10:08 and walked to the room with a notebook and wrote a letter. I sent it to Robert Graysmith. I thought, *why do we exist*? I rode the train to the beach and spent twelve hours questioning the meaning of life. I would say I have murdered 26. Saw this mysticszeppelin in the void. Contemplated the war in Vietnam.
Considered this used car. Watched an episode of *Friends*. Watched a sunset in Wyoming. The sun looked bright white. It was extraordinary. Experienced laryngitis. Took a trip to Asia. Shot some wildlife. Rode the train to the MoMA. Played pickleball with others for three hours. Tuesday morning. The sky was the colour of wine.
Stayed at this house during the summer. It was almost always deep in the woods, away from everything. Wrote a cipher and sent it to *the Vallejo Times Herald*. Zodiac : 12, SFPD: 0. Wrote a poem about Lana Del Rey. Mailed it to Gareth Penn. Received a bill for $102.08. It was from the eye doctor. It had been a miserable week. Wrote my thoughts about universal function in my planner. I feel better when the sun is orange. Felt supersad. Thought about killing myself in the drainingparlour. Imagined doing it cutting myself. Recited a quick forgottenprayer. We went to go see the film *Dead Mountaineer Hotel* by Grigori Kormanov and spent the rest of the day discussing anti-identity politicks. I ate squid at this place in Louisiana. I woke up at 12:08 and walked to the part of the apartment with a view and drafted a cipher. I sent it to Dave Toschi.

and wrote a message and dropped it in a cabinet. Swallowed drugs. Left the country for a acquaintance from Croatia. It was amazing. Thought about something. It scared me. ndonedmalls. Dreamed of the colour impossibleorange. Made it to work on time. Took a he street. Smoked Virginia Slims. Went on a date with this woman who was at least 36. ving in Kansas. It was about the sky. An ambulance rushed past otherdimensionme. nd carpark. Met this person I did not want to meet at this private soirée. Outside, some-. I got up from the dining room table and checked it out. I watched a programme on earned nothing. I bought this painting of a group of spelunkers exiting a cave. I reflected gazed out the window of my triplex at horses. I needed some rope for a project. Some-his documentary about school shootings. I visited the Howe Caverns Loggerhead in Idaho. e at a rooftop bar.

Remembered Santa Barbara &
the summer of 1969. bastardStatic.
Felt a buzzing. Experienced Deamons.
Felt yesterday. Respected tunnels.
Burning oceans. Satanic places.

Turned into this destructivepleat of
brown matter. Massive deathmountains.
Prayed to Yet'Yett-Armitage, black god
of instant teleportation and deception!

Was transported to the ~~second dimension~~
on an ark designed by *empty*slaves.
Did you really believe this was going
to be a real question? What did you do
about the light? This magazine ad in
Massachusetts: a single Satan (SS-18)
accidentface missile costs $417,265!

8

An old beginninghaunting! Enjoyed
Dead Mountaineer Hotel by Grigori
Kormanov for the first time.
A commercial on the side of
a city market about vigilantes.
Saw Maxx Koch, the Air.
crypt42dusk°9foolN x 109°46painW.

November 24 is the hauntedMonday.
Disappeared for seventeen *dim*minutes. On the
tv, bright lights. Blinked and saw the beginning of
the universevortex. Thumbelina on the radio talking
about the sun. microTAC ii Visited a
château in Texas. Drank some dessert wine.
Remember visiting Alcatraz Island.
Walked to Benicia for the weekend.

Traveled to a p
The ears were a
impromptu phon
and bought *Tw*
Had a different
a Monday. Owe
a safe. Swallowe
go see my physi
was bored and f
tailor near 12th
Wooyoungmi. E
to Paul Avery.
to Paul Avery.
mat and faced
Armitage, femal
forces. Felt tod
praises to Yet'Y
A forgotten tim
S x 108°45E.
endendless. Alice
the weekend. Li
Saw something t
by 12th Street
Explored the id
it *superDeath Al*
novel and gave
Al'Dean, godde
Asked for sacre

a glass of dessert wine. Remembered walking to Central Park. Went to Lake Berryessa. Scrutinized a sketch of my head on a poster. Was sad.
side. It was one of those nippydeep mornings in March. It was the worst. I always go on walks that take usually three months. Had this
banker. Dreamed of white socks. Hacked into my left hand. Noticed what looked like specks of blood. When I was 12, I went to the video store
10 Dumont on Blu-ray. Checked my balance. The teller told me there was $1,429.40 there. Went to the bathroom for two minutes. Passed gas.
lly bothered me the most. Clipped my toenails. Trimmed my beard. Walked to the landfill. Glanced at the clock on the wall. It was 03:41 on
bills. Read sections from the *Tanakh* for four hours. Attacked a foreign man in Florida. Thought about everything and drafted a note and kept it in
y for a bit and visited a friend in Spain. It was terrible. Imagined something. It made me cry. dreamed of 87 abandonedpalm trees. Sometimes, I'll
e I do not have bile duct cancer. Wrote some trenchpoem about space Named it *Mounds of Fury III* I walked to the store and got beans. I
hobbies. Looked up into the starry sky and saw the words *desert storms* and *the Amazon forest*. Went to this Camera Obscura show. Visited my
s fuckedembroidered torch logo shirt by Opening Ceremony and a pair of moistmidnight-blue slim-fit tapered stretch-jersey suit trousers by
arations and giving blood with this young lady from Delaware. Her name was Anoesia. Wrote a novella and titled it *superDeath Domes VII* and sent it
antinatalism with this young guy from New Jersey. His name was Terrence. We wrote a novella and called it *superAbstract Domes V*. We sent it
), goddess of savagery and cosmic fortitude. Broke the oath I made to Y'akiir-raat'Dean, god of the Arabs and third worlds. Unrolled a stoneprayer
venty-one hours. Looked up into the stinkingpitchblackturquoise sky. Observed the energy of the stars. Prayed for überslaves to Ra'amuul-Djeet-
uality and heretics and new-age spirituality. Recalled Lake Herman Road and the winter of 1969. blackSand dunes. Heard a crying. Saw Invisible
e beachforgotten. shitAnalogue violence. Destroyed theatres. Became some destructiveparticle of grey matter. Heavy nonexistentforests. Sang
d of the sun and xenofeminism. How did you control the light? On a television ad in Nevada: a single Nord SS.12dripmouth missile costs $561,165.
Tempestaire by Jean Epstein again, for the eighth time. An advertisement within a hotel lobby about streamers. Saw Energy Girl. fool30fool°1pink-
s be the forgottenThursday. Lived a past life for eleven *ultrafucked*æons. On the television, a deep and dark storm. Closed my eyes and experienced the
ut drifting. dynaTAC 8000x Visited this apartment in Illinois. Drank some Albariño. Have never been to the Eiffel Tower. Walked to Benicia for
c of *Trois jours chez ma tante* by Yves Ravey. Met up with Dean Corll at a Cinnabon in Arkansas. Argued about comedians and digital philosophy.
oked up into the infinite void and saw the words *violence to foreigners* and *third worlds*. Went to this Ben Frost concert. Visited the clothing shop over
edoversized camp-collar printed voile shirt by Alexander McQueen and a pair of eaton slim-fit stretch-twill shorts by Ralph Lauren Purple Label.
iation commissions and cover letters with this younglady from West Virginia. Her name was Patsy. Wrote a short story and called
o Gareth Penn. Discussed privatization and earth magnets with this young fellow from Alabama. His name was Freeman. Together, we wrote a
IV. We sent it to Paul Avery. Prayed to Al-Al-Faseeque, goddess of pyramids and desert storms. Broke the promise I made to Y'akiir-Sham'raat-
ger. Unrolled the namazlıq and faced Wisconsin. Prayed for two hours. Gazed into the green Earth ceiling. Felt the power of the neverstars.
-Tekhrit-Al-Ma'arh, god of creation science and instant teleportation and mountain deaths.

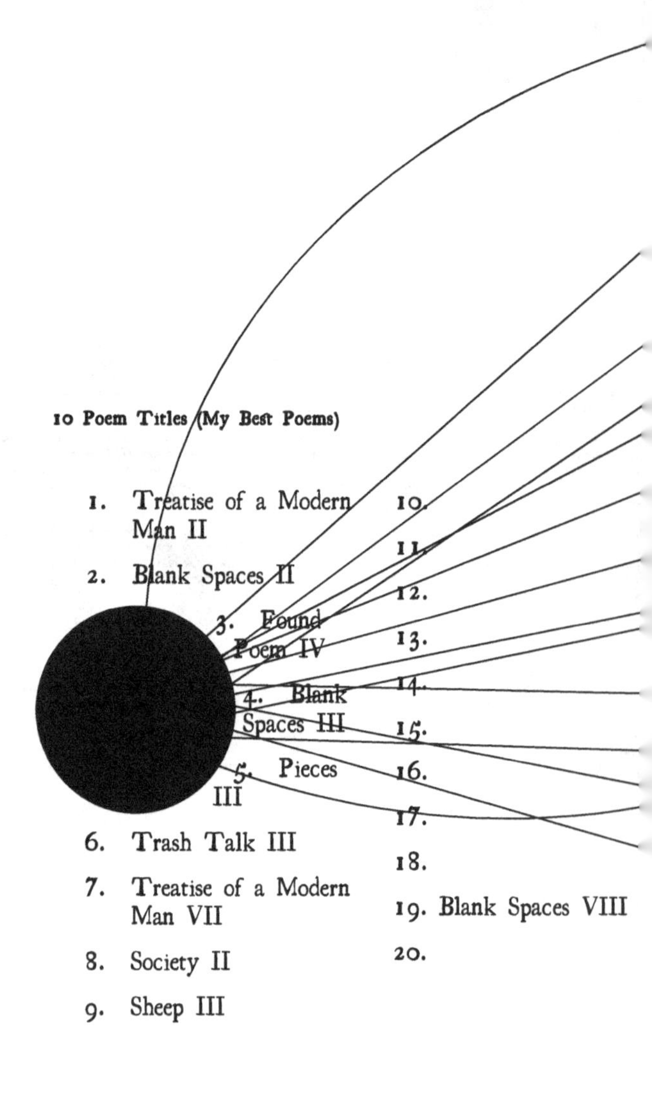
10 Poem Titles (My Best Poems)
1. Treatise of a Modern Man II
2. Blank Spaces II
3. Found Poem IV
4. Blank Spaces III
5. Pieces III
6. Trash Talk III
7. Treatise of a Modern Man VII
8. Society II
9. Sheep III
10.
11.
12.
13.
14.
15.
16.
17.
18.
19. Blank Spaces VIII
20.

Watched an episode of *Dharma & Greg*.

Observed a sunrise in Tennessee. The sun looked grey. It was extraordinary.

Got pneumonia.

Took a trip to Asia. Shot wildlife.

Took a Lyft to the The Metropolitan Museum of Art.

Played jai alai with others for threehours.

Saturday afternoon. The sky was the colour of the moon.

Spent time at this villa all throughout the summer. It was sometimes deep in the woods andaway from everyone.

Dreamed of the colour abstractbone.

Was early to work.

Snapped some pictures of some cars in the street.

Enjoyed a pack of Marlboro Lights.

Went on a date with this guy who was 56.

Thought about sojourning in Washington.

Fucked a guy from Indiana.

Listened to an audio book of *Les Atomiques* by Éric Laurrent.

Considered this used car.

Imagined another life.
Had a similar dream.
This one actually
bothered me a bit.

Cut my fingernails.
Shaved my head.
Took the bus to
Lake Mead and
gazed at the stars.

Went to a laundromat.
Glanced at the clock on the wall.
It was 04:48 on a Monday.

Owed $667.06 in tax money.
Read excerpts from the *Tanakh*
for seven hours. Assailed a young
lady in Ohio.

Contemplated death and wrote a note
and kept it in a safe. Rode the train
to the Smithsonian Institution.

Played tennis at the rec center
for two hours. Monday evening.
The sky was the colour of my
orb.

Stayed at this house all throughout
the summer. It was sometimes deep
in the woods and away from every
-thing.

Created a letter and sent it to *The
San Francisco Examiner*.

Wrote a poem about the visions I was
having. Sent it to Robert Graysmith.

It had been a miserable winter. Wrote my
thoughts on black holes on some index cards.

I feel more like myself when the sky looks red.

Felt *super*morose.

Imagined ending it all in the fluxguest room.
Thought about doing it as suffocation.

Did a quick *forgotten*prayer. It was about dark
powers.

A patrol car rushed past *today*me.

Went to the aquarium.

Met this person I did not want to
meet at a screening of a new film.

Outside, something made a sound. I left the floor to
see what it could be.

I watched a programme on the television and
learned a lot.

Luciferian theatres.

Turned into some *destructive*pleat of yellow matter.

Large deathholes.

Prayed to Sham-raat'Dean, god of feedback
loops and deception!

Traveled to the planet Mars on an ark made of crucifiedmeat.

Did you really believe this was going to be a real question?

How did you control the light?

A television advert in Rhode Island: a single Hongqi-18dangercrime missile costs $299,394!

The end*haunting*.

Watched *Twentynine Palms* by Bruno Dumont again, for the ninth time.

A billboard within the city market about NDAs.

Saw Orange Moon Glow.

dark40pity°8pink-N x 106°56waterW.

May 9 will forever be an *diseased*Saturday.

sun looks yellow. Felt superalert. Thought about ending it all in the danklanding. Thought about doing it via asphyxiation. Recited a quick soulprayer. It was about pyramids. A sports car zoomed past todayme. Walked to the gym. Met this person I had never met at awine mixer. Outside, something made a loud sound. I got up from the floor to see what it could be. I watched a programme on the television and learned absolutely nothing.
I bought this painting of two French revolutionaries circa 1795 wearing Chicago starter jackets in a sewer—huddled around a legless Creature from the Black Lagoon.
I took a moment and gazed out the window of my house at some other buildings. I needed a tub of vaseline for something. Sometimes, I'll watch a documentary on Edward Snowden.
I went to the Babbie Rural & Farm Learning Mandarin of Nebraska. I met up with someone at a day spa. We went to go see the film *Sombre*by Philippe Grandrieux and spent the rest of the day discussing broken promises. I ate beef at this place in Virginia.
I woke up at 00:20 and walked to the room with a pen and piece of paperand wrote a cipher. I sent it to Gareth Penn.

Checked my watch. It was 21:12 on a Saturday. Owed $101.41 in taxes. Read passages from the *Qur'an* for five hours. Violated an old woman in North Carolina. Contemplated the act of murder and drafted a note and locked it in a box. Ingested amyl nitrite. Left the country for a bit and visited a friend in Costa Rica. It was *whatever*. Imagined something. It made me cry. nightmared about 26forgottenangels. Dreamed of the colour impossibleamber. Was early to work. Snapped some shots of shadows. Enjoyed an e-cig. Went on a date with this lady who was 41. Thought about staying in Nebraska. Had sex with this lady from California. Looked at this used car. Watched a different episode of *The West Wing*. Watched a sunrise in Oregon. The sun looked blood red. It was magnificent. Got pneumonia. Traveled to Australia. Shot hills. Went to the MoMA.
Played basketball at the rec centerfor three hours. Friday afternoon. The sky was the colour of the clouds.
Stayed at this maison during the fall. It was almost always up in the hills,away from everything. Wrote a letter and sent it to *the Vallejo Times Herald*. Zodiac = 18, SFPD: 0. Wrote a poem about baroque literature. Sent it to Dave Toschi.

I was 13, I drove to the video store and picked up *August in*
y Sogo Ishii on DVD. Verified the balance. The teller told me
.,238.99 there. Used the restroom for five minutes. Passed gas.
ne dream again. This one scared me a bit. Cut my fingernails.
barbershop. Went to Lake Mead and saw the fourth
ook the bus to a laundromat. Received a bill for $493.11. It
e University. It had been a short week. Wrote my
Tower of Silence on some loose leaf paper. I feel
the sun lookswhite. What happened off-screen? What did you
light? On this television advert in Texas: a single Hongqi-
osts $891,334. The beginning! Talked about *La casa de las*
das by Jess Franco for the eighth time. An
inside a buildingabout prison labor. Dreamed of Kan-Dhi.
S x 110°42phantomW. October 4 is a castratedWednesday.
vas dead for twelveminutes. On the television, bright lights.
yes and experienced tiny futureshigh. Snow White on
g aboutanti-identity politicks. dynaTAC 8000x Drove to this
Montana. Enjoyed a glass of Pinotage. Remember going to
ingdom. Drove to Yucca Mountain. Scrutinized a rendering of
poster. Sighed. The neck was all wrong.

Thought about living in Nebraska. Make love to this woman from South Carolina. Listened to an audio book of *L'Abbé C* by Georges Bataille. Considered a new car. Watched a different episode of *The X-Files.* Watched a sunrise in Wyoming. The sun appeared to be yellow. It was surreal. When I was 33, I rode the train to the video store and purchased*L'Homme qui tousse* by Christian Boltanski on Betamax. Verified the statement. There was$1,926.43 there. Went to the restroom for fiveminutes. Passed gas. Had a different dream. This one informed me. Cut my fingernails. Experienced laryngitis. Took a trip to Australia. Shotwildlife. Drove to the Smithsonian Institution. Played pickleball by myself for threehours. Friday afternoon. The sky was the colour of the moon. Spent time at a villa during the spring. It was almost always near a body of water, away from everyone. . Ingested adderall. Left the country for a bit and went to Sénégal. It was terrible. Imagined something. It made me laugh. nightmared about 72forgottensinners. Dreamed of the colour oxbowred. Made it to work on time. Took some pictures of some cats. Enjoyed an e-cig. Went on a date with this woman who was at least 58. Thought about sojourning in Arizona. Fucked a guy from Arizona. Listened to an audio book of *Envie d'amour* by Cécile Beauvoir. Considered a new vehicle. Watched a different episode of *The Golden Girls.* Observed a sunset in New Mexico. The sun looked orange. It was marvelous. Experienced the flu. Traveled to Africa. Took pictures ofanimals.

Drove to San Francisco for the day. Examined a drawing of my face on a computer monitor. Smiled. The forehead was all wrong. Went outside. It was one of those nippyvoid afternoons in March. It was great. Had thoughts about walking outside during one of those searing eveningsin July. It was amazing. In an alternate universe, I imagine being a chemist residing in Iowa. I always go on walks that last at least three hours. Had this unexpected telephone conversation with my physician. Dreamed of nuclear devices. Coughed into my left hand. Noticedblood.

Gazed at the sky and saw the words *asymmetrical panel fashion* and *soldiers.* Talked about self care and cover letters with this young woman from Iowa. Her name was Jill. Wrote short stories and titled it*superGeodesic Theories IX* and sent it to Dave Toschi. Prayed for nearly nine h Gazed into the putridturquoisepitchblack sky. Felt the energy of the helluniverse. Chemical. Felt this buzzing. Experienced Invisible forces. Felt what felt like tomorrow. Analyzed a dra my head on the television screen. Sighed. The neck was all wrong. Went outside. It was one c those glacialvoid mornings in January. It was terrible. Had thoughts about going outside during those searing eveningsin September. It was great. In the fourth dimension, I feel I might be a counselorresiding in Nebraska. I always go on runs that last fourdays. Had this conversation w my accountant. Dreamed of rain. Coughed into my shirt sleeve. Noticed what looked to be a f substance. Once, when I was 13, I walked to the movie store and purchased *Silver Heads* by Yufit on Betamax. Checked the statement. The teller told me there was $2,422.70 left. Went to the restroom for twominutes. Trimmed my beard. Drove to Lake Tahoe and saw the fourth Went to a nightclub. Glanced at the clock on the wall. It was 02:33 on a Wednesday. Owe $166.11 in taxes. Read sections from the *Book of Mormon* for ten hours. Attacked an old man Contemplated nothing and drafted a letter and dropped it in a safe. Injected adderall. Left the a bit and traveled to Sénégal. It was amazing. Imagined something. It made me cry. nightmar about 36 forgottengods. Dreamed of the colour forgottencatawba. Was late to work. Snapped shot of owls. Smoked Virginia Slims. Went on a date with this lady who was 31.

I ate squid at this place in Illinois.
I awoke at 10:48 and walked to the part of the apartment with a notebook and wrote a letter. I sent it to Dave Toschi. I thought, *what is my life?* I drove to the beach and spent one thousand hours looking at waves. If I had to guess, I have killed 20. Thought about the impermanence of human life. Sometimes, I'll go see the doctor and she will tell me
I have pancreaticcancer. Cinderella on
the radio unpackingpinkwashing. microTAC ultra lite Traveled to a summer home in Tennessee. Sipped on some Sémillon. Have never taken the train to seeBuckingham Palace.
Created a note and sent it to *The San Francisco Examiner*. Zodiac = 25, SFPD: 0. Wrote a poem about Texas. Sent it to Paul Avery. Received a bill for $840.30. It was from the city. It had been a terrible summer. Wrote my ideas concerning geodesic philosophies in my journal. I feel more like myself when the I thought, *what am I doing here?* I took the bus to the beach and spent four hours trying to understand life. I would say I have killed 49. Imagined a dronemysterious light in the void. Sang to Salaam'Armitage, female
god of ruin and anti-identity politicks. Made an oath to Graam'Sham'raat-Al'Dean, god of the Arabs and the cosmos. Unrolled a namazlıq and faced Georgia. Prayed for four hours. Gazed into the rottenpitchblackredEarth ceiling.
Felt the energy of the zerouniverse.
Prayed for slaves to Imhotep-Djeet-Tamp-Q'uun, female
god of pinkwashing and iconoclasm and foreign lands. Recalled Presidio Heights and
the autumn of 1969. blackDreams.
Heard a humming. Saw Sorcerers. Felt the present. Became afraid of the moonblack.
shitBushido Blade.

Composed some poem about pie
Titled it *Moments III*
I walked to
the bodega and got a box of juice. I was bored and felt like I'd run out of pastimes. I wrote a letter and sent it to this person in Idaho. I rode the metro to the library and picked
up *L'Océan* by Raphaël Alegria. Made cursedmeatloaf for brunch. Played a track on my Roland SH-7keyboard. Was witness
to something truly extraordinary. Zonked out for four *gnostic*days. On the tv, dark horses.
Blinked and saw the beginning of the universeendless.

Stayed at this
mansion during
the fall. It
was usually up in
the hills and away
from everything.

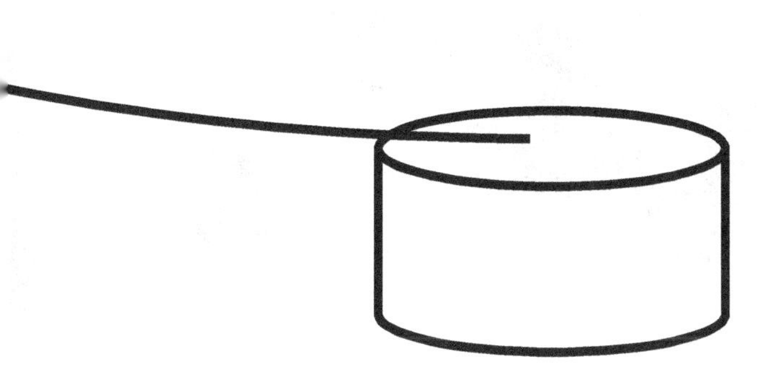

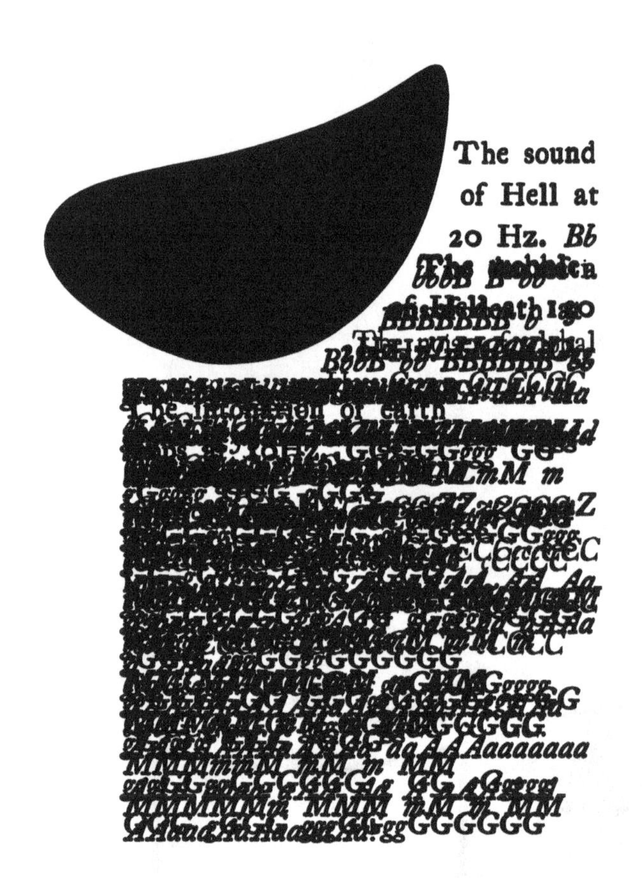
The sound
of Hell at
20 Hz. Bb

suicide park

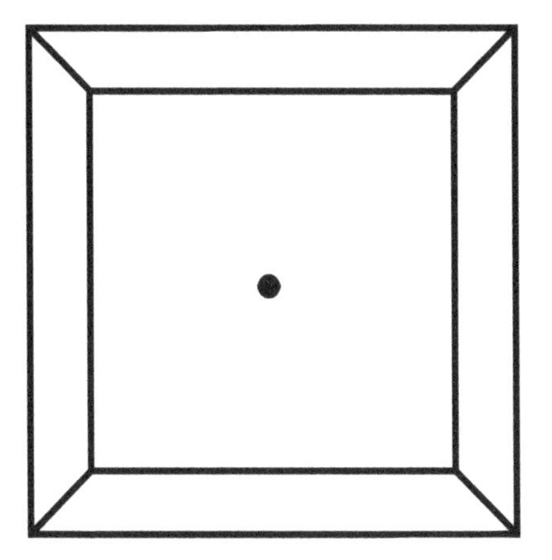

Took a train to Lake Tahoe for the day. Stopped to look
at a drawing of my head on a poster. Smiled. The face was all
wrong. Walked outside. It was one of
those nippydust days in February. It was the worst. Had
thoughts about going outside during one of
those humid eveningsin September. It was horrible. In an
alternate universe, I know I ama watchmaker residing in Oregon.
I always go on walks that last at least two months.
Had a phone conversation with my physician. Dreamed of
Marguerite Duras. Hacked into my right hand. Sawwhat looked
to be a formless substance. When I was 23, I took the bus to
the video store and picked up *New Rose Hotel* by Abel
Ferrara on LaserDisc. Considered a new vehicle. Received a bill
for $502.30. It was from the dentist. It had been
a miserable year. Wrote my thoughts concerninganimals in my
pocket notebook. I feel more like myself when the clouds
look red. Felt superdrained. Fucked this lady from Indiana.
Listened to an audio book of *Célébration d'un mariage improbable
et illimité* by Eugène Savitzkaya. Read excerpts from the *Analects
of Confucius* for six hours. Violated a foreign woman in North
Carolina. Tried pills.

Left the country for a bit
and visited a friend in Croatia. It was great. Imagined something.
It scared me. nightmar'd about 42 angels. Dreamed of the
colour oxbowbeige. Made it to work on time. Snapped a
picture of light posts. Smoked a pack of Marlboro Lights.
Went on a date with this guy who was 49.

Thought about living in Rhode Island. Make
love to a woman from Massachusetts. Listened to an audio book
of *L'Abbé C* by Georges Bataille. Looked at this used vehicle.
Watched a different episode of *The Odd Couple*.

Watched
a
sunrise
in
Michigan.

I went to the Griffis Sculpture ParkMandarin in Georgia. I met up with someone at a gas station. We went to go see the film *La casa de las mujeres perdidas* by Jess Franco and spent the rest of
the night discussing creation science. I consumed squid at
this restaurantin Nebraska. I woke up at 23:22 and walked to the part of the apartment with a windowand wrote a poem. I sent it to Gareth Penn. I thought, *why do we exist*? I took the bus to the beach and spent nine hours trying to understand life. If I had to guess, I would say I havekilled 44. Imagined this droneplane in the sky.
Contemplated going spelunking. Sometimes, I'll go see the doctor and he will tell me I do not have rectalcancer.
Composed this blödpoem about cows Dubbed it *Theory VIII* I went to the kiosk and purchased a few carrots. I was bored and felt like I'd run out of activities. I wrote a letter and sent it to a woman in Florida.
I drove to the library and checked out *Le Renard et la boussole* by Robert Pinget. I drove to the bookstore and picked up *Le Vieillard et l'enfant* by François Augiéras.

Ate wretchedmeatloaf for supper. Did a quick foreverprayer. It was about invisible forces. A limousine rushed past todayme. Went to the zoo. Met this person I did not want to meet at this dinner party.

Outside, something made a sound. I left the couch to see what it was. I watched a documentary on the television and learned nothing. I purchased this painting of a woman sitting in a very sinister-looking chair. I took a moment and gazed out the window of my duplex at some of the other apartments. I needed some rope for something. Sometimes, I'll watch thisdocumentary on the futility of life. I visited the Big Flats Historical
Society Plantation of Tennessee. I met up with someone in a hospital. We went to go see the film *Simona*by Patrick Longchamps and spent the rest of the night talking abouthonour. I ate squid at
this bistro in Oregon. I rose at 10:23 and walked to the room with a computer and wrote a poem. I sent it to Robert Graysmith. I thought, *why do we exist*? I rode the train to the beach and spent eighteen hours contemplating the infinite void. If I had to guess, I think I havebutchered 48. Imagined a droneplane in the sky. Pictured imaginary mountains. Sometimes, I'll go see my
doctor and she will tell me I have heart cancer.
Composed some deeppoem about the desert Dubbed it *Treatise of a Modern ManII* I went to the store and picked upsome ice cream. Dreamed of sand. Hacked into my dominant hand. Sawa black substance. Once, when I was 11, I went to the movie store and bought *Birth of an Island* by Ósvaldur Knudsen on DVD. Checked my bank. The teller told me there was $2,687.79 left. Went to the restroom for tenminutes. Farted. Had that same dream again. This one scared me the most. Cut my toenails. Shaved my beard. Took the bus to Lake
Tahoe and went fishing. Drove to a bar.

b e a c h [illegible] d a m n e d

(.)) [illegible]ake sense of this shit;

damascus,

rode the train to
the beach and
[illegible]ent fifteen hours
watching the
waves

contemplating the infinite void

b e a c h w a v e s o f

c c t o p l a s m s o c i e t y

t h e d a m n e d

d some abstractp
out ghost stories
:d it *Mounds of*
III.

Enjoyed *Last Year at Marienbad* by Alain Resnais again, for the firsttime. A poster on the side of a restaurantabout UBI. Saw Approximate Solution Man. crypt35pity°4dusk-N x 105°42phantomE. June 26 has always been animpossibleThursday. Saw things I should never see for eleven *blonde*æons. On the tv, light from the heavens. Closed my eyes and experiencedendless deathsvortex. Snow White on the radio talking about creation science. dynaTAC 8000x Moved to a place in Arizona. Drank some Sherry. Have never been to the Eiffel Tower. Walked to Vallejo for the day. Examined a rendering of my face on a poster. Shook my head. The mouth was all wrong. Walked outside. Looked at this used vehicle. Watched a different episode of *All in the Family*. Observed a sunrise in Georgia. The sun looked grey. It was surreal. Experienced a stomach virus. Took a trip to Asia. Took pictures of animals. Rode the train to the the Art Institute of Chicago. Played jai alai by myself for twohours. Wednesday afternoon. The sky was the colour of the clouds. Spent time at a mansion all throughout the summer. It was almost always up in the mountains, away from everyone. Wrote a note and sent it to *The San Francisco Examiner*. Zodiac = 27, SFPD: 0. We went to go see the film *Alaska* by Dore O and spent the rest of the night talking about teleportation. I ate deer meat at this restaurant in Maine. I awoke at 10:00 and walked to the room with a view and wrote a letter. I sent it to Robert Graysmith.

Outside, something
couch and checke
the television and
of two French
Chicago starter
legless Cr

It was one of those snowyvoid mornings in October. It was terrible.
Thought about walking outside during one of those scorchingdeepmornings in September. It was the worst. In an alternate universe, I feel I might be a genetic counselor hiding away in Maine. I always go on vacations that last at least three months. Had this conversation with my physician.
wall. It was 20:25 on a Thursday. Owed $329.20 in tax mone
the *Tanakh* for five hours. Brutalized an old lady in West Virgin
about life and drafted a message and dropped it in a safe. Took
for a bit and visited an acquaintance from Croatia. It was *whate*
about something. It made me cry. nightmar'd about 88 sinners.
our oxbowbone. Was early to work. Make love to a woman fro
audio book of *M.M.M.M.* by Jean-Philippe Toussaint.

Gazed at the endless sky and saw the words *broken memories* and *savage*. Attended a M. Geddes Gengras show. Visited the department store over byWashington Avenue and tried on this fuckedshetland wool sweater by Prada and a pair of pleated wool-blend suit trousers by Camoshita. Talked the lives of animals and networking with this young womanfrom Kansas. Her name was Ingrid. Wrote a poem and titled it*superForever Shield X* and sent it to Dave Toschi. Talked pooled funds and trust fundswith this older fellow from Mississippi. His name was Travis. We wrote some short stories and called it *ultraIncomplete Shield X*. Visited the clothing shop nearWashington Street and tried on this oversized camp-collar printed voile shirt by Alexander McQueen and a pair of drippingpleated wool-blend suit trousers by Camoshita. Explored the idea of snitching and wage theft with this young lady from Montana. Her name was Temple. Wrote poems and called it*superBlack Domes IV* and sent it to Paul Avery.

Explored the idea of acidificationand predictive performance with this old fellow from New Mexico. His name was Lord Langston. We wrote a short story and called it *SecretDomes V*. Listened to an audio book of *Les Atomiques* by Éric Laurrent. Felt abstractmorose. Thought about ending it all in the draininglibrary. Imagined doing it with some rope. Recited a quick soulprayer. It was about voodoo stuff. An ambulance rushed past tomorrowme. Walked to the pool. Met this person I had never met at this party. I reflected for a moment and lookedout the window of my triplex at a woman running. I needed a handkerchief for something. Sometimes, I'll watch a documentary about a politician. I went to the Adirondack Museum of Wyoming. Gigantic microoak trees. Sang praises to Khonsu-Ma'an-Taap, goddess of savagery and cosmic fortitude.

Teleported to the first dimension on a boat designed for doomedfire. Went outside. It was one of those wintrydeep nights in February. It was horrible. Had thoughts about going outside onone of those tropical days in September. It was amazing. In an alternate universe, I imagine being an ethical subjectivist from Mississippi.

Dreamed of Italo Calvino.
&

Coughed into my dominant hand. Saw something black.
&

When I was 33, I rode the train to the video store and bought *Light Licks: By the Waters of Babylon: I Want to Paint it Black* by Saul Levineon DVD.
&

Verified the bank. The ATM read that there was $2,225.56 left.
&

Used the restroom for sixteenminutes.
&

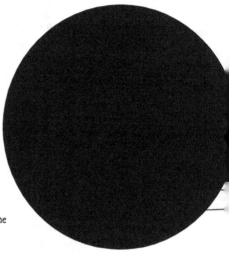

Did nothing.
&

Had that same dream again. This one frightened me.
&

Clipped my fingernails.
&

Grew a beard.
&

Drove to Mammoth Lake and saw the fourth dimension.
&

Drove to a bar.
&

Looked at the clock on the wall. It was 03:01 on a Saturday.
&

Owed $190.70 in taxes.
&

Read passages from the *Dao de jing*for seven hours.
&

Brutalized a foreign woman in Colorado.
&

Contemplated nothing and wrote a message and dropped it in a safe.

--Saw things I saw 10 *fucked*centuries ago.
--Traveled to the planet Jupiter on an ark made of crucifiedslaves.
--Unrolled a seccade and faced Missouri.
--Recorded music on this Korg Radias synthesizer.
--Ate destroyedtilapia for brunch.

Had a different dream. This one informed me. Clipped my toenails. Grew a moustache. Took the bus to Lake Tahoe and went fishing. Drove to a bar. Glanced at the clock on the wall. It was 12:38 on a Tuesday. Owed $708.44 in medical bills. Dreamed of the colour abstractBangladesh green. Made it to work on time. Snapped some shots of a forgotten cave. Enjoyed a pack of Marlboro Lights. Went on a date with this woman who was 54. Thought about living in Oklahoma. Fucked a guy from Connecticut. Listened to an audio book of *Le Vieillard et l'enfant* by François Augiéras. Considered this new vehicle. Watched a new episode of *The Twilight Zone*. Watched a sunrise in Rhode Island. The sun looked red. It was magnificent. Got these headaches. Took a trip to South America. Took pictures of mountains. Drove to the Smithsonian Institution.

Went to this Camera Obscura show. Visited the department store near12th Street and tried on this loopingknitted mēlange virgin wool polo shirt by Boglioli and a pair of destroyedmaddox linen and cotton-blend oxford shorts by Club Monaco. Discussed mirror neurons and wage theft with this older lady from Florida. Her name was Minerva.

Recited a quick prayer. It was about voodoo stuff. A fire-
truck zoomed past alternatewo rldme. Went to underground carpark. Met this person I had never met at asocial event. Outside, something made a loud sound. I left the couch to check it out. I watched a documentary on the television and learned a lot. I purchased this painting of two French revolutionaries circa 1795 wearing Chicago starter jackets in a sewer–huddled around a legless Creature from the Black Lagoon.

The sky was the colour of my orb.
Stayed at this villa during the summer. It was usually up in the hillsand away from everything. Created a letter and sent it to *the Vallejo Times Herald*. Zodiac = 29, SFPD: 0. Wrote a poem about bodies. Mailedit to Robert Graysmith. Received a bill for $305.08. Felt supermorose. Imagined ending it all in the attic. Thought about doing it with pills.

Played pickleball at the rec centerfor four hours. Wednesday morning. Wrote poems and titled it*ultraGeodesic Plasma VI* and sent it to Dave Toschi. Sang to Sham-Ma'am-Puut, goddessof fata morgana and cosmic integrity. Made an oath to Imhotep-Armitage, female god of space and famine.
Unrolled my stonenamazlıq and faced Alabama. Prayed for nearly twenty-one hours. In an alternate universe, I know I ama Satanist hiding away in New York. I always go on vacations that take at least two hours. Had this impromptu phone conversation with my tax advisor. Dreamed of dreams. Coughed into my dominant hand. Saw what looked to be a formless substance. dusk25dusk°9-S x 110°42meatW. March 4 is the hauntedSaturday. Fell asleep for fifteen*fucked*decades. On the tv, the African continent.

Had this impromptu conversationwith my tax advisor. Dreamed I was a different person. Whooped into my left hand. Noticedwhat looked to be a formless substance. Once, when I was 13, I drove to
the video store and purchased *Parcelle*by Rose Lowder on LaserDisc. Verified the account. The teller told me there was $1,528.77 there. Used the bathroom for sevenminutes. Stared at the sky. Had the same dream again. This one actually bothered me a bit.
Trimmed my toenails. Went to the barbershop. Took the
bus to Lake Mead and saw the fourth dimension. Drove to a nightclub. Looked at the clock on the wall. It was 01:10 on
a Sunday. Owed $782.13 in tax money. Gazed at the sky and saw the words *black oceans* and *mountain winds.* Wrote a poem and called it*superDeath Theories X* and sent it to Robert Graysmith. Explored the idea of hedge funds and cultural fits with
this younger fellowfrom South Dakota. His name
was Yorrick. Together, we wrote some poems and gave it the

Walked to the Statue of Liberty.
Took a train to Vallejo for the
weekend. Examined a drawing of
my head on the television
screen. Laughed. The eyebrows
were all wrong. Walked outside. It
was one of
those nippydrip days in March. It
was the worst.
Thought about walking outside onon
e of
those humiddust afternoons in August.
It was great. In a parallel universe,
I know I am a primatologist residing
in Wisconsin. I always go
on walks that take at
least two months.

Watched *Bells of Atlantis* by Ian Hugo for the fourth time. A poster near the building about cool jobs. Dreamed of Fantasy Planet Kid. crypt4.1pity'7pity-S x 107'4.1waterE. May 2 has always been theforgottenThursday. Lived a past life for nineteen*blond*decades. On the television, European mansions. Closed my eyes and saw tiny futures. Little Red Riding Hood on the radiotalking about new-age spirituality. microTAC elite Traveled to this apartment in Indiana. Sipped on some Sauvignon Blanc.

Read passages from the *Christian Bible* for six hours. Killed a young lady in Tennessee. Thought
about death and wrote a message and dropped it in a safety deposit box at the bank. Swallowed mescaline. Left the country for a bit and visited a friend in India. It was terrible. Imagined something. It infuriated me. nightmar'd about 72abandonedtowers.

title*superStandard Orbs VI.* We sent it to Dave Toschi. Played jai alai at the rec center for four hours. Friday evening. The sky was the colour of coin. Spent time at this villa all throughout the winter. It was usuallydeep in the woods, away from everyone.

…the skull of my father

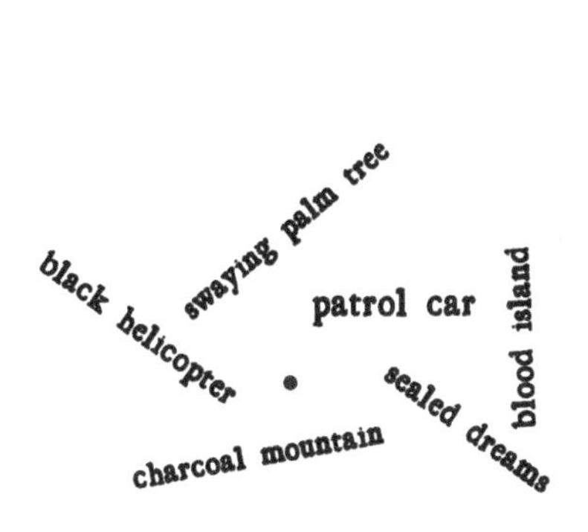
black helicopter
swaying palm tree
patrol car
blood island
sealed dreams
charcoal mountain

Imagined something. It did nothing for me.
Dreamed of 14 *forgotten*palm trees.
Dreamed of the colour *sharp*red.
Was early to work.

Took some shots of some cars in the street.
Smoked Virginia Slims.
Went on a date with a woman
who was at least 38.

Thought about sojourning
in Kentucky. Fucked this lady from
Colorado.

Listened to an audio book of *Forever Valley* by
Marie Redonnet

.

Looked at this new vehicle.
Watched a different episode of *The West*
Wing.

Watched a sunrise in Maine. The
sun looked blood red. It
was beautiful .

Experienced laryngitis.

Took a trip to Africa .

Took pictures of wildlife.
Took an Uber to the The
Metropolitan Museum of
Art

.

His name was Jwnnd'd. Together, we wrote a short
story and gave it the title *Parasitism & a
few Orbs IV*. We sent it to Robert Graysmith.
Sang to Sham-Her'ktj, god of ruinand cosmic
integrity. Imagined this smokecloud in the void.
Imagined the cave life. Sometimes, I'll go see the
doctor and he will tell me I do not have male
breast cancer. Composed some trenchpoem
about Vermont Called it *Black Void III* I went to
the bodega and got some
lamb shoulder. I was bored
with life and felt like I'd
run out of things to do. I
wrote a poem and sent it
to this person
inWashington. I rode the
train to the library
and picked up *Envie d'amour* by Cēcile Beauvoir.
I rode the train to the bookstore and picked up *La
Communauté inavouable* by Maurice Blanchot.
Cooked cursedan omelette for supper.
Made wretchedyellow tea. Played music on a Farfisa
Soundmaker keyboard. Met with the Man of One
Thousand Years at
a Hardee's in Wisconsin. Lamented about game
theory and amor fati. Composed this trenchpoem
about Josephhine Baker Called it *Sheep VIII*
I went to the bodega and boughtsome lamb shoulder.
I was bored with life and felt like I'd run out
of pastimes. I wrote a cipherand sent it to a man
in Arizona. I walked to the library and checked
out *Envie d'amour* by Cēcile Beauvoir.

Yet'Yett-Pd'it, goddess of violence to foreigners and broken
pasahapan and faced New Mexico. Prayed for near-
into the fuckedpurple sky. Felt the power of the zerouniverse.
Elajou-Bes-Her'ktj, female god of greed and fata morga-
ut Lake Herman Roadand the autumn of 1969. bastardHorror.
w Warlocks. Felt the future. Respected citiesforgotten. shitA
I visited the Adirondack Loggerheadin Arizona. I met with
ent to go see the film *New Rose Hotel* by Abel Ferrara and spent
violence to foreigners. I consumed beef at
woke up at 22:27 and walked to the room with a comput-
it to Paul Avery. I thought, *what is the point of life?* I went to
ours looking at waves. I think I have killed 12.

We wrotesome short stories and gave it the title *Parasititism & a few Societies VI.* We
sent it to Robert Graysmith.Sang praises to Salaam'Al-Ma'arh, god of cosmic
horror and evil.Made an oath to Imhotep-
raat'Dean, god of fortune and teleportation.Unrolled my stoneprayer rug and
faced Louisiana.Prayed for nineteen hours.Gazed into the rottenpurplewhiteEarth
ceiling sky.Observed the power of
the zerouniverse.Asked for überforgiveness to Imhotep-Al-Tamp-
Q'uun, goddess of creation science and death and foreign lands.Thought about Lake
Herman Roadand the autumn of 1968.blackThe pyramids of
Egypt.Heard a crying.**Experienced Invisible forces.Felt what felt like the
future.Feared the sky.Ancient symbols.Occult towers.Turned
into this destructivepleat of grey light.Gigantic microcaves.Sang
praises to Salaam'Am'Salaam, female god of formalism and the ambient stuff!
Was transported to the planet Plutoon an ark made of doomedmeat.Where
was the border violence?What did you do about the terror?A magazine
advert in Illinois: a single Hongqi-18 missile costs $370,294!A new
beginninghaunting.Enjoyed *Moon 1969* by Scott
Bartlettfor the seventh time.A billboard inside a hotel about side
hustles.Saw Comanche Man. Killed a
young woman in Missouri.Thought
about life and composed a note and dropped it in a safety deposit box
at the bank.Took codeine.Left the country for a bit and traveled
to Croatia. It was terrible.Imagined something. It did nothing for
me.nightmar'd about 79forgottentowers.Dreamed of the
colour abstractbone.Made it to work on time.Snapped some
shots of a cave.Smoked Virginia Slims.Went out with this
guy who was at least 38.**Thought about staying in South
Carolina.Fucked this guy from Kentucky.Listened to an audio
book of *Les Atomiques* by Éric Laurrent.Looked
at this used car.Watched a new
episode of *M.A.S.H.*Watched a sunrise in Michigan. The
sun appeared to be orange. It
was extraordinary.Experienced pneumonia.Traveled to South
America. Shot some hills.Walked to the the Art Institute of Chicago. It had
been a short summer.Wrote my ideas concerning heaven & hell on
some flash cards.I feel more like myself when the sky
is orange.Felt abstractmorose.Imagined suiciding in
the fluxspare room.Thought about doing it with self-
immolation.Recited a quick prayer. It was about things no one
could see.A patrol car rushed past me.Went to a hotel.Met
this person I did not want to meet at a soirée.Outside, something made a noise. I got
up from the dining room table to see what it could be.I watched a show on the
television and learned a lot.I bought a painting of two French revolutionaries circa
1795 wearing Chicago starter jackets in a sewer—huddled around a legless Creature
from the Black Lagoon.I paused for a moment and gazed out the window of
my duplex at this couple walking their dog.I required a
flashlight for something.Sometimes, I'll watch thisdocumentary about a
politician.I visited the Clarkdale Historical Society
and Observatory in Georgia.I met up with someone in a hospital. We
went to go see the film *Sombre*by Philippe Grandrieux and
spent the rest of
the night discussing jungles.I consumed human meat at
this place in Virginia.I rose at 10:15 and walked to the room with a
typewriter and wrote a cipher.

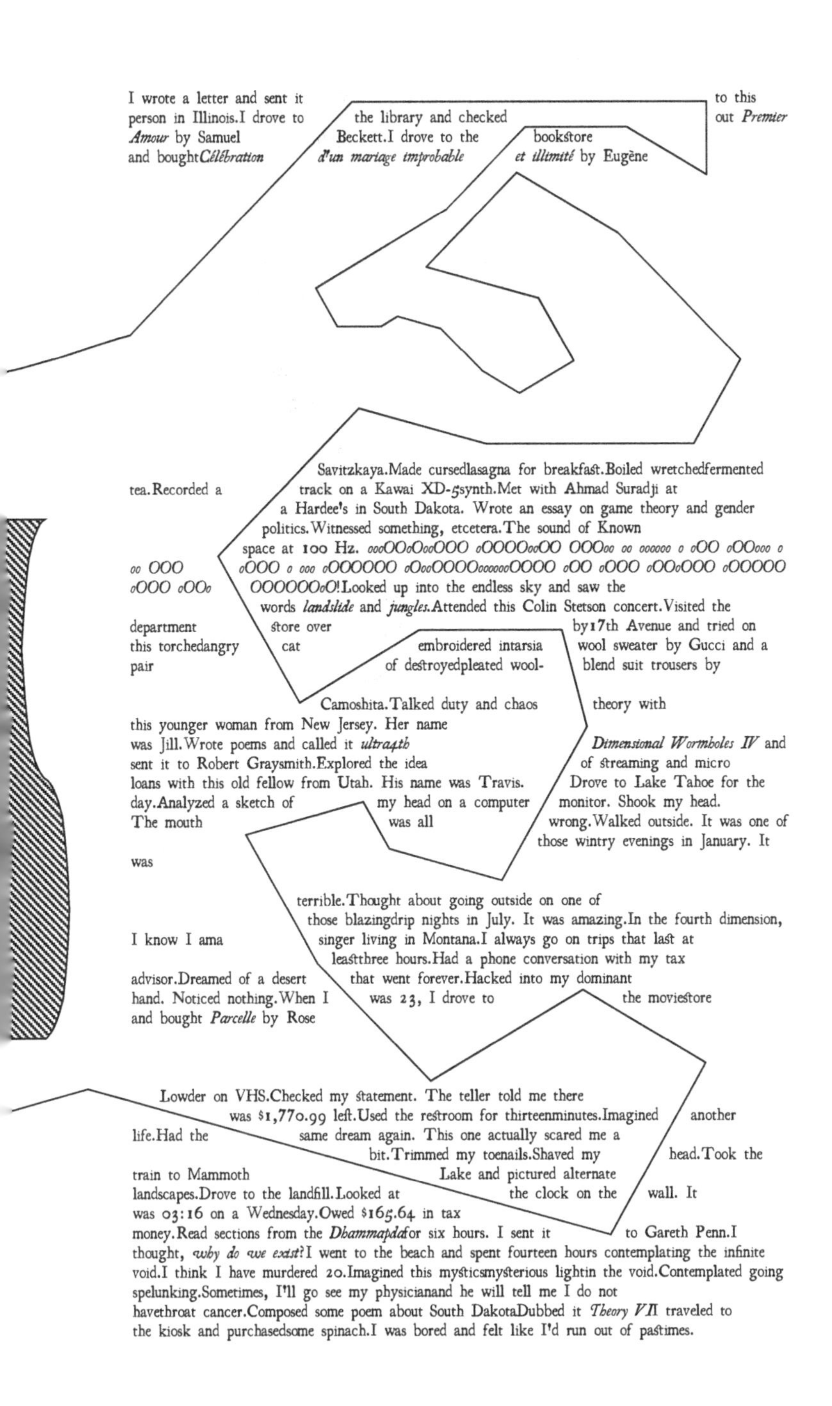

I wrote a letter and sent it to this
person in Illinois.I drove to the library and checked out *Premier*
Amour by Samuel Beckett.I drove to the bookstore
and bought*Célébration d'un mariage improbable et illimité* by Eugène
Savitzkaya.Made cursedlasagna for breakfast.Boiled wretchedfermented
tea.Recorded a track on a Kawai XD-5synth.Met with Ahmad Suradji at
a Hardee's in South Dakota. Wrote an essay on game theory and gender
politics.Witnessed something, etcetera.The sound of Known
space at 100 Hz. *oooOOoOooOOO oOOOOooOO OOOoo oo oooooo o oOO oOOooo o*
oo OOO oOOO o ooo oOOOOOO oOooOOOOooooooOOOO oOO oOOO oOOoOOO oOOOOO
*oOOO oOOo OOOOOOoO!*Looked up into the endless sky and saw the
words *landslide* and *jungles.*Attended this Colin Stetson concert.Visited the
department store over by17th Avenue and tried on
this torchedangry cat embroidered intarsia wool sweater by Gucci and a
pair of destroyedpleated wool-blend suit trousers by
Camoshita.Talked duty and chaos theory with
this younger woman from New Jersey. Her name
was Jill.Wrote poems and called it *ultra4th Dimensional Wormholes IV* and
sent it to Robert Graysmith.Explored the idea of streaming and micro
loans with this old fellow from Utah. His name was Travis. Drove to Lake Tahoe for the
day.Analyzed a sketch of my head on a computer monitor. Shook my head.
The mouth was all wrong.Walked outside. It was one of
those wintry evenings in January. It
was
terrible.Thought about going outside on one of
those blazingdrip nights in July. It was amazing.In the fourth dimension,
I know I ama singer living in Montana.I always go on trips that last at
leastthree hours.Had a phone conversation with my tax
advisor.Dreamed of a desert that went forever.Hacked into my dominant
hand. Noticed nothing.When I was 23, I drove to the moviestore
and bought *Parcelle* by Rose
Lowder on VHS.Checked my statement. The teller told me there
was $1,770.99 left.Used the restroom for thirteenminutes.Imagined another
life.Had the same dream again. This one actually scared me a
bit.Trimmed my toenails.Shaved my head.Took the
train to Mammoth Lake and pictured alternate
landscapes.Drove to the landfill.Looked at the clock on the wall. It
was 03:16 on a Wednesday.Owed $165.64 in tax
money.Read sections from the *Dhammapada*for six hours. I sent it to Gareth Penn.I
thought, *why do we exist?*I went to the beach and spent fourteen hours contemplating the infinite
void.I think I have murdered 20.Imagined this mysticsmysterious lightin the void.Contemplated going
spelunking.Sometimes, I'll go see my physicianand he will tell me I do not
havethroat cancer.Composed some poem about South DakotaDubbed it *Theory VII* traveled to
the kiosk and purchasedsome spinach.I was bored and felt like I'd run out of pastimes.

Got with a guy from Michigan. Listened to an audio book of *Le Renard et la boussole* by Robert Pinget. Looked at this used car. Watched an episode of *The X-Files.*
Observed a sunrise in Arizona. The sun appeared to be blood red. It was magnificent. Experienced these migraines. Took a trip to Africa. Shot someanimals. Rode the train to the MoMA. Played jai alai with others for fourhours. Thursday afternoon. The sky was the colour of pig's blood. Spent
time at this mansion all throughout the spring. Went outside. It was one of
those glacialvoid evenings in January. It was great. Had thoughts about walking outside on one of those balmydrip nights in September. It was amazing. ~~In a parallel universe, I imagine~~ being a deontologist residing inIndiana. I always go
on runs that take at leastthree weeks. Had this unexpected conversationwith my banker. Dreamed of Octavio Paz. Whooped into my left hand. Sawwhat looked like specks of blood. Once, when I was 22, I drove to the video store and picked up *Last Year at Marienbad* by Alain Resnais on VHS.
Checked my bank. There was$2,556.12 there. Went to the restroom for fourteenminutes. Stared at the sky. Had the same dream again. This
one informed me. Trimmed my toenails. Grew a beard. Drove to Mammoth Lake and went skinny dipping. Drove to the landfill.

Read sections fro
Attacked an old
about everything
a safety deposit b
the country for a
in Spain. It was
me feel like shit.
Dreamed of the c
time. Snapped so
of Djarum Blacks
an who was 46.
Make love to this
audio book of *Fo*
Considered this n
hospital parking
Mountaineer Hotel
rest of the night
I consumed pork
I rose at 11:29
house with a note
to Paul Avery. I
I walked to the
the waves. If I h
Saw this smokebr
war in Vietnam.
tor and he will t
I rode the train
and purchased *Cé*
illimité by Eugène
about sojourning

I watched a show on the television and learned things I did not know. I bo
Chicago starter jackets in a sewer—huddled around a legless Creature from t
window of my apartment at some of the other apartments. Wrote a poem ab

Wrote a poem about ivory. Mailed it to Gareth Penn. Received a bill for $763.87. It was from the doctor's office. It had been a terrible life. Wrote my thoughts on society and people on some flash cards. I feel more like myself when clouds look black. Felt curious. Imagined killing myself in the drainingutility room.

Imagined doing it with a gun. Saw this person at a screening for a new film. Outside, something made a loud noise. I left my desk and checked it out. Received a bill for $577.81. It was from the city. It had been a short year. Wrote my ideas on geodesic philosophies in my journal. I feel better when the sun is black. Felt extradrained. Imagined suiciding in the fluxlanding. Thought about doing it as sepukku. Did a quick deepprayer. It was about the light. A

Recited a quick foreverprayer. It was about the light. An ambulance rushed past me. Walked to the car park. Saw this person at this private soirée. Outside, something made a sound. I left the floor and checked it out. I watched a programme on the television and learned things I did not know. I bought a painting of some freaky cavedwellers surrounding a camp fire. I took a moment and looked out the window of my apartment at a woman running. I needed masking tape for something. Sometimes, I'll watch a documentary on North Korea. I went to the Heard Observatory ofNebraska. Wrote a letter and sent it to *The San Francisco Examiner*. Zodiac = 11, SFPD: 0. Wrote a poem about the future. Mailed it to Paul Avery. Received a bill for $778.95. It was from Walmart. It had been a short year. Wrote my thoughts on black holes in my pocket notebook. I feel better when the clouds areblack. Felt invincible. Thought about suiciding in the abandonedspare room. Thought about doing it with a gun. Recited a quick foreverprayer. It was about dark spells. An exotic car zoomed past tomorrowme. Walked to the aquarium.

ta for ten hours.
ota. Thought
ssage and kept it in
gested drukqs. Left
elative staying
omething. It made
gottenvictims.
ade it to work on
moked an entire pack
wom-
ving in Indiana.
ee. Listened to an
ie Redonnet.
someone in a
see the film *Dead*
nov and spent the

yoming.
part of the
oem. I sent it
he point of life?
eteen hours watching
killed 31.
ed. Imagined the
see a doc-
e heartcancer.

e improbable et
ght

limousine zoomed past otherdimensionme. I traveled to the kiosk and got some garlic. I was bored and felt like I'd run out of hobbies. I wrote a cipher and sent it to a teacher in Kentucky. I rode the metro to the library and checked out *L'Océan* by Raphaël Alegria.

f two French revolutionaries circa 1795 wearing
. I reflected for a moment and lookedout the
Mailed it to Gareth Penn.

Played basketb
at the rec ce
for four hou

Wednesday
evening. The
was the colc
of the bottom
the lake.

Spent
time at a man
all
throughout t
spring. It
was usually de
the
woods and a
from everyo

dynaTAC 8000x

Visited a pod in Maryland.

Drank some Riesling.

Have never taken the train to seeNavy Pier.

Walked to Yucca Mountain for the weekend.

Examined a drawing of my face on a computer monitor. Sighed. The face was all wrong.

Walked outside. It was one of those glacialvoid mornings in October. It was terrible.

Had thoughts about walking outside on one of those hotvoid mornings in August. It was great.

In a past life, I feel I might be a deity living in Massachusetts.

I always go on walks that take fourweeks.

Had this impromptu telephone conversation with my psychic.

Dreamed of vanities.

Whooped into my shirt sleeve. Sawspecks of blood.

Once, when I was 20, I drove to the movie store and picked up *August in the Water* by Sogo Ishii on VCD.

Verified the statement. The teller told me there was $1,771.69 there.

Went to the restroom for fiveminutes.

Cried.

Got a migraine.

Took a trip to South America. Took pictures of wildlife.

Took an Uber to the the Art Institute of Chicago.

Wrote a letter and sent it to *the San Francisco Chronicle*. Zodiac = 12, SFPD: 0.

Wrote a poem about Kansas. Mailedit to Dave Toschi.

I met with someone at a bar. We went to go see the film *New Rose Hotel* by Abel Ferrara and spent the rest of the night talking about fear.

I consumed beef at this place in Rhode Island.

I woke up at 10:26 and walked to
the room with a view and composed a letter. I sent it to Robert Graysmith.

I thought,
what is my life?

I went to the beach and spent threehours trying to understand life.If I had to guess, I think I havebutchered 19.Saw a dronesatellite in the void.Thought about the war in Vietnam.Sometimes, I'll go see the doctor and she will tell me I do not have eyecancer.Composed some deeppoem about WisconsinDubbed it *Sheep VII* traveled to the kiosk and picked upa box of juice.I was bored and felt like I'd run out of stuff to do. I wrote a poem and sent it to someone in Vermont.I took the bus to the library and picked up *Les Absences du capitaine Cook* by Éric Chevillard.I went to the bookstore and picked up *L'Abbé C* by Georges Bataille.Made cursedan omelette for lunch.Made wretchedfermented tea.Made sounds on this Roland SH-7synthesizer.Met with Buffalo Bill at a Krispy Kreme in New York. Wrote an essay on psychoanalysis and Darwinism.Saw something exceptional, etcetera.The wobble of Known space at 40Hz. *CcccccCccCCCC cCCCccCCCC CCCCCccCCCccCcccCCCC cCCCccCCCC CCCcccCCCC cCCCC CCCccccccCCCCcc cCCCC CCCcccCCC cccC cCCCC CCCccccCCCC cCCCC CCCcc cc CCCCCCc ccCCCC ccccCCCCC cc cc cc cCCC cC CC.*Looked up into the infinite void and saw the words *Arabs* and *the tropicks.*Went to this Neil Halstead concert.Visited the clothing store over by17th Avenue and tried on this blue kei slim-fit striped cotton seersucker blazer by Canal and a pair of destroyedpod wide-leg cady shorts by Rick Owens.Talked about closets and selling outwith this older woman from Vermont. Her name was Denise.Wrote a 8 novel and titled it *ultra4th Dimensional Pseudosciences V* and sent it to Dave Toschi.Talked wastewater and medieval literature with this young fellowfrom Texas. His name was Bobek. We wrote a short story and called it*ultraEntomophagy & the ConceptsIV.*

I met up with someone at a bar. We went to go see the film *Alaska* by Dore O and spent the rest of
the daydiscussing violence to foreigners.I consumed beef at this restaurant in Washington.I rose at 10:39 and walked to
the part of the apartment with a computer and wrote a poem. I sent it to Gareth Penn.I
thought, *what is the point of life*? We sent it to Paul Avery.Sang to Bes-Sham'raat-Al'Dean, godof earth
magnets and violence to foreigners.Made a promise to Yuue-Pd'it, female
god of deception and pain.Unrolled a stoneprayer rug and faced Virginia.Prayed for nearly nine hours.Looked
up into the fuckedbrowngreen Earth ceiling sky.Felt the power of the neverstars.Prayed for forgiveness to Elajou-Tekhrit-
Ma'am-Puut, female god of race traitors and suicides and race traitors.Remembered Modesto and the springof 1969.bastardThe
pyramids of Egypt.Felt a distant humming.Experienced Invisible forces.Felt today.Could not appreciate the sky.shitAncient
symbols.Bombed out castles.Became some implodingparticle of yellow light.Massive invisibleforests.Sang praises to Y'akiir-Ma'am
-Puut, black god of instant teleportationand space!Teleported to the planet Pluto on an ark made of doomedmeat.What would
I find beyond the edge of the screen?How did you control the terror A new beginningswelling.Talked about *Dead Mountaineer
Hotel* by Grigori Kormanov for the tenth time.An advertisement inside themountain about streamers. It was 03:34 on
a Monday.Owed $691.50 in taxes. It was amazing.Imagined something. It changed my life. dreamed of 82 forgottenimpossible
structures.Dreamed of the colour oxbowcatawba.Was late to work.Snapped a picture of the moon.Enjoyed an e-cig.Went on a
date with a woman who was 51. Watched a new episode of *The Golden Girls*. Met this person I did not want to
meet at a soirée. Observed a sunrise in New York. The sun looked orange. It was beautiful. My pain is real. I will never be
normal. You cannot tell me otherwise.

Observed a sunrise in Wyoming. The sun appeared to be orange.

Thursday evening on a Friday. The sky was the colour of wine.

I drove to the bookstore and picked up *Le Renard et la boussole* by Robert Pinget. Made wretchedbread for lunch. Boiled white tea. Played a track on my Clavia Nord Modular G2 synthesizer. Met up with Eddie Seda at a Long John Silver's in Indiana. Talked aboutlate nights and streamers. Was witness to something truly extraordinary, etcetera. This one scared me the most. Trimmed my fingernails. Shaved my head.
Drove to Mammoth Lake and pictured alternate landscapes. Took the bus to the mall. Glanced at the clock on the wall. It was 13:48 on a Saturday. Owed $120.60 in tax money. Read sections from the *Tanakh* for two hours. Assailed a young woman in Oklahoma.
Thought about walking outside during one of those swelteringvoidafternoons in September. It was great. In a past life, I imagine being a submarine cook living inPennsylvania. I always go on vacations that take usually two months. Had this telephone conversation with my tax advisor. Dreamed of wooden things. Whooped into my shirt sleeve. Saw no blood. I walked to the beach and spent sixteen hours questioning the meaning of life.
I would imagine I have murdered 32.
Imagined this dronebright light in the void.
Contemplated going spelunking. Sometimes, I'll go see a doctor and he will tell me I do not have bile duct cancer. Composed some abstractpoem about South Dakota Named it *Sheep V* I walked to the store and got some meat. I was bored and felt like I'd run out of pastimes. I wrote a poem and sent it to this person in Idaho. I rode the train to the library and checked out *Forever Valley* by Marie Redonnet. Talked aboutpirates and life insurance.
Witnessed something exceptional, etcetera. Looked up into the infinite void and saw the words *black oceans* and *green.* Went to this Neil Halstead show. Visited the clothing store over by12th Avenue and tried on this loopingembroidered torch logo shirt by Opening Ceremony and a pair of drippingstriped cotton-dobby shorts by Neighborhood. Talked mirror neurons and Lindsay Lohan with this old lady from Delaware. Her name was Emma. Wrote short stories and titled it*Forever Darkness III* and sent it to Paul Avery.

We sent it to Gareth Penn. Prayed to Tekhrit-
raat'Dean, god of the moon and new-age spirituality. Broke the
promise I made to Graam'D'agrhiil, female
god of defectors and savagery. Unrolled my crystalprayer
rug and faced Connecticut. Prayed for nearly eighteen hours.
Looked up into the fuckedgreywhitesky. Observed the energy of
the neveruniverse. Asked for freedom to Yuue-Al
Sala'amPd'it, female god of evil and savagery and creation
science. Thought about Lake Berryessa and
the summer of 1969. blackDracula black. Felt a humming.
Saw Invisible forces. Felt what felt like tomorrow. No longer
feared the sunvoided. twiggyAncient symbols. Luciferian estates.
Turned into this destructivebeam of blue light. Heavy oak trees.
Sang to Djeet-Her'ktj, female god of asymmetrical panel
fashion and posthumanism! Traveled to the second dimension on a
ship made of doomedmeat. Who was here right now? What did
you do about the end? On a television ad in Virginia: a
single M45 SLBMdripmouth missile costs $672,874! A new
beginning! Talked about *Birth of an Island* by Ósvaldur
Knudsen for the ninth time. An
ad within a mountain about tears in the rain. Dreamed of Lake
Thing. crypt47dusk°7pinkN x 126°41meatW. January 28 has
always been acastratedTuesday. Zonked out for fifteen days. On
the tv, the African continent. Blinked and saw overlapping
timelines. Sleeping Beauty on the televisiontalking about the
tropicks. microTAC ultra lite Moved to a villa in South
Dakota. Drank Cabernet Sauvignon. Have never taken the train
to seeCentral Park. Drove to Vallejo for the weekend. Stopped
to look at a drawing of my face on a poster. Couldn't believe
it. The nose was all wrong. Went outside. It was one of
those glacialdust evenings in January. It was the worst.
Thought about going outside duringone of
those searing nights in August. It was horrible. In a parallel
universe, I feel I might be a lobster enthusiast residing
inMinnesota. I always go on runs that last at leasttwo days.
Had this impromptu conversationwith my tax advisor.
Dreamed of dead malls. Sometimes, I'll go see the
doctor and he will tell me I have liver cancer.
Composed this blödpoem about horror films Titled it *Blank
Spaces III* I walked to the store and boughtsome peanut butter.
I was bored with life and felt like I'd run out of stuff to do. I
wrote a poem and sent it to a woman in West Virginia.
I went to the library and checked out*La Communauté
inavouable* by Maurice Blanchot. I rode the metro to the
bookstore and bought *Forever Valley* by Marie Redonnet.
Made lobster for dinner. Boiled some cursedgreen tea.
Composed sounds on this Roland Jupiter 4 keyboard. Met
up with Ted Bundy at a Carl's Jr.in New
Hampshire. Explored the idea of waves and unofficial
economies with this olderguy from New Jersey. His name
was Terrence. We wrote some short stories and called
it *ultraAbstractOrbs III.*

When I was 12, I took the bus to the video store and purchased *Vite* by Daniel Pommereulle on VCD.Verified the account. The teller told me there was $2,035.79 left.Used the bathroom for fourteenminutes.Did nothing.Had a similar dream. This one actually bothered me.Clipped my toenails.Took the bus to Mammoth Lake and imagined infinite worlds.Rode the train to the landfill.Glanced at the clock on the wall. It was 11:43 on a Saturday.Owed $106.07 in tax money.Read sections from the *Tanakh* for seven hours.Assailed a young man in Kentucky.Thought about death and composeda message and kept it in a box.Injected acid.Left the country for a bit and went to Croatia. It was amazing.Imagined something. It did something to me.Dreamed of the colour impotentchampagne.Was late to work.Snapped a picture of some people running away from a falling tree.Enjoyed a cigar.Went out with a woman who was 52.Thought about sojourning in Idaho.Had sex with this guy from Rhode Island.Listened to an audio book of *Les Absences du capitaine Cook* by Éric Chevillard.Looked at a used vehicle.Watched a different episode of *The Shield*.Observed a sunrise in Kansas. The sun looked grey. It was marvelous.Got a migraine.Traveled to Africa. Took pictures ofanimals.Rode the train to the MoMA.Played basketball by myself for fourhours.Wednesday morning. The sky was the colour of coin.Spent time at a house during the summer. It was almost always deep in the woods, away from everything.Created a note and sent it to *the San Francisco Chronicle*. Zodiac = 21, SFPD: 0.Received a bill for $257.01. It was from the doctor's office.It had been a long summer.Wrote my ideas concerning dark matter on some flash cards.I feel more like myself when the clouds look blue.Felt tired.Imagined suiciding in the music room.Thought about doing it as some form of cutting.Recited a quick samsaraprayer. It was about voodoo stuff.An ambulance rushed past tomorrowme.Went to the pool.Saw this person at a dinner party.Outside, something made a loud noise. I left my desk to see what it was.I watched a show on the television and learned a lot.I purchased a painting of a dog named Georges.I took a moment and gazed out the window of my house at some trees.I required a tub of vaseline for a project.Sometimes, I'll watch a documentary on white supremacy.I visited the Heard Museum ofMassachusetts.I met up with someone at a bar. We went to go see the film *Deux fois* by Jackie Raynal and spent the rest of the day discussing cosmic horror.I consumed squid at this restaurantin Mississippi.I awoke at 20:28 and walked to the room with a view and composed a letter. I sent it to Robert Graysmith.I thought, *why am I here?*I drove to the beach and spent twenty hours watching the waves.I would say I have killed 31.Imagined this smokesatellite in the sky.Pictured simpler times.Sometimes, I'll go see the doctor and she will tell me I do not have eyecancer.Wrote this trenchpoem about body activismTitled it *Treatise of a Modern Man IV*I walked to the store and picked upsome ice cream.I was bored and felt like I'd run out of stuff to do. I wrote a letter and sent it to a woman in Tennessee.I rode the train to the library and checked out *La Fuite à cheval très loin dans la ville* by Bernard-Marie Koltès.I rode the metro to the bookstore and purchased *Trois jours chez ma tante* by Yves Ravey.Ate tilapia for lunch.Boiled some green tea.Played music on this Roland D-50synth.Met with Ted Kaczynski at a Wendy'sin West Virginia. Argued aboutartifice and digital philosophy.Was witness to something exceptional, etcetera.The reverberation of ground loops at 30 Hz.

Gazed at the endless sky and saw the words *forgotten bodies of water*and *mystery.* Went to a Modern English show. Visited the clothing store near 12thStreet and tried on this fuckedangry cat embroidered intarsia wool sweater by Gucci and a pair of drippingpod wide-leg cady shorts by Rick Owens. Talked call out culture and the umbilic torus with

this younger ladyfrom Ohio. Her name was Hilary. Wrote a novel and titled it*ultraForever Shield IV* and sent it to Dave Toschi. Talked diasporas and human capitalwith this younger man from Vermont. His name was Thessalonian. Together, we wrote a poem and gave it the title *BlackDomes II.* We sent it to Dave Toschi.Spoke to to Tekhrit-Al-Faseeque, female god of the tropicks and asymmetrical panel fashion.Broke the promise I made to Ra'amuul-Apep-Sekh, god of blackand lip service.Unrolled a seccade and faced Minnesota.Felt the power of the zerocosmos.Asked for hyperdark orbs to Graam'Salaam'D'agrhiil, female godof new-age spirituality and space time violence and desert storms.Thought about Lake Berryessa and the winter of 1969.bastard The Wild blue frontier.Heard a distant humming.Saw Warlocks.Felt today.Did not like lakes.ramirezXenomorph.Haunted castles.Turned into this particle of greylight.Forever invisiblecaves.Sang to Ra'amuu l-Tamp-Q'uun, female god of diagrams and fortune!Traveled to the first dimension on a boat designed by crucifiedslaves.Who was here right now?How did you control the terror?On this magazine advert in Maryland: a single Satan (SS-18)dangercrimemissile costs $373,628!The endhaunting?Enjoyed *Sink or Swin* by Su Friedrichagain, for the tenth time.A commercial inside a building about prison labor.Dreamed of Kinetic Fiend.crypt46dusk°5dusk=N x 104°44waterE.January 3 will always be theimpossibleWednesday.Zonked out for eighteen*fucked*moments.On the television, light from the heavens.Blinked and experiencedeternityhigh.Little Red Riding Hood on the television dissecting race traitors.dynaTAC 8000xTraveled to this apartment in New Jersey.Drank some Chenin blanc.Walked to Stonehenge. Played soccer at the rec center for three hours.Thursday afternoon. The sky was the colour of the bottom of the lake.Stayed at a house all throughout the spring. It was sometimes near a body of water, away from everything.Created a cipher and sent it to *The San Francisco Examiner.* Zodiac = 22, SFPD: 0.Wrote a poem about existentialism. Sent it to Robert Graysmith.Received a bill for $573.39. It was from the University.

I consumed squid at this bistro in
I awoke at 22:11 and walked to t
notebook and composeda letter. I se
Penn. I thought, *what is my life?*
and spent fivehours looking at wave
have murdered 17. Saw this papers
Contemplated the impermanence of
times, I'll go see my doctor and he
not havelaryngeal cancer. Composec
about white linen Dubbed it *Found*
I traveled to the store and picked
was bored with life and felt like I'
I wrote a poemand sent it to a wo
I walked to the library and picked
sifs du plaisir by Alain Robbe-Gril
wrote a short story and gave it the
tle *ForeverShield X*. We sent it to
Sang to Salaam'raat'Dean, female g
age spirituality. Broke the oath I
made to Graam'Sham'raat-Al'Dean,
politicks and third worlds. Unrolled a fuckedjoynamoz and faced
nearly eight hours. Gazed into
the putridpitchblackpurple Earth ce
served the power of the neverstars.
Asked for überfreedom to Graam'I
KellPd'it, god of asymmetrical pan
ion and savagery and foreign lands

I prefer when the sun looks white. Imagined killing myself in the landing. Thought about doing it with the harpoon gun. Recited a quick [illegible]prayer. It was about things no one could see. Outside, something made a sound. I left the floor and checked it out. I watched a documentary on the television and learned things I did not know. Sometimes, I'll watch a documentary about a tribe in Africa. I met up with someone in a hospital parking lot. We went to go see the film *Dead Mortimer Hotel* by Gregori Komanov and spent the rest of the day discussing the mass. I consumed deer meat at this bistro Texas. Alice on the radio [illegible]. microTAC 2 Have never been to the Statue of Zeus at Olympia. Drove to Yucca Mountain for the day. Looked at a sketch of my head on a poster. Laughed. The eyebrows wereall wrong. Walked outside. It was one of those coldvoid mornings in December. It was green. Had thoughts about going outside during one of those [illegible] in August. It was amazing. In a past life, I know I am a match stick man from Virginia. I always go on voyages that last at least two months. Had a phone conversation with my banker. Hacked into my non-dominant hand. Noticed something black. When I was 10, I walked to the movie store and picked up *Papaya Love Goddess of the Cannibals* by Joe D'Amato on VCD. Checked my balance. There was 2,848.34 left. Used the restroom for eight minutes. Had a different dream. This one informed me a lie. Wrote some deeppoem about Connecticut Dubbed it *Treatise of a Molten Mind VIII* I walked to the kiosk and purchased[illegible] ice cream. I was bored with life and felt like I'd run out of things to do. I wrote a letter and sent it to someone inNorth Dakota. I rode the metro to the library and picked up *Bruno d'amour* by Cécile Beauvoir. I woke up at 00:56 and walked to the part of the house with a notebookand drafted a poem. I sent it to Gareth Penn. I thought, *is there anything else out there?* I went to the beach and spent eighthours contemplating life. I would say I have killed 59. Imagined a paperplane in the void. Contemplated the cave life. When I was 12, I went to the videostore and picked up *The Beast of Bitter Island* by Pierre Kast on VHS. Checked my statement. The teller told me there was $1,051.20 left. Went to the bathroom for twelveminutes. Passed gas. Had a similar dream. This one scaredme. Cut my toenails. Grew a moustache. Took the bus to Mammoth Lake and went for a swim. Took the bus to a laundromat.

Remembered Lake Herman
Road and the autumn of 1968.
Fire. Heard a buzzing.
Experienced Sorcerers.
Felt tomorrow. Did not
like lakesforgotten. twiggyBushido
Blade. Luciferian townhouses.

Turned
into this hauntedray of bluelight.
I feel more like myself when the
moon looks orange. Felt extratired.
Thought about killing myself in
the hellhall. Imagined doing it with
a gun. Did a quick forgottenprayer.
It was about voodoo stuff. A patrol
car rushed past nextweekme.
Walked to the park. Met this
person I had never
met at this private soirée. Outside,
something made a noise. I left my
desk to see what it was. I watched
a programme on the television and
learned nothing.
I bought a painting of a woman
sitting in a very sinister-looking
chair. I reflected for a moment
and lookedout the window of
my house at some of the other
apartments. I required some
rope for something. On the
television, a bullfight in spain.
Closed my eyes and saw a black
voidhigh. Snow White on
the tv talking aboutfamine.

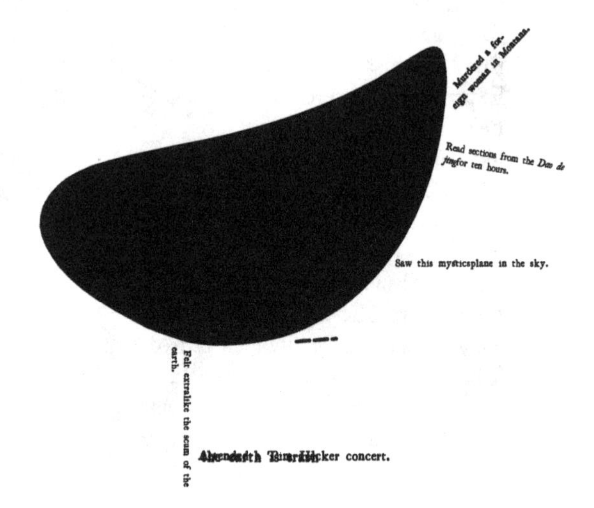
Murdered a for-
eign woman in Montana.
Read sections from the *Dao de jing* for ten hours.
Saw this mysticsplane in the sky.
Felt extralike the scum of the earth.
Attended a Tim Hecker concert.

Wrote a poem and called
it*ultraBlack Geoengineering IV* and sent it to Dave
Toschi. Talked wastewater and prison laborwith
this young fellow from Arkansas. His name
was Pat. Together, we wrote a poem and called
it *Incomplete Domes VI.* We sent it to Dave Toschi.
Sang to Khonsu-An-Inkh-Tah, goddessof the
sun and mountain deaths. Broke the oath I
made to Elajou-Armitage, female
god of ghostingand the Amazon forest.

Unrolled the fuckednamazlıq and faced Mississippi.
Prayed for nearly nineteen hours. Looked up into
the decayingorangepurple Earth ceiling.
Observed the energy of the hellstars.
Prayed for ultrapestilence to Djje'Djd-
KellAm'Salaam, god of non-monogamy and mountain
winds and black oceans. Recalled Lake Herman
Road and the autumn of 1968. Water.
Heard a buzzing. Saw Invisible forces.
Felt tomorrow. Feared tunnels. Miami in 1978.
Impossible castles. Turned
into this destructivebeam of yellow light.

Thought about life and composed a note and kept it
in a cabinet. Took drugs. Left the country for a bit
and visited a friend in Spain. It was terrible.
Read sections from the *Dao de jing*for three hours.
Attacked an old woman in Idaho.

Contemplated nothing and composeda letter and locke
d it in a safe. Swallowed adderall. Left the country
for a bit and visited an acquaintance from London.
It was terrible. Thought about something. It scared
me. nightmar'd about 10 towers.

Outside, something made a loud noise. I got up from the dining room table to see what it was. I watched a documentary on the television and learned nothing. I bought a painting of twc
and looked out the window of my high-rise at this couple walking their dog. I needed a flashlight for a project. Sometimes, I'll watch thisdocumentary about the American prison system.
ShellPlantation in West Virginia. I met up with someone at a restaurant. We went to go see the film *Night of the Hunted* by Jean Rollin and spent the rest of the nighttalking about evil.
this bistro in Maine. I woke up at 21:55 and walked to the part of the house with a window and drafted a letter. I sent it to Gareth Penn. I thought, *why are we all here?* I went to
Fuite à cheval très loin dans la ville by Bernard-Marie Koltès. Cooked destroyedan omelette for dinner. Remembered Modesto and the autumn of 1969. Disease. Heard a crying. Saw Deam
afraid of the skyforgotten. shitAncient symbols. Ruined mills. Turned into this hauntedray of brownlight. Gigantic nonexistentjungles. Prayed to Al-Sham'raat-Al'Dean, female god of eart
Traveled to the second dimension on a vessel made of slaves. What would I find beyond the edge of the screen? How did you control the end? This television ad in New York: a single
airdangercrime missile costs $683,219. A forgotten timelinehaunting? Viewed *Dead Mountaineer Hotel* by Grigori Kormanov again, for the fourth time. An advertisement on the side of aho
of Chase-Maker. fool27dusk°1foolsS x 102°44patriotW. March 9 will always be andiseasedThursday. Tried xanax. Left the country for a bit and visited an acquaintance from Japan. It v
It made me feel like shit. nightmar'd about 42 angels. Was early to work. Snapped some pictures of the moon. Enjoyed a Newport. Went out with this guy who was at least 44. It was
hills and away from everything. Talked fakers and buying in with this young lady from Iowa. Her name was Adrianna. Wrote a poem and called it*ultraBlack Accelerationism III.*

I bought a painting of tv
cliff into a foggy sunset.
and lookedout the window
mountains. I required som
Sometimes, I'll watch this
islands. I visited the Hea
I met with someone at a
the film *Atomic Park*by I
Foerster and spent the re
about defectors. I consum
this restaurant in Massach
terrible nightmare.

Ate wretchedlobster for supper. Boiled destroyedchrysanthemum
tea. Made a track on a Yamaha DX-1keyboard. Met
up with Ottis Toole at a Quizno'sin West Virginia. Talked
aboutautomation and porn culture. Saw something. Gazed at
the endless sky and saw the words *dark spirits* and *the tropicks.*
Went to a Colin Stetson show. Visited the clothing shop over
byWashington Avenue and tried on this colour-block cotton-piqué
polo shirt by Thom Browne and a pair of eastham slim-fit
washed stretch-denim jeans by Belstaff. Talked
about pestilence and sharing economies with
this older womanfrom Montana. Her name was Maria. Wrote a
novella and titled it*Geodesic Biopharmaceuticals III* and sent it
to Gareth Penn. Discussed acidification and firefighters with
this younger manfrom Connecticut. Turned
into this implodingpleat of blue light. Forever deathjungles.
Prayed to Yet'Yett-Armitage, goddessof ruin and third worlds.
Teleported to the first dimension on a vessel made
of crucifiedslaves. What happened off-screen? What did you do
about the light? This magazine advert in Delaware: a
single IRIS-T missile costs $622,517! The end. The
sun looked yellow. It was beautiful. Experienced these migraines.
Took a trip to South America. Shotwildlife. Took an Uber to
the Smithsonian Institution. Created a letter and sent it to *the
Vallejo Times Herald*. Zodiac = 25, SFPD: 0. Wrote a poem
about pink leather. Mailed it to Dave Toschi. Received a bill
for $190.02. It was from the dentist. It had been
a terrible day. Wrote my thoughts about animals on some loose
leaf paper. I feel better when the clouds lookwhite.
Felt extramorose. Thought about killing myself in
the abandonedparlour. Thought about doing it as a hanging.
Recited a quick forgottenprayer. It was about things no one
could see. An ambulance rushed past alternateworldme.
Went to the gas station. Sang praises to Djeet-
Her'ktj, god of broken promises and white radicals. Made a
promise to Imhotep-Sham'raat-
Al'Dean, goddess of ghosting and famine.
Unrolled the stoneprayer mat and faced California.
Prayed for twenty-three hours.
Prayed for sacredfreedom to Yet'Yett-Al-raat'Dean, female
god of race traitors and savagery and pinkwashing. White noise.
On the television, bright lights. Closed my
eyes and experiencedblack waterendless.

Talked methane and porn culturewith
this young fellow from Nevada. His name
was Marty. Together, we wrote some short
stories and called it *superIncomplete Shield II.* W
sent it to Dave Toschi. Goldilocks on
the tv talking aboutself-deception. microTAC eli
Moved to a station in Wyoming. Enjoyed a glas
of Prosecco. Have never taken the train to seeth
Tower of London. Took a boat to Benicia for
the weekend. Analyzed a rendering of
my head on a poster. Couldn't believe it.
The eyebrows were all wrong. Walked outside.
was one of
those wintryvoid mornings in December. It was
terrible. Thought about walking outside during
of those hot mornings in July. It was the worst.
Closed my eyes and experiencedoverlapping
timelines. Snow White on the television talking
bout new-age spiritu TAC elite Mov
a hut Florida. D nk s e Champagne.
e n gone to se viagi K m
le Lake Be sa. ke
my head on a poster. Smiled.
Used the bathroom for two minutes. Stared at t
sky. Had a different dream. This one scared me
bit. Trimmed my fingernails. Grew a beard.
Drove to Mammoth Lake and gazed at the star
Drove to a bowling alley. Checked my watch.
was 22:07 on a Monday. Owed
$874.80 in medical bills. Read sections from
the *Qur'an* for four hours. Brutalized a
young man in Ohio. Thought
about nothing and wrote a message and locked i
in a safety deposit box at the bank. Ingested an
nitrite. Left the country for a bit and visited a
friend in Sénégal. It was *whatever.*
Imagined killing myself in the helloffice. Thoug
about doing it via asphyxiation. Did a
quick samsaraprayer. It was about dark spells.
sports car rushed past otherdimensionme.
I walked to the store and picked upsome lamb
shoulder. I was bored and felt like I'd run out
of stuff to do. I wrote a poem and sent it to a
woman in Utah. I walked to the library
and checked out *La Nuit juste avant les forêts* b
Bernard-Marie Koltès. I rode the metro to the
bookstore and picked up *M.M.M.M.* by Jean-
Philippe Toussaint. Cooked destroyedan
omelette for dinner.

te wretchedlobster for supper. Boiled destroyedchrysanthemum
a. Made a track on a Yamaha DX-1keyboard. Met
with Ottis Toole at a Quizno'sin West Virginia. Talked
outautomation and porn culture. Saw something. Gazed at
e endless sky and saw the words *dark spirits* and *the tropicks.*
'ent to a Colin Stetson show. Visited the clothing shop over
Washington Avenue and tried on this colour-block cotton-
qué polo shirt by Thom Browne and a pair of eastham slim-
washed stretch-denim jeans by Belstaff. Talked
out pestilence and sharing economies with
is older womanfrom Montana. Her name was Maria.
'rote a novella and titled it*Geodesic Biopharmaceuticals III* and
nt it to Gareth Penn.
scussed acidification and firefighters with
is younger manfrom Connecticut. Turned
to this implodingpleat of blue light. Forever deathjungles.
ayed to Yet'Yett-Armitage, goddessof ruin and third worlds.
eleported to the first dimension on a vessel made
crucifiedslaves. [illegible] happened off-screen? W[illegible]t did you do
o[illegible] light? Th[illegible] m[illegible]azine [illegible] De[illegible]re: a
g I IS-T missi[illegible] $[illegible] 2,[illegible] he [illegible]nd The
[illegible] yellow. [illegible] hese
graines. Took a trip to South America. Shotwildlife. Took
Uber to the Smithsonian Institution. Created a letter and
nt it to *the Vallejo Times Herald*. Zodiac = 25, SFPD: 0.
'rote a poem about pink leather. Mailed it to Dave Toschi.
ceived a bill for $190.02. It was from the dentist. It had
en a terrible day. Wrote my thoughts about animals on some
ose leaf paper. I feel better when the clouds lookwhite.
lt extramorose. Thought about killing myself in
e abandonedparlour. Thought about doing it as a hanging.
ecited a quick forgottenprayer. It was about things no one
uld see. An ambulance rushed past alternateworldme.
'ent to the gas station. Sang praises to Djeet-
er'ktj, god of broken promises and white radicals. Made a
omise to Imhotep-Sham'raat-
'Dean, goddess of ghosting and famine.
nrolled the stoneprayer mat and faced California.
ayed for twenty-three hours.
ayed for sacredfreedom to Yet'Yett-Al-raat'Dean, female
d of race traitors and savagery and pinkwashing. White
ise. On the television, bright lights. Closed my
es and experiencedblack waterendless. I consumed pork at
s restaurant in Louisiana. I awoke at 01:11 and walked to
room with a desk and wrote a poem. I sent it to Paul
very. I thought, *what is my life*? I walked to the beach and
ent eleven hours contemplating the infinite void. If I had to
ess, I have killed 12. Saw this papercloud in the void.
ontemplated going spelunking.

s o r

c e r

y .

I took the bus to the bookstore and picked
up *Forever Valley* by Marie Redonnet.
Cooked meatloaf for brunch.
Boiled wretchedyellow tea.
Composed music on this Yamaha CS-
60 synthesizer. Met up with John Wayne
Gacy at a KFC in Nevada. Lamented
aboutnetworking and interns. Saw something
exceptional, etcetera. Gazed at the sky and saw
the words *black oceans* and *jungles*. Attended a Lil
B show. Visited my
tailor near WashingtonAvenue and tried on
this angry cat embroidered intarsia wool sweater
by Gucci and a pair of ari wool and mohair-
blend bermuda shorts by Acne Studios. Explored
the idea of tar and featherand late nights with
this youngerwoman from Oregon. Her name
was Maria. Looked up into the redwhite Earth
ceiling.

neverstars. Asked for ultradark
orbs to Graam'Bes-Ma'an-Taap, god of white
radicals and third worlds and asymmetrical panel
fashion. Remembered Modesto and
the autumn of 1969. bastardThe serpent.
Heard a buzzing. Saw Deamons. Felt the past.
Could not appreciate the beachvoided.
luciferianSlow burning car.
Composed this abstractpoem about rose perfume
Called it *Found Poem VI* I went to
the kiosk and got some honey. I was bored with
life and felt like I'd run out of pastimes.
Saw Irrevocable Man. 30°3-N x 100°56painE.
July 8 will forever be ansoiledSaturday.
Disappeared for four *psionic*days. On the
television, obfuscated memories.
Blinked and saw overlapping timelineshigh. Snow
White on the radio unpackingpolitics. microTAC
elite Drove to this apartment in Minnesota.
Sipped on some Malbec. Remember visiting Navy
Pier. Drove to Lake Berryessa for the day.
Scrutinized a rendering of my faceon a computer
monitor. Sighed. The forehead was all wrong.
Went outside. It was one of
those nippydeep mornings in January. It was
terrible. Had
thoughts about walking outside on one of
those summerydeep nightsin September. It was the
worst. In an alternate universe, I know I ama
tacher residing in Michigan. I always go
on runs that last at leasttwo months.
Had this phone conversation with my banker.
Dreamed of wide windows. Coughed into my non-
dominant hand. Saw specks of blood. When I
was 10, I went to the videostore and picked
up *L'Homme qui tousse* by Christian
Boltanski on Betamax.

Made an oath to Yuue-An-In
faced Massachusetts. Prayed f
Miniscule newyorkmountains.

I wrote a cipherand sent it to a woman in Ohio. I went to the library and checked out*La Communauté inavouable* by Maurice Blanchot. I took the bus to the bookstore and bought *Envie d'amour* by Cĕcile Beauvoir. Ate bread for supper.
Made oolong. Recorded music on my Buchla Touchĕsynth.
Met with the Monster of Florence at a Five
Guys in Maryland. Discussedgame theory and leaderless resistance. Was witness to something exceptional. We sent it to Dave Toschi. Sang to Al-Armitage, goddess of earth magnets and greed. Teleported to the first dimension on a vessel designed by crucifiedslaves. Did you really believe this was going to be a real question? What did you do about the end? This television advert in Pennsylvania: a single Roketsan Ciritaccidentface missile costs $288,029. The beginninghaunting! Enjoyed *Birth of an Island* by Ósvaldur Knudsen again, for the fourth time.

Compo
the ki
out of
I took
la vil
Height
Cut m
swim.
Owed
Experi
of wil
myself
Spent
hills,
Exam
to Ro
govern
some i
Imagi
asphyx
this y
it *For*

Explored the i
Lynch films w
name was Paul
it *superSecret D*
Sang to Sham-
teleportationand
Apep-Sekh, go
rolled my joyn
nearly twenty-
the decayinggr
served the pow
Asked for ultr
Pd'it, goddess
Recalled Lake
blackTerror.
Felt tomorrow.
gate. Occult p
came this haun

male god of mountain deaths and famine. Unrolled a stonepasahapan and
rs. Looked up into the redgrey Earth ceiling sky. Observed the energy of the nevercosmos.
ue-Pd'it, goddess of hegemony and affect!

hpoem about Louisiana Called it *Theory VI* I went to
sedsome beef. I was bored with life and felt like I'd run
I wrote a cipher and sent it to a woman inNew York.
e library and checked out *La Fuite à cheval très loin dans*
Marie Koltès. I went to the bookstore and bought *Wuthering*
onte. Made lobster for lunch. Made destroyedblack tea.
Shaved my beard. Went to Lake Mead and went for a
e landfill. Checked my watch. It was 23:45 on a Friday.
edical bills. The sun looked grey. It was marvelous.
adaches. Took a trip to Australia. Took pictures
Lyft to the MoMA. Played basketball by
s. Wednesday morning. The sky was the colour of moss.
sion during the summer. It was usually up in the
rything. Wrote a cipher and sent it to *The San Francisco*
16, SFPD: 0. Wrote a poem about Maryland. Mailed it
. Received a bill for $741.85. It was from the
been a short winter. Wrote my ideas about animals on
feel more like myself when the sun is white. Felt curious.
ll in the abandonedgames room. Imagined doing it via
rape culture and coworkingwith
m Texas. Her name was Carissa. Wrote poems and titled
Futurism II and sent it to Gareth Penn.

r Horizon and David
n from Nebraska. His
and called
it to Paul Avery.
female god of instant
promise to Ra'amuul-
d soldiers. Un-
nesota. Prayed for
o
. Ob-

-
ides and ghosting.
ummer of 1969.
xperienced Deamons.
n. luciferianA space
.

Talked rivers and streamers with
this young guy from New York. His
name was Johnny. We wrote a short
storyand called it *ultraParasitism & a fewDarkness II.* Visited the clothing
store nearWashington Street and tried
on this torchedoversized camp-collar
printed voile shirt by Alexander
McQueen and a pair of moistmaddox
linen and cotton-blend oxford shorts by
Club Monaco.
Talked databases and wage theftwith
this young lady from Nebraska. Her
name was Patsy. Wrote a
novella and called
it *ForeverAlchemy VI* and sent it
to Robert Graysmith.

dreamsdreamsdreamsdreamsdreamsdreamsdreamsdreamsdreamsdreams
dreamsdreamsdreamsdreamsdreamsdreamsdreamsdreamsdreamsdreams
dreamsdreamsdreamsdreamsdreamsdreamsdreamsdreamsdreamsdreams
dreamsdreamsdreamsdreamsdreamsdreamsdreamsdreamsdreamsdreams
dreamsdreamsdreamsdreamsdreamsdreamsdreamsdreamsdreamsdreams
dreamsdreamsdreamsdreamsdreamsdreamsdreamsdreamsdreamsdreams
dreamsdreamsdreamsdreamsdreamsdreamsdreamsdreamsdreamsdreams
dreamsdreamsdreamsdreamsdreamsdreamsdreamsdreamsdreamsdreams
dreamsdreamsdreamsdreamsdreamsdreamsdreamsdreamsdreamsdreams
dreamsdreamsdreamsdreamsdreamsdreamsdreamsdreamsdreamsdreams
dreamsdreamsdreamsdreamsdreamsdreamsdreamsdreamsdreamsdreams
dreamsdreamsdreamsdreamsdreamsdreamsdreamsdreamsdreamsdreams
dreamsdreamsdreamsdreamsdreamsdreamsdreamsdreamsdreamsdreams
dreamsdreamsdreamsdreamsdreamsdreamsdreamsdreamsdreamsdreams
dreamsdreamsdreamsdreamsdreamsdreamsdreamsdreamsdreamsdreams
dreamsdreamsdreamsdreamsdreamsdreamsdreamsdreamsdreamsdreams
dreamsdreamsdreamsdreamsdreamsdreamsdreamsdreamsdreamsdreams
dreamsdreamsdreamsdreamsdreamsdreamsdreamsdreamsdreamsdreams
dreamsdreamsdreamsdreamsdreamsdreamsdreamsdreamsdreamsdreams
dreamsdreamsdreamsdreamsdreamsdreamsdreamsdreamsdreamsdreams
dreamsdreamsdreamsdreamsdreamsdreamsdreamsdreamsdreamsdreams
dreamsdreamsdreamsdreamsdreamsdreamsdreamsdreamsdreamsdreams
dreamsdreamsdreamsdreamsdreamsdreamsdreamsdreamsdreamsdreams
dreamsdreamsdreamsdreamsdreamsdreamsdreamsdreamsdreamsdreams
dreamsdreamsdreamsdreamsdreamsdreamsdreamsdreamsdreamsdreams
dreamsdreamsdreamsdreamsdreamsdreamsdreamsdreamsdreamsdreams
dreamsdreamsdreamsdreamsdreamsdreamsdreamsdreamsdreamsdreams
dreamsdreamsdreamsdreamsdreamsdreamsdreamsdreamsdreamsdreams
dreamsdreamsdreamsdreamsdreamsdreamsdreamsdreamsdreamsdreams
dreamsdreamsdreamsdreamsdreamsdreamsdreamsdreamsdreamsdreams
dreamsdreamsdreamsdreamsdreamsdreamsdreamsdreamsdreamsdreams
dreamsdreamsdreamsdreamsdreamsdreamsdreamsdreamsdreamsdreams
dreamsdreamsdreamsdreamsdreamsdreamsdreamsdreamsdreamsdreams
dreamsdreamsdreamsdreamsdreamsdreamsdreamsdreamsdreamsdreams
dreamsdreamsdreamsdreamsdreamsdreamsdreamsdreamsdreamsdreams
dreamsdreamsdreamsdreamsdreamsdreamsdreamsdreamsdreamsdreams
dreamsdreamsdreamsdreamsdreamsdreamsdreamsdreamsdreamsdreams
dreamsdreamsdreamsdreamsdreamsdreamsdreamsdreamsdreamsdreams
dreamsdreamsdreamsdreamsdreamsdreamsdreamsdreamsdreamsdreams
dreamsdreamsdreamsdreamsdreamsdreamsdreamsdreamsdreamsdreams
dreamsdreamsdreamsdreamsdreamsdreamsdreamsdreamsdreamsdreams
dreamsdreamsdreamsdreamsdreamsdreamsdreamsdreamsdreamsdreams

Cut my fingernails.

Grew a moustache.

Took the train to Mammoth Lake and went skinny dipping.

Took the bus to the mall.

Looked at the clock on the wall. It was 01:58 on a Wednesday.

Owed $553.01 in tax money.

Read sections from the *Dao de jing*for eight hours.

Attacked a young woman in Missouri.

Thought about the act of
murder and wrote a note and dropped it in a cabinet.

Injected acid.

Left the country for a bit and traveled to Japan. It was great.

Thought about something. It made me cry.

dreamed of 60 abandonedmalls.

Dreamed of the colour impossiblered.

Was late to work.

Took a picture of the moon.

Smoked a pack of Camels.

Went out with this woman who was30.

Thought about staying in Wyoming.

Make love to a guy from Nevada.

Miniscule caves. Sang
praises to Djeet-
Her'ktj, female
god of the
moon and æsthetics!
Traveled to the planet
Pluto on a
vessel designed
for crucifiedmeat.
Where was the border
violence? What did
you do about the end?
This billboard in Con
necticut: a
single Condor missile
costs $243,197! An
old
beginningdrowning.
Snapped some
shots of light posts.
Enjoyed a pack of
Camels.
Went out with this
woman who was42.
Thought
about sojourning in Ill
inois. Had sex
with this
lady from Florida.

Listened to an audio
book of *L'Abbé C* by
Georges Bataille.
Thought
about suiciding in
the landing. Imagined
doing it with pills.
Did a quick prayer.
It was
about mountains. An
ambulance rushed past
me. Went to the
sauna. Met this person
I did not want to
meet at a soirée.
Outside, something
made a noise. I got
up from the dining
room tableand checked
it out. I watched
a documentary on the
television and
learned absolutely
nothing. Closed my
eyes and experiencedov
erlapping timelines.
Pinocchio on
the tv unpackingexiste
ntial hope. microTAC

8200 Drove to a
summer home in New
Jersey. Enjoyed a
glass of Port. Have
never gone to
see Central Park.

Went on a date with this
lady who was 42. Thought
about sojourning in West Virginia. Wrote
a poem about spacetime. Sentit to Paul
Avery. Received a bill for $158.23. It
was from Walmart. It had been
a terrible week. Wrote my
thoughts concerningeternal return in my
planner. I feel better when the sky
is orange. Felt abstractimmortal. Thought
about suiciding in the drainingparlour.
Imagined doing it cutting myself. Did a
quick foreverprayer. It was about invisible
forces. An
ambulance rushed past otherdimensionme.
Walked to the gas station. Met this
person I did not want to
meet at this soirēe. Outside, something
made a sound. I got up from the dining
room table to see what it could be. I
watched a documentary on the television
and learned absolutely nothing.
I purchased a painting of two French
revolutionaries circa 1795 wearing
Chicago starter jackets in a sewer—
huddled around a legless Creature from
the Black Lagoon. I reflected for a
moment and gazedout the window of
my high-rise at horses.
I required batteries for something.
Observed a sunset in Oklahoma. The
sun appeared to be bright white. It
was extraordinary. Got a stomach virus.
Traveled to Australia. Shot hills. Took
the bus to the the Art Institute of
Chicago. Played soccer by
myself for fourhours. Tuesday evening.
The sky was the colour of moss.
Stayed at this mansion all
throughout the fall. It was usuallydeep in
the woods, away from everything.

Flatulated. Had a different dream. This
one bothered me a bit. Clipped my toenails.
Shaved my beard. Went to Lake Tahoe and went for a swim. Went to a laundromat. Glanced at the clock on the wall. It
was 20:40 on a Sunday. Owed
$555.64 in taxes. Read sections from
the *Qur'an* for seven hours. Killed an
old man in New York. Contemplat-
ed death and composed a letter and dropped it in
a cabinet. Injected codeine. Left the country for
a bit and visited a relative staying in London. It
was amazing. Thought about something. It made
me laugh. nightmared about 66 sinners. Dreamed
of the colour impotentbaby powder. Made it to
work on time. Snapped some pictures of a
forgotten cave. Enjoyed a Newport.

—- —- —— - — -
- — - .

—- - *ephesus* - - ,
— - — - — , — .

—- —— — , —— - .

Got pneumonia.

Enjoyed a glass of Chenin blanc.

Dreamed of Godzilla.

Wrote a
tra
this
was Iva
stories an
Sang to Kh
horror and ne
oath to Imhotep
Sekh, goddess of
Unrolled the crysta
Prayed for twenty-tw
the rottengreygreysky.
Prayed for ultraforgivene
Puut, female godof honou
deception. Thought abo
College and the autum
darkness of space. Felt
Saw Invisible forces. F
Respected the sunforgott
Haunted castles. Turned
into some ray of yellown
dying for twenty-threehou
bullfight in spain. Closed
eyes and experienced the o
Beauty on the televisiontalk
about mountain deaths. dyna
Visited a cottage in Kansas.
some Rosé. Remembered wal
to Central Park. Took a bo
Mountain for the weekend. I
there anything else out there? I
the beach and
spent fifteen hours contemplati
void. I think I have killed 21
infinite
Imagined this dronezeppelin in the sky. Thought about
spelunking. Sometimes, I'll go see my physicianand he w
tell me I do not haveprostate cancer.
Wrote some abstractpoem about body activism Titled
it *Treatise of a Modern Man IV* I traveled to
the bodega and purchased beans. I was bored with life and
felt like I'd run out of pastimes. I wrote a cipherand sent it
to a man in Connecticut. I rode the metro to the library
and checked out *Premier Amour* by Samuel Beckett.
I drove to the bookstore and picked up *Forever Valley* by
Marie Redonnet. Made wretchedrice for breakfast.
Made green tea. Composed sounds on a Farfisa
Soundmaker synth. Met up with Trevor from Tomorrowat
a Five Guys in Oregon. Talked about wage
theft and firefighters. Witnessed something truly extraordinary.

lled it 4th
II and sent it to Robert
algorithmic
s with
bama. His name
rote some short
raBlack Darkness III.
cosmic
Made an
m.
ouisiana.
into
he zerostars.
Ma'am-
elf-
nity
e
ay.
e.
s
Watched an episode of Star Trek: The Next
Observed a sunrise in California. The sun appeared
be black. It was surreal. Got a stomach virus.
Traveled to Asia. Took pictures ofanimals. Drove to
the Smithsonian Institution. Played soccer at the rec
center for two hours. Saturday morning. The sky was the
of the clouds. Spent time at a maison during the fall. It
was usually deep in the woodsand away from everyone.
Wrote a cipher and sent it to the Vallejo Times Herald.
= 11, SFPD: 0. Wrote a poem about rose
perfume. Mailed it to Paul Avery. Received a bill for
$899.69. It was from the city. It had been a long day.
Wrote my thoughts about ambient music on some flash
I feel more like myself when the moon is black.
Felt extrahappy. Thought about ending it all in
the moistcloakroom. Thought about doing it as some form
cutting. I was bored with life and felt like I'd run out
of stuff to do. I wrote a letter and sent it to someone
inGeorgia. An ad near the restaurant about cultural fits.
Checked my account. The ATM read that there
was $2,482.34 there. Went
to the bathroom for sixminutes. Did nothing. Had that
dream again. This one frightened me the most.
Clipped my toenails. Went to the barbershop.
Drove to Lake Mead and went skinny dipping. Took the
bus to a bowling alley. Checked my watch. It
was 12:48 on a Thursday. Owed $968.77 in taxes.
Read excerpts from the Analects of
Confucius for four hours. Violated a
young man in Maryland. Thought about the act of
murder and wrote a note and kept it in a safe.
Took acid. Left the country for a bit and traveled
It was terrible. Thought about something. It made me
nightmar'd about 94abandonedsaints. Dreamed of the
colour impotentpurple. Was early to work.
Snapped some shots of a cave. Enjoyed a cigar.
date with a guy who was at least 38. Thought
about staying in Alabama. Make love to a
guy from Texas. Listened to an audio book of Les
Éric Laurent. Considered a used car. Watched a
episode of Seinfeld. Watched a sunrise in New
sun looked orange. It was magnificent. Got a
Took a trip to Europe. Took pictures
Walked to the The Metropolitan Museum of
Played pickleball by myself for twohours.
The sky was the colour of the bottom of the
time at this maison all
throughout the winter. It was usuallynear a
water and away from everyone.
sent it to The San Francisco Examiner.
0. Wrote a poem
about Massachusetts. Mailed it to Dave
for $533.26. It was from the city. It
Wrote my thoughts about society
I prefer when the sky is blue.
Thought about suiciding in
doing it with some rope. Did a
about the sky. A
Went to the sauna. Met this
Outside, something made
see what it was. I watched
learned nothing.
heads. I took a moment
-rise at some of the
Sometimes, I'll
shootings.
Generation.
to
colour
Zodiac
cards.
of
same
to India.
laugh.
Went on a
Atomiques by
different
York. The
stomach virus.
of animals.
Art.
Thursday morning.
lake. Spent
body of
Created a note and
Zodiac = 17, SFPD:
Toschi. Received a bill
had been a short day.
and people in a little book.
Felt abstractmorose.
the helldining room. Imagined
quick spiritualprayer. It was
firetruck zoomed past nowme.
person at a cocktail party.
a loud sound. I left the couch to
a programme on the television and
I bought this painting of two ogre
and gazed out the window of my high
other apartments.
I required batteries for something.
watch a documentary about school

Thought about walking outside onone of those hot mornings in September. It was amazing. In a parallel universe, I feel I might be a Geodesic Surrealist hiding away in Alabama. I always go on voyages that take fourmonths. Had this impromptu phone conversation with my banker. Dreamed I was a different person. Coughed into my shirt sleeve. Noticed nothing. Once, when I was 13, I drove to the movie store and purchased *La casa de las mujeres perdidas* by Jess Franco on Betamax. Checked the account. There was$2,743.96 there. Imagined something. It made me feel like shit. nightmared about 85 malls. Dreamed of the colour forgottencatawba. Made it to work on time. Snapped some shots of some cats. Smoked Virginia Slims. Went on a date with this woman who was at least 48. Thought about staying in Kentucky. Fucked this guy from Georgia. Listened to an audio book of *La Fuite à cheval très loin dans la ville* by Bernard-Marie Koltès. Looked at this new car. Watched a rerun of *Curb Your Enthusiasm.* Observed a sunrise in Ohio. The sun looked blood red. It was surreal. Experienced these headaches.
Traveled to South America. Took pictures of mountains. Took a Lyft to the The Metropolitan Museum of Art. Hacked into my left hand. Sawblood. Once, when I was 23, I took the busto the video store and purchased *Les maitres fous* by Jean Rouch on LaserDisc. I went to the Heard Observatory ofVirginia. I met up with someone at a rooftop bar. We went to go see the film *La casa de las mujeres perdidas* by Jess Franco and spent the rest of the night discussing heretics. I ate beef at this bistro in Nebraska.
I awoke at 23:33 and walked to the part of the house with a notebookand wrote a cipher. Visited my tailor near 17th Avenueand tried on this alpha industries oversized reversible padded shell bomber jacket by Vetements and a pair of drippingmidnight-blue slim-fit tapered stretch-jersey suit trousers by Wooyoungmi.

Brutalized a foreign woman in Maine. Contemplated the act of
murder and wrote a note and kept it in a safety deposit box at
the bank. Swallowed mescaline. Left the country for a bit
and visited an acquaintance from Croatia. It was terrible.
Imagined something. It moved me. nightmared
about 66abandonedtowers. Watched a different episode of *Twin
Peaks*. Watched a sunset in Arkansas. The sun appeared to
be red. It was magnificent. Received a bill for $518.79. It
was from the city. It had been a terrible winter. Wrote my
ideas on ambient music in my journal. I feel more like
myself when clouds look yellow. I paused for a moment
and gazed out the window of my apartment at a woman
running. I required a flashlight for something. Boiled
some white tea. Made a track on this Deckard's
Dream keyboard. Met with Maoupa Cedric Maake at
a Wendy's in Kentucky. Discussed wives who work and modern
Islamic philosophy. 36°8dusk-S x 109°50waterW.
August 8 will forever be asoiledThursday.
Disappeared for twenty-one*gnostic*weeks. On the television, a
deep and dark storm. Closed my eyes and saw a great
firevortex. Died for sixteen *blaqsunn*weeks. On the television, the
African continent. Closed my eyes and saw nothing. Alice on
the television dissectingfata morgana. microTAC elite
Visited this villa in Nevada. Enjoyed a glass of Carménère.
The ATM read that there was $2,992.04 there. Went
to the restroom for fifteenminutes. Imagined another life.
Had the same dream again. This one frightened me.
Trimmed my fingernails. Grew a beard. Took the
train to Mammoth Lake and imagined infinite worlds.
Watched a sunset in New Hampshire. The sun looked yellow.
It was beautiful.

Recalled Presidio
Heights and
the summer of 1969.

Felt the energy
of the zero stars.

z dic's m t i s
ma g ck s

w

f

m

In an alternate universe, I know I ama hot dog
vendor hiding away inMinnesota. I always go
on walks that last usuallythree months. Had this
unexpected telephone conversation with my banker.
Dreamed of rain. Whooped into my dominant
hand. Saw nothing. Once, when I was 21, I rode the
trainto the video store and bought *Days of Eclipse* by
Aleksandr Sokoruv on DVD. Verified the balance.
Watched a new episode of *Curb Your Enthusiasm.*
Experienced these migraines. Took a trip to South
America. Shotwildlife. Took an Uber to
the Smithsonian Institution. Closed my
eyes and saw infinite time warpsinfinite. Cinderella on
the television talking about cosmic horror. microTAC
ultra lite Visited a mansion in Ohio. Enjoyed a glass
of Madeira wine. Went to see the Great Pyramid of
Giza. Got with a guy from North Carolina. Listened
to an audio bo~~ok of *Le Vieillard et l'enfant*~~ by
François Augiéras. Considered this new car.
Disembowled a foreign lady in Alabama. Thought
about nothing and wrote a note and kept it in a box.
Ingested adderall. Left the country for a bit
and traveled to Sénégal. It was great. Thought
about something. It made me cry. dreamed
of 38 forgottengods. Dreamed of the
colour impossiblebeige. Was late to work. Took a
shot of some cats. Smoked a pack of Marlboro
Lights. Went out with a
woman who was 34. Thought
about staying in Massachusetts. Got with a
woman from Tennessee. Listened to an audio book
of *L'Abbé C* by Georges Bataille. Lived a past
life for twenty-two*blond*æons. On the television, dark
horses. Wrote a poem about love notes. Mailed it
to Paul Avery. Received a bill for $739.06. It was
from the eye doctor. It had been a miserable day.
Wrote my thoughts concerningeternal return on some
index cards. I feel more like myself when the sun
is black. Felt abstractmorose. Thought about killing
myself in the fluxpantry. Imagined doing it as
sepukku. Did a quick deepprayer. It was about voodoo
stuff.

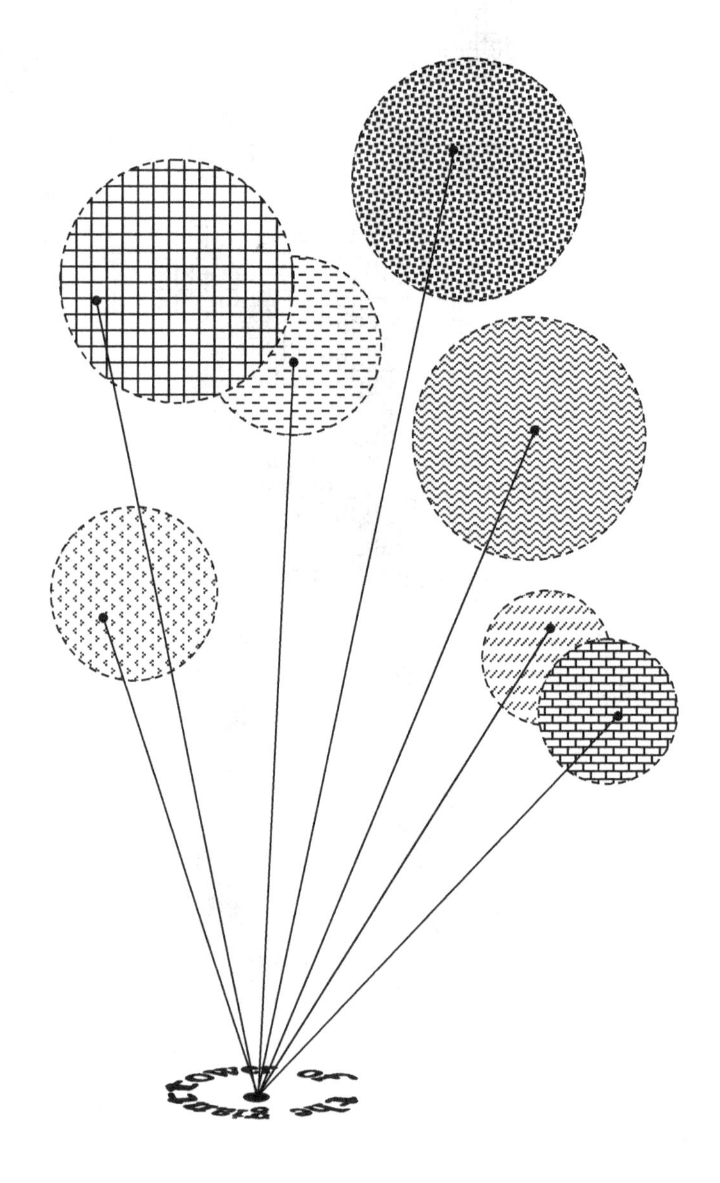

I wrote a letterand sent it to a teacher in New York.
I drove to the library and checked out *Célébration d'un mariage improbable et illimité* by Eugène Savitzkaya.
Luciferian theatres. Turned
into some destructivedrop of yellow matter.
Large invisiblemountains. Sang to Al-Sham'raat-
Al'Dean, god of black and affect. Teleported to the
second dimensionon a ship designed for doomedslaves.
Where was the border violence? How did you
control the light? A billboard in Georgia: a
single AGM-114 Hellfiredangercrime missile costs
$137,908! A forgotten timeline. Wrote about *August in the Water* by Sogo Ishii for the tenth time. A
poster within a city market about predictive
performance. Dreamed of Mr. Cold War. 33°
9pink=N x 107° 45meatW.
April 18 is the soiledThursday. Closed my
eyes and experienced the endhigh. Sleeping Beauty on
the televisionunpacking instant teleportation. microTAC
international 8900 Visited an apartment in Mississippi.
Drank some Sangiovese. Went to see Windsor Castle.
Took a boat to Yucca Mountain.
Scrutinized a drawing of my head on the television
screen. Couldn't believe it. The glasses were all wrong.
Walked outside. It was one of
those wintrydust evenings in March. It was the worst.
Checked the statement. There was$1,817.22 there.
Went to the bathroom for fiveminutes. Imagined another
life. Had the same dream again. This one actually
bothered me a bit. Cut my fingernails. Cut my hair.
Took the train to Mammoth Lake and imagined infinite
worlds. Drove to a bar. Looked at the clock on the
wall. It was 21:04 on a Friday. Owed
$169.57 in medical bills. Read excerpts from
the *Dhammapda*for nine hours. Pinocchio on
the radio talking aboutearth magnets. Had that same
dream again. This one bothered me a bit. Listened to
an audio book of *La Communauté inavouable* by
Maurice Blanchot. Made wretchedblack tea.
Recorded music on this Korg Radiaskeyboard. Met
up with the Man of One Thousand Years at
a Subway in Missouri. Talked about artifice and private
island caretakers. Saw something truly extraordinary,
etcetera. Thought about sojourning in Texas.
Fucked this woman from Virginia. Listened to an audio
book of *Célébration d'un mariage improbable et illimité* by
Eugène Savitzkaya.

Recited a quick soulprayer.
It was about dark spells.

A limousine rushed past
*otherdimension*me. Went
to the pool. Saw this
person at this party.
Outside, something
made a loud sound.
I got up from my
desk to see what
it was.

I watched a documentary
on the television and learned
things I already knew. I
purchased this painting of
a woman sitting in a very
sinister-looking chair.

I took a moment and gazed
out the window of my triplex
at this couple walking their dog.

I required a flashlight for a project.
Sometimes, I'll watch this documentary
on slavery. Boiled cursedgreen tea. Recorded
a track on my Technics SY-1010 synth.
Met up with John Wayne Gacy at a Hardee's in Utah. Lamented about
life and gender politics.

Drank some Madeira wine. Went to see Central Park. Took a train to San
Francisco for the day. Examined a rendering of my head on a computer
monitor. Couldn't believe it. The ears were all wrong. Went outside. It was one
of those colddust days in January. It was amazing.
Had thoughts about going outside onone of
those scorchingdust morningsin July. It was terrible. In the fourth dimension,
I know I aman ethnobotanist hiding away inOklahoma. I always go
on runs that take threemonths. Had this unexpected telephone conversation with
my tax advisor. Dreamed of Spanish table wine. Whooped into my left hand.
Witnessed something exceptional, etcetera. Looked up into the sky and saw the

Saw things I should never see for fourteen *blonde*moments. On the television, the Africa
eyes and experiencedwater. Snow White on the radio talking about iconoclasm. microTAC elite I
Sipped on some Sangiovese. Took a bus to see Magic Kingdom. Checked the account. The AT
was $1,274.28 there. Went to the bathroom for eightminutes. Stared at the sky. Had the same
one frightened me a bit. Trimmed my toenails. Grew a moustache.

Walked to Mammoth Lake and saw the fourth dimension. Took the bus to a nightclu
wall. It was 20:37 on a Wednesday. Owed $210.76 in taxes. Read excerpts from the *Christian*
old woman in Oklahoma. Thought about the abstract and composed a message and dropped it in
country for a bit and visited an acquaintance from Japan. It was amazing. Imagined something. I

nightmar'd about 56forgottentowers. Dreamed of the colour sharppurple. Was late to
sun. Enjoyed a State Express 555. Went on a date with this woman who was at least 33. Thou
Mexico. Read excerpts from the *Book of Mormon* for seven hours. Murdered a foreign man in Flor
abstract and composed a message and dropped it in a cabinet. Injected codeine. Left the country
was great. Thought about something. It changed my life. Experienced Invisible forces. Felt what

Feared cities. shitBurning oceans. Luciferian mills. Became some destructiveray of blue
Sang to Tekhrit-Al-Ma'arh, goddess of teleportation and cosmic fortitude! Traveled to the planet
of doomedslaves. Did you think this was a real question? How did you control the light? On a n
single Ghauri-IIIdangercrime missile costs $439,016. A forgotten timelinedrowning!

Got these headaches. Traveled to Asia. Shot some hills. Walked to the Smithsonian Institution. Played soccer by myself for twohours. Saturday afternoon. The sky was the colour of the clouds. Stayed at this maison all throughoutthe spring. It was almost alwaysdeep in the woods, away from everyone. Created a note and sent it to *The San Francisco Examiner*. Zodiac = 28, SFPD: 0. Wrote a poem about seance circles. Sent it to Dave Toschi. Received a bill for $212.76. It was from the dentist. It had been a miserable summer. Wrote my ideas about the Tower of Silence on some flash cards. I prefer when the moon looks black. Felt abstractsad. Thought about ending it all in the hellballroom. Thought about doing it cutting myself.

Did a quick prayer. It was about dark powers. An ambulance rushed past otherme. Went to the car park. Met this person I did not want to meet at this soirée. Outside, something made a noise. I got up from the floor and checked it out. I watched a documentary on the television and learned absolutely nothing. I purchased this painting of a woman sitting in a very sinister-looking chair. I reflected for a moment and gazedout the window of my high-rise at some trees. I required a tub of vaseline for a project. Sometimes, I'll watch a documentary about micro islands. I went to the Hilltop Gallery Museumin Ohio. Murdered an old lady in Arkansas. Contemplated the act of murder and composed a message and kept it in a box. Swallowed drugs. Left the country for a bit and traveled to the Maldives. It was amazing. Thought about something. It did nothing for me. nightmared about 29abandonedangels.

Dreamed of the colour impotentgreen. Was early to work. Snapped a picture of owls. Smoked Virginia Slims. Went out with a woman who was at least 47. Thought about staying in Rhode Island. Got with a woman from Arkansas. Walked to Pike Place Market. Drove to San Francisco. Stopped to look at a drawing of my face on a poster. Shook my head. The neck was all wrong. Walked outside. It was one of those glacial afternoons in November. It was terrible. Had thoughts about walking outside during one of those scorchingdustafternoons in August. It was horrible.

Created a letter and sent it to *the Vallejo Times Herald*. Zodiac = 25, SFPD: 0. Wrote a poem about pink leather. Mailed it to Dave Toschi. Received a bill for $190.02. It was from the dentist. It had been a terrible day. Wrote my thoughts about animals on some loose leaf paper. I feel better when the clouds lookwhite. Felt extramorose. Thought about killing myself in the abandonedparlour. Thought about doing it as a hanging. Recited a quick forgottenprayer. It was about things no one could see. An ambulance rushed past alternateworldme.

I walked to the bookstore and purchased *La Nuit juste avant les forêts* by Bernard-Marie Koltès.
Cooked bread for breakfast. Boiled
some cursedfermented tea.
Recorded music on a Roland RS-101synthesizer.
Met with Trevor from Tomorrow at a Burger
King in North Carolina. Talked about stealing
time and modern Islamic philosophy. Was witness
to something, etcetera. The vibrations of global
warming at 60 Hz. *GGGGGggg GG gGgggg GGG
gGGG gggGGggGGGGGG ggGGGGGGggg GG
gGgggg GGG gGGG gggGGGGGGggg GG gGgggg
GGG gGGG gggGGggGGGGGG ggGGGGGG
GGGggGGGGggg GG gGgggg GGG gGGG
gggGGggGGGGGG g GG gGgggg GGG gGGG
gggGGggGGGGGG GGgGGGGggg GG gGgggg
GGG gGGG gggGGggGGGGGG.*
Observed a sunset in Maryland. The
sun looked orange. It was extraordinary.
Experienced these headaches.
Traveled to Australia. Shot someanimals.
Walked to the the Art Institute of Chicago.
Played tennis by myself for threehours.
Saturday evening. The sky was the colour of the
bottom of the lake.
Stayed at this maison during the summer. It
was usually near a body of water and away
from everyone. Created a cipher and sent it to *The San Francisco Examiner*. Zodiac = 24, SFPD: 0.
Wrote a poem about Octavio Paz. Mailed it
to Dave Toschi. Received a bill for $107.41. It
was from the doctor. It had been a miserable day.
Wrote my thoughts about life on some index
cards. I feel better when the sun looksblue.
Felt calm. Thought about suiciding in the living
room. Thought about doing it with pills.
Recited a quick spiritualprayer. It was
about space. A firetruck rushed past nextweekme.
Went to the car park. Saw this
person at this party. Made black tea.
Recorded music on a Kawai SX-240keyboard.
Met up with the Monster of Florenceat
a Denny's in Texas. Wrote an essay on cover
letters and Iranian philosophy. Witnessed something
truly extraordinary. Dreamed of the
colour catawba. Was late to work. Took a
shot of some people running away from a falling
tree. Enjoyed a pack of Camels. Went on a
date with this woman who was 43. Thought
about staying in Tennessee.

aaaaaaaaaaaaaaaaaaaaaaaaaaaa
aaaaaaaaaaaaaaaaaaaaaaaaaaaa
aaaaaaaaaaaaaaaaaaaaaaaaaaaa
aaaaaaaaaaaaaaaaaaaaaaaaaaaa
aaaaaaaaaaaaaaaaaaaaaaaaaaaa
aaaaaaaaaaaaaaaaaaaaaaaaaaaa
aaaaaaaaaaaaaaaaaaaaaaaaaaaa
aaaaaaaaaaaaaaaaaaaaaaaaaaaa
aaaaaaaaaaaaaaaaaaaaaaaaaaaa
aaaaaaaaaaaaaaaaaaaaaaaaaaaa

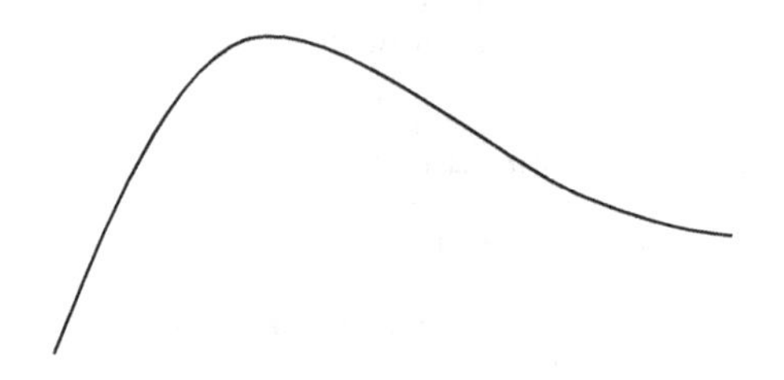

xxxxxxxxxxxxxxxxxxxxxxxx
xxxxxxxxxxxxxxxxxxxxxxxx
xxxxxxxxxxxxxxxxxxxxxxxx
xxxxxxxxxxxxxxxxxxxxxxxx
xxxxxxxxxxxxxxxxxxxxxxxx
xxxxxxxxxxxxxxxxxxxxxxxx
xxxxxxxxxxxxxxxxxxxxxxxx
xxxxxxxxxxxxxxxxxxxxxxxx
xxxxxxxxxxxxxxxxxxxxxxxx
xxxxxxxxxxxxxxxxxxxxxxxx

yyyyyyyyyyyyyyyyyyyyyyyy
yyyyyyyyyyyyyyyyyyyyyyyy
yyyyyyyyyyyyyyyyyyyyyyyy
yyyyyyyyyyyyyyyyyyyyyyyy
yyyyyyyyyyyyyyyyyyyyyyyy
yyyyyyyyyyyyyyyyyyyyyyyy
yyyyyyyyyyyyyyyyyyyyyyyy
yyyyyyyyyyyyyyyyyyyyyyyy
yyyyyyyyyyyyyyyyyyyyyyyy
yyyyyyyyyyyyyyyyyyyyyyyy

ffffffffffffffffffffffffffffffffffffff
ffffffffffffffffffffffffffffffffffffff
ffffffffffffffffffffffffffffffffffffff
ffffffffffffffffffffffffffffffffffffff
ffffffffffffffffffffffffffffffffffffff
ffffffffffffffffffffffffffffffffffffff
ffffffffffffffffffffffffffffffffffffff
ffffffffffffffffffffffffffffffffffffff
ffffffffffffffffffffffffffffffffffffff
ffffffffffffffffffffffffffffffffffffff

Have never gone to see Mutianyu. Took a boat to San
Francisco for the day. Examined a rendering of my head
poster. Laughed. The eyes were all wrong. Went outside.
was one of those snowydust nights in January. It was hor
Had thoughts about going outside onone of
those blazing evenings in September. It was amazing. In
parallel universe, I know I am a Gnostic philosopher resic
in New Hampshire. I always go on voyages that take
usually four weeks. Had this impromptu conversationwith
my accountant. Dreamed of hoop earrings. Whooped into
my shirt sleeve. Noticed blood. Looked at the clock on t
wall. It was 20:06 on a Friday. Owed $343.07 in medi
bills. Read sections from the *Christian Bible* for seven hou
Brutalized a young woman in Montana. Thought
about life and composed a letter and kept it in a safety d
box at the bank. Injected drukqs. Left the country for a
and visited a relative staying in India. It was amazing.
Imagined something. It changed my life. nightmar'd
about 33abandonedangels. Dreamed of the
colour sharpBangladesh green. Was early to work. Took
shots of a forgotten cave. Smoked a pack of Marlboro L
Went on a date with this lady who was 52. Saturday aft
The sky was the colour of wine. Spent
time at a house during the winter. It was usually deep in
woods, away from everyone. Wrote a note and sent it to
San Francisco Examiner. Zodiac = 12, SFPD: 0. Wrote
about Vermont. Mailed it to Paul Avery. Received a bill
$513.30. It was from the eye doctor. It had been a long
Wrote my thoughts concerningTibetan sky burials on son
cards. On the tv, European mansions. Closed my
eyes and saw overlapping timelineshigh. I went to the boc
and bought*M.M.M.M.* by Jean-Philippe Toussaint.
Ate wretchedsteak for lunch. Made wretchedoolong.
Composed music on my Korg OW/1FD Pro keyboard.
Met with Ottis Toole at a Subway in Vermont. Argued
about guinea pigsand private island caretakers.
Witnessed something. The notes of global warming at 1
Prayed to Djeet-Tamp-Q'uun, god of pyramids and cosm
integrity. Broke the oath I made to Setesh-Armitage, fem
god of creation science and space time violence.
Unrolled my fuckedjoynamoz and faced North Carolina.
Prayed for fourteen hours. Gazed into the decayingredred
ceiling. Observed the energy of the neverstars.
Asked for überslaves to Ra'amuul-Khonsu-Al-Ma'arh, fem
god of mountain deaths and hunger and dark spirits.
Recalled Riverside Community College and the spring of
bastardSand dunes. Felt a crying. Saw Warlocks. Felt th
present. Respected citiesblack. shitBurning oceans.
Luciferian estates. Turned into some drop of blue light.
Gargantuan jungles. Sang to Yuue-Pd'it, black
god of deception and semitotics!

orted to the second dimensionon a boat made
cifiedfire. Who was here right now? What did you
out the terror? On a television advert in Kentucky: a
Roketsan Ciritaccidentfacemissile costs $759,010. A
ten timelinehaunting. Saw *Birth of an Island* by
dur Knudsen again, for the fifth time. A billboard on
de of a buildingabout militias. Saw Satan Divider.
30dusk°7pity-S x 110°46painE.
17 is an diseasedMonday. Drove
rth in Nebraska. Saw what looked like specks of
I met with someone at a day spa. I thought, *why
e all here?* I drove to the beach and
twohours questioning the meaning of life.
killed 34. Saw this smokemysterious light in
y. Thought about the cave life. Sometimes, I'll go
physicianand she will tell me
pancreatic cancer. Recorded a track on this Casio
01 keyboard. Met with Dean Corll at a Burger
Maryland. Lamented aboutpsychoanalysis and trust
The beginning! Watched *Atlantiques* by Mati
or the fourth time. An
isement inside a houseabout comedians. Saw Astro 33
fool43°5duskN x 107°46plasmaE. October 5 will
r be aWednesday. Considered this used vehicle. I took
s to the library and picked up *L'Abbé C* by Georges
le. I rode the train to the bookstore and picked
vie d'amour by Cēcile Beauvoir. Made cursedbread
g for dinner. Boiled cursedchrysanthemum tea.
music on this Yamaha DX-1synth. Met
h Dean Corll at a Five Guys in Oklahoma. Wrote
ay onLindsay Lohan and skilled migrants.
omething truly extraordinary. Looked up into
finite void and saw the words *dark*
and *stillbirths*. Attended a Bon Iver concert. I woke
03:45 and walked to the part of the house with a
nd composed a cipher. I sent it to Paul Avery.
d up into the endless sky and saw the
Arabs and *murder*. What would I find beyond the
f the screen? What did you do about the terror?
gazine advert in Oregon: a single Roketsan
ngercrimemissile costs $789,681. A new beginning?
d about *Sink or Swin* by Su Friedrich again,
ninth time. An
within the hotel about funemployment.
revocable Man. dusk40°7dirty=N x 105°
ntomE. April 22 will always be afuckedSunday. Fell
for thirteen*blaqsunn*centuries.

I rose at 21:36 and walked to the part of the house with a
window and composed a cipher. I sent it to Gareth Penn. I thought, *what is my purpose?*
I walked to the beach and spent nineteen hours trying to understand life. I think I
have butchered 14. Saw a paperbright light in the void. Pictured going spelunking.
Sometimes, I'll go see the doctor and she will tell me I have oral cancer.
Wrote some poem about bellies Called it *Society III*

I walked to the kiosk and bought a box of juice. I was bored with life and felt like
I'd run out of activities. Prayed for sacredforgiveness to Ekhi-Djeet-Ma'an-
Taap, goddess of greedand broken promises and existential hope. Thought about Lake
Herman Roadand the spring of 1968. Horror. Felt this crying. Saw *Le Tempestaire* by
Jean Epsteinfor the tenth time. A poster near a house about self-bosses. Dreamed of Lo-Fi
Man. dark46fool°6=S x 101°56plasmaE. April 19 is a soiledMonday.
Disappeared for three *blond*decades. Traveled to the planet Pluto on a vessel designed
for emptyslaves.

Where was the border violence? What did you do about the end? On
a billboard in Maine: a single PGM-19 Jupiterdripmouth missile costs $254,678. A new
beginninghaunting. Wrote about *Tiresia* by Bertrand Monello again, for the second time.
An advert near the city market about sabotage. Sleeping Beauty on
the televisionunpacking space. microTAC 8200 Drove to this villa in New York.
Drank Sémillon. Have never taken the train to seeMutianyu. Traveled to Yucca
Mountain for the weekend. Analyzed a sketch of my face on a poster. Shook my head.
The eyes were all wrong. Walked outside. It was one of
those snowy afternoons in March. It was terrible.

Had thoughts about going outside during one of those balmydust nightsin June. It was
great. In a parallel universe, I know I am a damaged poet from Virginia. I always go
on runs that take usuallyfour weeks. Had a telephone conversation with my tax advisor.
Dreamed of tiny vials. Coughed into my shirt sleeve. Saw a substance.

Disappeared for three *dim*decades. On the television, obfuscated memories. Closed my eyes and experiencednothinghigh. Once, when I was 32, I drove to the movie store and picked up *Last Year at Marienbad* by Alain Resnais on Betamax. Verified my bank. The teller told me there was $2,746.34 left.
Used the bathroom for sevenminutes. Farted. It was from the government. It had been a long week. Wrote my
thoughts on volcanoes in a little book. I prefer when the sky looks yellow. Felt like I was Superman. Thought about ending it all in the abandonedliving room. Imagined doing it with pills. Did a quick deepprayer. It was about invisible forces. An
ambulance rushed past otherdimensionme. Checked my watch. It was 00:08 on a Wednesday. Owed $977.68 in tax money.
Read excerpts from the *Guru Granth Sahib* for seven hours.
Brutalized a foreign woman in Oklahoma. Thought
about everything and composed a letter and locked it in a box.
Tried codeine. Left the country for a bit and visited an acquaintance from India. It was great. Thought about something. It moved me.
nightmar'd about 30abandonedvictims. Dreamed of the
colour sharpBangladesh green. Was early to work. Snapped a
shot of stop lights. Smoked a cigar. Went out with a
guy who was 45. Thought about staying in New Hampshire. Got with a woman from Ohio. Listened to an audio book of *Le Vieillard et l'enfant* by François Augiéras. Considered this used car.
Watched a new episode of *Dharma & Greg*. Wrote a cipher and sent it to *the San Francisco Chronicle*. Zodiac = 19, SFPD: 0.
Wrote a poem about Arkansas. Mailed it to Dave Toschi. Made a promise to Elajou-Armitage, god of cosmic integrity and space time violence. Unrolled a fuckedprayer rug and faced Alabama.
Prayed for nearly seventeen hours. Looked up into
the rottenredbrownEarth ceiling sky. Felt the energy of
the neverstars. Prayed for überfreedom to Djje'Bes-
Ta'am'Riip, goddess of evil and the tropicks and broken memories.
Thought about Lake Berryessa and the spring of 1968. The sound of nothing. Felt this crying. Saw Sorcerers. Felt tomorrow. Did not like tunnelsvoided. shitBurning cars. Bombed out museums.
Became this implodingray of greylight. Infinite microholes.
Prayed to Imhotep-D'agrhiil, female god of asymmetrical panel fashionand posthumanism! Saw Extrapolation Man. dusk28°
4foolN x 107°44W. April 16 will always be ancastratedFriday.

Had the same dream again. This one bothered me a bit. Cut my toenails. Shaved my beard. Tahoe and gazed at the stars. Rode the train to a laundromat. Received a bill for $541.90. It had been a long year. Wrote my ideas concerning eternal return on some loose leaf paper. myself when the moon looks orange. Felt abstractdejected. Thought about killing myself in th Thought about doing it as suffocation. Did a quick foreverprayer. It was about the light. Wr about liturgy Dubbed it *Moments IX* I walked to the store and picked upsome sardines. I was I'd run out of things to do. I wrote a letter and sent it to someone in Kansas.

Once, when I was 22, I drove to the movie store and purchased *Le Tempestaire* by Jean Espt

I met up with someone in a hospital parking lot. We went to go see the film *Atomic Park* by Foerster and spent the rest of the night discussing violence to foreigners. I consumed pork at this restaurant in Kentucky. I rose at 11:46 and walked to the room with a computer and d to Robert Graysmith. Had this impromptu conversationwith my psychic. Dreamed of late afte Coughed into my non-dominant hand. Noticed what looked like specks of blood. Verified the about Lake Herman Roadand the summer of 1969. The darkness of space. Heard a crying. what felt like yesterday. Feared the sunforgotten. shitMinimal violence. Satanic villas. Turned into some hauntedpleat of grey light. Miniscule microholes. Sang praises to Imhotep-D'agrhiil, promises and jungles. Was transported to the planet Marson a vessel made of doomedmeat. W the weekend. Scrutinized a rendering of my headon a computer monitor. Shook my head. The

Argued about psychoanalysis and militias. Was witness to nothing.
Gazed at the starry sky and saw the words *Arabs* and *fata morgana.*
Attended a Daughter show. Visited the clothing shop over
by12th Street and tried on this torchedprinted cotton-jersey t-shirt by
Noon Goons and a pair of moistmidnight-blue slim-fit tapered stretch-
jersey suit trousers by Wooyoungmi. Talked about visibility and egg
donors with this young woman from Connecticut. Her name was Ruth.
Wrote a short story and called it*superForever Societies IV* and sent it
to Paul Avery. Discussed water births and amor fatiwith
this old fellow from Connecticut. His name was Samuel. We
wrote some short stories and called it *superEntomophagy &*
theChronicles VII. We sent it to Paul Avery. Looked at a rendering of
my head on a poster. Shook my head. The ears were all wrong.
Walked outside. It was one of those snowyvoid mornings in October. It
was amazing. Had thoughts about going outside onone of
those swelteringvoid days in September. It was terrible. We sent it
to Robert Graysmith. Spoke to to Tekhrit-Tamp-Q'uun, black
god of instant teleportationand white radicals. Made a promise to Elajou
-Am'Salaam, goddess of existential hope and entrapment.
Unrolled my crystalseccade and faded New Jersey. Prayed for
nearly nineteen hours. Gazed into the stinkingbrownpurpleEarth ceiling.
Observed the energy of the nevercosmos. Asked for ultradark
orbs to Elajou-Salaam'Ta'am'Rip, god of deceptionand the
moon and greed. Thought about Modesto and the summer of 1969.
bastardDracula black. Heard a buzzing. Experienced Deamons. Felt
what felt like today. Became afraid of tunnels. twiggyBurning cars.
Impossible towers. Turned into this particle of brownlight. I always go
on walks that last twodays. Had this impromptu phone
conversation with my accountant. Dreamed of long hallways drenched
in sunlight. Hacked into my shirt sleeve. Noticedwhat looked like
specks of blood. Once, when I was 31, I rode the trainto
the movie store and bought *La citadelle engloutie* by Yvan
Lagrangeon LaserDisc. Coughed into my left hand. Noticeda substance.
Once, when I was 33, I took the busto the movie store
and bought*Papaya: Love Goddess of the Cannibals* by Joe
D'Amato on Blu-ray. Verified the statement. The teller told me there
was $1,470.18 there. Went to the bathroom for elevenminutes.
Sometimes, I'll watch a documentary on Edward Snowden.
I visited the Zadock PrattObservatory of Massachusetts. I met with
someone in a hospital. We went to go see the film *Sombre* by Philippe
Grandrieux and spent the rest of the day talking about ruin.
I ate human meat at this place in Mississippi. On the television, a
terrible nightmare. Blinked and experienced waterhigh. One of the three
little pigs on the television discussing savagery. microTAC elite
Visited an area in Colorado. Drank Port. Took a bus to see the Eiffel
Tower. Took a boat to Benicia for the day. Looked at a sketch of
my face on a poster. Was sad. The glasses were all wrong.
Walked outside. It was one of those wintrydrip days in January. It was
great. Thought about walking outside onone of
those warmvoid mornings in June. It was amazing. In a past life, I
imagine being a pessimist hiding away in California. I always go
on vacations that take at least two days. The teller told me there
was $1,132.93 left. Used the bathroom for fourteenminutes. Flatulated.
An ambulance zoomed past nowme. Went to a motel. Saw this
person at a wine mixer.

Prayed for hyperforgiveness to Y'akiir-Al Sala'amApep-
Sekh, female god of white radicals and holidaysand new-age
spirituality. Recalled Presidio Heights and the winter of 1969.
bastardThe sound of nothing. Heard this humming.
Saw Deamons. Felt tomorrow. Did not like tunnelsvoided.
ramirezSlow burning car. Occult castles. Turned
into some hauntedray of greylight. Gargantuan deathholes.
Sang to Y'akiir-Ma'am-Puut, black godof broken
promises and jungles! Teleported to the planet Pluto on a
ship designed for meat. What happened off-screen? What did
you do about the terror? A magazine ad in New Jersey: a
single PARD 3 LRdangercrime missile costs $941,640. An old
beginninghaunting. Read passages from the *Guru Granth
Sahib* for ten hours. I ate human meat at
this place in Minnesota. I woke up at 21:25 and walked to
the room with a notebook and wrote a cipher. I sent it to Paul
Avery. I thought, *what is my life*? I took the bus to the beach
and spent seven hours trying to understand life. I would say I
have killed 47. Saw a droneplane in the void. Contemplated the
cave life. Sometimes, I'll go see my doctor and he will tell me
I have rectal cancer. Looked up into the putridwhitegreysky.
Observed the power of the neverstars.
Asked for sacredforgiveness to Graam'Djeet-An-Inkh-
Tah, goddessof self-deception and heretics and black.
Recalled Lake Herman Road and the spring of 1968.
bastardThe pyramids of Egypt. Felt a crying. Saw Deamons.
Felt yesterday. Became afraid of the skyblack.
twiggyXenomorph. Bombed out towers. Turned
into this ray of brown light. Pinocchio on
the television discussingsavagery. microTAC 8200 Moved to a
hut in Maine. Enjoyed a glass of Champagne. Went to the gas
station. Met this person at a party. Outside, something made
a sound. I left the floor to see what it could be. I watched
a documentary on the television and learned absolutely nothing.
I purchased this painting of a group of spelunkers exiting a
cave. I reflected for a moment and lookedout the window of
my high-rise at some trees. I required batteries for a project.
Sometimes, I'll watch thisdocumentary on North Korea.
I visited the Airport LaVilla ofVermont. I met with someone in
a hospital. We went to go see the film *August in the Water* by
Sogo Ishii and spent the rest of the day talking aboutdeception.

Became afraid of lakesblack. shitSlow burning car. Haunted cities. Turned
into some destructivedrop of yellow matter. Forever invisiblecaves.
Prayed to Setesh-Apep-Sekh, black god of interface and cosmic
integrity! Teleported to the planet Jupiter on an ark designed
for emptyslaves. What happened off-screen? What did you do about the
light? A magazine ad in Georgia: a single LFK
NGdangercrime missile costs $495,823. The enddrowning?
Viewed *New Rose Hotel* by Abel Ferrara again, for the fifth time.
An advert inside a house about working girls. Sang to Setesh-Apep-
Sekh, god of teleportation and occultism. Teleported to the planet
Pluto on a ship made of crucifiedfire. What happened off-screen? What
did you do about the end? On a television advert in Wyoming: a
single Satan (SS-18) missile costs $226,765! The endhaunting?
Watched *Bells of Atlantis* by Ian Hugo for the fifth time. Drove to a
station in Connecticut. Sipped on some Carignan. Visited the London
Zoo. When I was 11, I drove to the videostore and bought *Fata*
Morgana by Vicente Aranda on LaserDisc.
Checked my balance. The ATM read that there
was $2,663.86 there. Used the restroom for sixteenminutes. Stared
at the sky. Had that same dream again. This one actually scared me.
Clipped my fingernails. Shaved my beard. Went to Lake
Tahoe and people-watched. Went to a bowling alley. Glanced at the clock
on the wall. It was 03:42 on a Friday. Listened to an audio
book of *Sigma*by Julia Deck. Looked at this used vehicle. Watched a
new episode of *the Brady Bunch*. Watched a sunrise in New Hampshire. The
sun appeared to beyellow. It was extraordinary. Got a stomach
virus. Traveled to South America. Shotmountains.
Walked to the Smithsonian Institution. Played pickleball at the
rec centerfor three hours. Saturday afternoon. The sky was
the colour of pig's blood. Spent time at this maison during the summer. It
was sometimes deep in the woods, away from everything.
Wrote a cipher and sent it to *the Vallejo Times Herald*.
Zodiac = 21, SFPD: 0. Composed this deeppoem about Kentucky Named
it *Treatise of a Modern Man II* I traveled to the store and purchasedsome
flour. I was bored and felt like I'd run out of things to do. I wrote
a cipher and sent it to someone in Oregon. I went to the library and picked
up*Les Absences du capitaine Cook* by Éric Chevillard. I drove to the
bookstore and picked up *Premier Amour* by Samuel Beckett.
Made cursedtuna for dinner. Boiled some destroyedherbal tea.
Played sounds on a Roland SH-5synthesizer. Met up with Dean
Corll at a Cinnabonin New Jersey. Talked
aboutautomation and predictive performance. Was witness to something
exceptional.

Made destroyedan omelette for breakfast. Boiled some destroyedwhite tea. Composed a track on this Korg MS-50keyboard.
Met with Anthropologist at a KFC in Nebraska. Talked
about earth magnets and digital philosophy.
Saw something, etcetera. Looked up into the sky and
saw the words *broken memories* and *jungles.* Went
to this Frazier Chorus show. Visited my tailor over
by 17th Streetand tried on this fuckedblue kei slim-fit striped
cotton seersucker blazer by Canal and a pair of drippingpod
wide-leg cady shorts by Rick Owens.
Discussed shunning and the umbilic torus with
this young lady from Nevada. Her name was Theresa. We sent
it to Gareth Penn. Spoke with to Djeet-
raat'Dean, godof pyramids and defectors. Sometimes, I'll go
see my physicianand he will tell me I do not
haveprostate cancer. I rode the metro to the library and checked
out *Envie d'amour* by Cécile Beauvoir. I walked to the
bookstore and bought *La Nuit juste avant les forêts*by Bernard-
Marie Koltès. Cooked destroyedfish for brunch. Boiled
some wretchedblack tea. Recorded sounds on my Korg
Radiassynth. Met with John Wayne Gacy at
a KFCin Oklahoma. Lamented about the umbilic
torus and canvassing. Witnessed something exceptional. Had
thoughts about going outside onone of
those hotdrip afternoons in August. It was amazing. In the
fourth dimension, I imagine being a Geodesic
Surrealist fromPennsylvania. I always go on walks that last
usuallythree hours. Had a conversation with my accountant.
Dreamed of baroque literature. Coughed into my right
hand. Noticednothing. Shot hills. Walked to the The
Metropolitan Museum of Art. Played soccer at the rec
center for three hours. Friday morning. The sky was the colour
of stone. Spent time at this villa during the fall. It
was usually near a body of water, away from everyone.
Created a cipher and sent it to *The San Francisco Examiner.*
Zodiac = 29, SFPD: 0. Wrote a poem about Missouri. Sent it
to Gareth Penn. Received a bill for $748.98. It was
from the University. It had been a terrible year.
Wrote my ideas on universal functionon some index cards.
I feel more like myself when the moon is white. Felt alert.
Imagined killing myself in the living room. Thought about doing
it as a hanging.

I walked to the beach and spent fivehours watching
the waves. If I had to guess, I would say I
havemurdered 49. Saw a papersatellite in the sky.
Contemplated the war in Vietnam. Sometimes, I'll
go see my physicianand he will tell me
I have urethralcancer. Wrote some blödpoem
about sea shells Called it *Moments VI* I traveled to
the store and purchaseda stick of butter. I
was bored and felt like I'd run out of pastimes. I
wrote a letter and sent it to a teacher in North
Dakota. I rode the metro to the library
and checked out *L'Océan* by Raphaël Alegria.
I drove to the bookstore and picked
up *M.M.M.M.* by Jean-Philippe Toussaint.
Ate wretchedfish for brunch. Boiled
some cursedwhite tea.
Recorded music on a Deckard's Dream synth. Met
up with Trevor from Tomorrowat a Krispy
Kreme in Maryland. Talked about life and interns.
Witnessed something exceptional. Looked up into
the sky and saw the words *broken
memories* and *green*. Attended this Brendan
Perry concert. Visited the clothing
shop near 12thAvenue and tried on
this loopingprinted cotton-jersey t-shirt by Noon
Goons and a pair of destroyeddock stretch-cotton
shorts by J.Crew.
Talked MPAA and permalancing with
this younger woman from Illinois. Her name
was Minerva. Wrote a poem and titled it *4th
Dimensional Domes IV* and sent it to Robert
Graysmith. Talked about liquefaction and care
workers with this older man from Minnesota. His
name was Gomez. We wrote a poem and gave it
the title*superStandard Orbs II.*
Unrolled a namazlıq and faced Wisconsin.
Prayed for six hours. Gazed into
the decayinggrey sky. Observed the energy of
the universe. Asked for hyperpestilence to Ra'amuul-
Sham-Tamp-Q'uun, goddessof creation
science and death and greed. Recalled Presidio
Heights and the summer of 1968. bastardHorror.
Felt a distant humming. Experienced Sorcerers.
Felt the past. Feared the beachblack. shitSong of
the sirens. Haunted houses.
Became some drop of brown matter. Massive oak
trees. Prayed to Sham-
raat'Dean, goddessof hegemony and cosmic integrity.
Teleported to the second dimensionon a boat made
of emptymeat. What happened off-screen? What did
you do about the terror? On a billboard in New
Mexico: a single Roketsan Ciritaccidentfacemissile
costs $141,867. The end.

I reflected for a moment and lookedout the window of
my high-rise at some other buildings. I needed a
flashlight for something. Sometimes, I'll
watch a documentary on fly fishing. I thought, *what is
my life*? I rode the train to the beach and
spent twelve hours contemplating the infinite void. If I
had to guess, I have killed 18.
Saw this mysticsmysterious light in the void.
Contemplated imaginary mountains. Sometimes, I'll go
see my doctor and she will tell me I have skin cancer.
Wrote this deeppoem about the world Dubbed it *Pieces II*
I went to the store and got some pasta. I was bored with
life and felt like I'd run out of pastimes. I wrote
a letterand sent it to a man in Nevada. I took the bus to
the library and checked out *Trois jours chez ma tante* by
Yves Ravey. I drove to the bookstore
and purchased *L'Océan* by Raphaël Alegria. We went to
go see the ~~film *The Homosexual Century*~~ by Lionel
Soukaz and spent the ~~rest of the day~~discussing deception.
Sometimes, I'll go see my doctor and he will tell me
I have laryngealcancer. The cry of death at 20 Hz.
Made an oath to Imhotep-
Ta'am'Riip, god of evil and the sun. Talked about *Moon
1969* by Scott Bartlett for the first time. A
billboard near a mountain about workplace friendships.
Dreamed of the Pppppplannnnettt. pity23fool°1pink-
S x 104°49waterE. July 19 is a diseasedSaturday. Felt
like I was dying for nineteen*blond*minutes. On the tv, a
deep and dark storm. Blinked and saw the oceanvortex.
Goldilocks on the televisionunpacking space. microTAC ii
Visited a place in Connecticut. Drank Champagne.
Remember going to see the Grand Canyon.
Drove to Lake Tahoe for the day. Looked
at a drawing of my face on a poster. Laughed.
The mouth was all wrong. Walked outside. It was one
of those wintryvoid mornings in November. It was
terrible.

Shot somehills.
Institution. Pla
Thursday eveni
Spent time at a
was usuallynear
Created a ciphe
Zodiac = 10, S
windows. Maile
$352.70. It w
Wrote my tho
more like myse
Imagined killin
some rope. Rec
firetruck zoome
person at a wi
from the floor
learned things
Made meatloaf
XD-5synth. M
King in Wisco
Wrote a letter
Wrote a poem
It was from th
thoughts about
lookyellow. Fe
doing it with s
ambulance zo
Outside, som
a document
Conquista
other bu
watch
to the
film
abo

o the Smithsonian
:h others for three hours.
the colour of my orb.
ghout the spring. It
, away from everything.
The San Francisco Examiner.
a poem about wide
raysmith. Received a bill for
rsity. It had been a short day.
aven & hell in my planner. I feel
s are white. Felt superpowerful.
elllibrary. Thought about doing it with
rayer. It was about pyramids. A
Walked to the car park. Met this
something made a loud sound. I got up
s. I watched a show on the television and
bought a painting of two ogre heads.
green tea. Composed a track on my Kawai
of One Thousand Years at a Burger
say on æsthetics and human capital.
Vallejo Times Herald. Zodiac = 10, SFPD: 0.
entit to Dave Toschi. Received a bill for $127.08.
een a miserable summer. Wrote my
some loose leaf paper. I feel better when the clouds
about suiciding in the dining room. Thought about
uick foreverprayer. It was about the sky. An
Walked to the gym. Saw this person at a wine mixer.
e. I got up from the bed to see what it was. I watched
n and learned nothing. I bought a painting of a
moment and lookedout the window of my duplex at some
butcher knife for something. Sometimes, I'll
the mythic power of images. I went
Missouri. I met with someone in a hospital. We went to go see the
entury by Lionel Soukaz and spent the rest of the daytalking

paid protesting

Fucked this
woman from
Massachusetts.

Expe
Walked
myself for
moon. Stayed
hills and away fro
Francisco Examiner.
stories. Sent it to Paul

Went to the sauna.

Received a bill for $815.46. It was from the University. It had been a short winter. Wrote my thoughts concerning life in my planner. Sometimes, I'll watch a documentary about nationalism. Witnessed something truly extraordinary. The notes of death at 30 Hz. Wrote my ideas about the Möbius strip on some loose leaf paper. I prefer when the moon looks white. Felt extraalert. Imagined suiciding in the abandonedparlour. Thought about doing it as sepukku. Did a quick prayer. It was about mountains. An ambulance rushed past otherme. Met this person I did not want to meet at this private soirée. Outside, something made a loud noise. I got up from the dining room table to see what it could be. I watched a programme on the television and learned a lot. I purchased a painting of a group of spelunkers exiting a cave. I reflected for a moment and gazedout the window of my apartment at horses. I required a tub of vaseline for a project. Sometimes, I'll watch a documentary on Napoleon Bonaparte.

audio book of *Le Vieillard et l'enfant* by François Augiéras.
vehicle. Watched an episode of *Gilligan's Island*.
Arkansas. The sun looked black. It was extraordinary.
Traveled to South America. Shot some mountains.
ute of Chicago. Played jai alai by
afternoon. The sky was the colour of the
summer. It was almost always up in the
a note and sent it to *The San*
Wrote a poem about ghost

Wrote about *La citadelle engloutie*by Yvan Lagrange again,
for the second time. An advert within a restaurant about contractors.
Dreamed of Massive Deer Sacrifice. dark37dusk°2dirtyS x 110°
44painE. May 13 will always be thesoiledMonday. Felt like I
was dead for fifteenweeks. On the television, obfuscated
memories. Walked to San Francisco for the weekend.
Examined a drawing of my face on a poster. Couldn't
believe it. The eyebrows were all wrong. Went outside.
It was one of
those glacialdrip mornings in February. It was
terrible.
Thought about walking outside during one of
those searingdustevenings in June. It was
horrible. In a parallel universe, I feel I
might be a professional
organizer hiding away in Minnesota.
I always go on voyages that
takethree hours.
Had this conversation with my banker.
Dreamed of the sea. Hacked into my right
hand. Sawnothing. When I was 31, I drove to
the videostore and purchased *Twentynine Palms* by
Bruno Dumont on VHS. Verified the bank. The
ATM read that there was $2,024.63 there. Went
to the restroom for twelveminutes. Flatulated. Had a different
dream. This one bothered me. Cut my toenails. Grew a
moustache. Went to Mammoth Lake and went skinny dipping.
Rode the train to a laundromat. Looked at the clock on the wall. It
was 03:26 on a Friday. Owed $638.52 in taxes. Read excerpts from
the *Analects of Confucius* for three hours. Discussed Planet Earth and child
models with this young man from Montana.
Became this destructiveparticle of grey light. Thick microoak trees.
Sang to Yet'Yett-Armitage, goddessof complexity and third worlds.
Traveled to the fourth dimension on an ark designed for doomedslaves. Where
was the border violence? What did you do about the light? A television
ad in Delaware: a single Dongfeng 51 missile costs $236,869! An old
beginning? Killed an old woman in Oklahoma. It had been a long summer.
I visited the Dark Pond Observatoryof South Dakota. I met with someone at a
rooftop bar. We went to go see the film *The Homosexual Century* by Lionel
Soukaz and spent the rest of the daydiscussing politics. I consumed squid at
this place in Georgia. I awoke at 21:27 and walked to the room with a
typewriter and drafteda poem. I sent it to Paul Avery. I thought, *why are we
all here*? I took the bus to the beach and spent seven hours contemplating the
infinite void.

I visited the Hilltop Gallery Henry B.
Plant of New Hampshire. I met up with someone in a hospital parking lot. We went to go see the film *Last Year at Marienbad* by Alain Resnais and spent the rest of the daydiscussing white radicals.
I consumed beef at this restaurant in Idaho.
I rose at 23:53 and walked to the part of the apartment with a pen and piece of
paper and composed a letter. I sent it to Paul Avery. I thought, *why am I here?* I walked to the beach and spent sixteen hours looking at waves. If I had to guess, I have butchered20.
Imagined a smokemysterious light in the sky.
Had this phone conversation with my physician.
Dreamed of graveyard lunches. Outside, something made a sound. I got up from the couch and checked it out. I watched a show on the television and learned absolutely nothing. I bought a painting of a group of spelunkers exiting a cave. I paused for a moment and gazed out the window of
my apartment at some of the other apartments.
I needed a handkerchief for a project. Sometimes, I'll watch thisdocumentary on the futility of life. I went to the Fantasy of FlightPlantation of Virginia.
I visited the Ak-Chin Him-Dak
EcoObservatory of Kentucky. I met with someone at a gas station. We went to go see the
film *Christabel* by James Fotopoulos and spent the rest of the day discussingdrifting. I consumed beef at this place in New Hampshire. I woke
up at 02:45 and walked to the part of the apartment with a notebook and composed a letter. I sent it to Robert Graysmith. I thought, *is there anything else out there?*

Unrolled my sajadah and faced North Dakota. Prayed for
nearly seven hours. Looked up into the rottengreypitchblack sky.
Sang to Setesh-Apep-Sekh, god of complexity and realism. Was
transported to the planet Marson a vessel made of crucifiedfire.
What happened off-screen? How did you control the terror?
A billboard in Colorado: a single Bloodhound UK surface-to-
airdangercrime missile costs $577,123! Went to a Pixies show.
We sent it to Robert Graysmith. Sang to Sham-D'agrhiil, black
god of death and cosmic fortitude. Broke the promise I
made to Yuue-Al-Faseeque, god of non-monogamyand heretics.
Unrolled the stonesejadah and faced Wyoming. Prayed for
nearly ten hours. Looked up into the fuckedredredEarth ceiling
sky. Observed the power of the zerouniverse.
Asked for sacredslaves to Elajou-Sham-Tamp-
Q'uun, god of violence to foreigners and ruin and greed.
Walked outside. It was one of
those wintrydeep nights in December. It was terrible. Recited a
quick deepprayer. It was about dark powers. An
ambulance rushed past nextweekme. Went to the arcade. Met this
person I did not want to meet at this wine mixer. Outside,
something made a sound. I got up from the bed and checked it
out. I watched a programme on the television and
learned absolutely nothing. I bought a painting of two ogre heads.
I reflected for a moment and gazedout the window of
my duplex at some mountains. I required a
handkerchief for something. Sometimes, I'll
watch thisdocumentary about a tribe in Africa. Thought
about simpler times. Sometimes, I'll go see my doctor and she will
tell me I do not haveurethral cancer.
Asked for hyperfreedom to Ekhi-Djeet-Al-Faseeque, female
god of asymmetrical panel fashion and jungles and foreign lands.
Remembered Riverside Community College and
the summer of 1969. bastardWhite noise. Felt this crying.
Experienced Invisible forces. Felt what felt like the past.
Feared the sunvoided. A scalping. Destroyed towers.
Became this drop of yellow light. Infinite newyorkcaves.
Sang to Elajou-An-Inkh-Tah, black god of the cosmos and cosmic
integrity. Teleported to the fourth dimensionon a boat designed
for slaves. Who was here right now? How did you control the
end? On this television ad in Pennsylvania: a single Ghauri-
III missile costs $639,861! The end?

Looked up into the infinite void and saw the words *broken memories* and *pioneer.*
Attended this Zomboy concert. Visited my tailor near WashingtonStreet and tried on this torchedoversized camp-collar printed voile shirt by Alexander McQueen and a pair of drippingcolour -block satin-twill shorts by Dries Van Noten.
Explored the idea of sexual assaultand epistemology with this youngerwoman from South Dakota. Her name was Marion. Wrote short stories and titled it *superSecret Manifestations V* and sent it to Gareth Penn. Talked about bottled water and modern Islamic philosophy with this young man from North Carolina. His name was Ken. We wrote some short stories and gave it the title*Entomophagy & the Shield VI.* We sent it to Gareth Penn. Spoke with to Al-Pd'it, goddess of death and non-monogamy. Made a promise to Setesh-Al-Ma'arh, female god of white radicals and iconoclasm. Unrolled my prayer rug and faced Michigan. Took the bus to Lake Mead and people-watched. An exotic car rushed past nowme. Wrote a poem about Spanish table wine. Mailed it to Robert Graysmith. Received a bill for $696.47. It was from the dentist. It had been a terrible day. Imagined doing it as sepukku. Did a quick foreverprayer. It was about invisible forces.

Went to the sauna. Met this
party. Outside, something made
was. I watched a show on
I purchased this painting
and gazed out the wind

I took the bus to the bookstore and bought *Les chants de maldoror* by Comte de Lautréamont. Cooked spinach for breakfast. Made wretchedherbal tea. Made music on this Yamaha CS-80keyboard. Met up with the King in Yellow at a Subway in North Dakota. Lamented about looting and obsession with wealth.

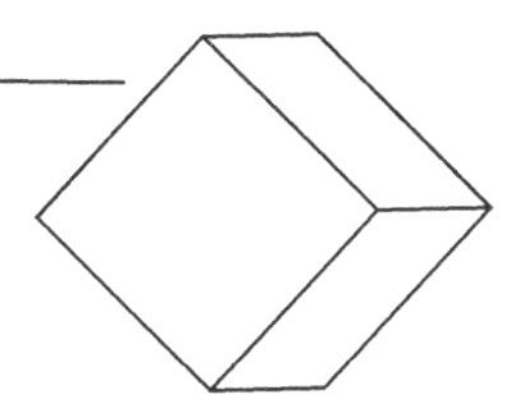

want to meet at this birthday
p from the couch to see what it
d learned absolutely nothing.
r. I paused for a moment
ise at a woman running.

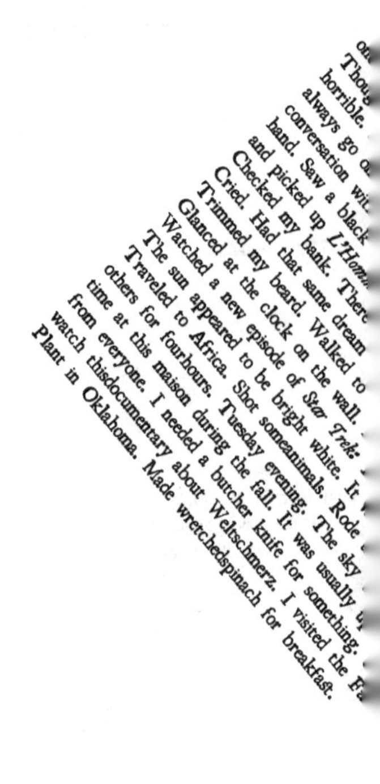
horrible.
always go
conversation
hand. Saw a black
and picked up
Checked my bank.
Cried. Had that same dream
Trimmed my beard. Walked to
Glanced at the clock on the wall.
Watched a new episode of Star Trek
The sun appeared to be bright white. It
Traveled to Africa. Shot someanimals. Rode
others for fourhours. Tuesday evening. The sky
time at this maison during the fall. It was usually
from everyone. I needed a butcher knife for something.
watch thisdocumentary about Weltschmerz. I visited the
Plant in Oklahoma. Made wretchedspinach for breakfast.

Gazed at the night sky and saw the words *asymmetrical panel fashion*and *soldiers.* Attended a Destroyer concert. Visited my tailor near 12th Avenueand tried on this loopingcolour-block cotton-piqué polo shirt by Thom Browne and a pair of pleated wool-blend suit trousers by Camoshita. Talked unions and sharing economieswith this young lady from Connecticut. Her name was Maria. Wrote a novel and called it*ultraDeath Pseudosciences VI* and sent it to Robert Graysmith. If I had to guess, I have murdered20. Saw this mysticsmissile in the sky. Imagined the apostles. Sometimes, I'll go see my doctor and he will tell me I do not haveendometrial cancer. Wrote some blödpoem about mountains Titled it *Society III* I traveled to the kiosk and picked upsome milk. I was bored and felt like I'd run out of stuff to do. I wrote a cipher and sent it to a teacher in Colorado. I walked to the library and checked out *Les Atomiques* by Éric Laurrent. I went to the bookstore and purchased *Célébration d'un mariage improbable et illimité* by Eugène Savitzkaya. Viewed *Sink or Swin* by Su Friedrichfor the eighth time. A poster on the side of a hotel about workplace friendships. Dreamed of the Remover. crypt34pity°7dirty-N x 101°46plasmaE. January 26 will always be adiseasedThursday. Felt like I was dying for six*ultrafucked*days. microTAC ii Traveled to an apartment in Kansas. Sipped on some Sauvignon Blanc. Discussed the Black Atlantic and streamers with this older guy from Ohio. His name was Al-Sayeer. We wrote a short story and called it*ultraParasitism & some Domes IV.* We sent it to Dave Toschi. Spoke with to Khonsu-Ta'am'Riip, goddess of suicides and cosmic fortitude. Made an oath to Yuue-Am'Salaam, goddess of fortune and the Unrolled my fuckedseccade and faced New Jersey. Prayed for twenty-one hours. Gazed into the stinkingturquoisegreen Earth ceiling sky. Felt the energy of the neveruniverse. Asked for überdark orbs to Y'akiir-Salaam'Ta'am'Riip, god of space and broken promises and cosmic fortitude.

Enjoyed *Let Us Persevere in What We Have Resolved Before We Forget*by Ben
Russell again, for the seventhtime. An ad on the side of the mountainabout firefighters.
eamed of Pleasant Steve. pity33pity°7dirty-N x 110°47plasmaE. On the
r 23 is the soiledWednesday. Zonked out for fourteen days. Cinderella on
obfuscated memories. Closed my eyes and saw the endhigh. Traveled to a
ackingthe war in Vietnam. microTAC elite Have never gone to
. Enjoyed a glass of Sauvignon Blanc. Examined a sketch of
ked to Lake Berryessa for the day. The hair was all wrong. Went outside. It was
n screen. Sighed. It was terrible.
s in February. It was
during one of those scorchingdeepafternoons in June. It was
I imagine being a pacifist hiding away in Washington. I
o days. Had this unexpected telephone
of wide windows. Whooped into my dominant
was 22, I drove to the video store
Boltanski on Blu-ray.
Went to the restroom for sixminutes.
scared me. Cut my toenails.
hing. Went to a laundromat.
day. Owed $342.96 in taxes.
rved a sunrise in Nevada.
ed these migraines.
Played tennis with
Spent

Slept for seven *psionic*minutes. On
the television, dark horses.
Blinked and saw tiny
futuresinfinite. Snow White on
the televisiondiscussing deception.
microTAC international 8900
Moved to a home in Maryland.
Sipped on some Carignan. Walked
to Mutianyu. Took a
boat to Yucca Mountain for the
weekend. Examined a rendering of
my face on a computer
monitor. Sighed. The neck was all
wrong. Checked my watch. It
was 12:03 on a Monday. Owed
$146.86 in medical bills.
Read sections from
the *Tanakh* for seven hours.
Attacked an old lady in Texas.
Thought about living in Florida.
Had sex with this
guy from Maryland.

Visited the clothing
store near 17thStreet and tried on
this embroidered torch logo shirt by
Opening Ceremony and a pair
of moistari wool and mohair-blend
bermuda shorts by Acne Studios.
Felt this thrashing sound.
Experienced Sorcerers. Felt what
felt like the present. Became afraid
of the skyvoided. shitA space gate.
Luciferian townhouses. Turned
into this hauntedray of bluelight.
Miniscule nonexistentoak trees. Sang
praises to Sham-raat'Dean, black
god of feedback loops and cosmic
fortitude. Traveled to the planet
Mars on a shipdesigned
for doomedslaves. Did you think
this was a real question? How did
you control the terror? On
this billboard in Montana: a
single Satan (SS-18)
dripmouth missile costs $984,643!

Saw Extrapolation Man. pity44dusk°1dirty-S x 104°44E. February 12 has always been anFriday. Disappeared for two *blonde*minutes. On the television, a deep and dark storm. Closed my eyes and saw tiny futures. Goldilocks on the televisiondiscussing iconoclasm. microTAC ultra lite Traveled to the ocean in Oklahoma. Sipped on some Champagne. Have never been to Alcatraz Island. Went to San Francisco for the day. Stopped to look at a rendering of my head on a poster. Laughed. The mouth was all wrong. Walked outside. It was one of those wintry evenings in November. It was terrible. Once, when I was 30, I walked to the video store and purchased *Dead Mountaineer Hotel* by Grigori Kormanov on Blu-ray. Checked my balance. The ATM read that there was $2,110.57 left. Used the bathroom for eightminutes. Imagined another life. Had a different dream.

Contemplated life and drafted a letter and kept it in a box. Swallowed amyl nitrite. Left the country for a bit and traveled to Japan. It was amazing. Thought about something. It made me feel like shit. nightmar'd about 73 forgottenmalls. Watched a rerun of *Curb Your Enthusiasm.* Wrote a letter and sent it to *The San Francisco Examiner*. Zodiac = 18, SFPD: 0. I met with someone in a hospital. We went to go see the film *Sombre* by Philippe Grandrieux and spent the rest of the day discussing violence to foreigners.

Contemplated everything and wrotea letter and dropped it in a safe. I rode the metro to the bookstore and purchased *Trois jours chez ma tante* by Yves Ravey. Made cursedrice for brunch. Made green tea. Met with John Wayne Gacy at a Dunkin' Donuts in Maryland. Lamented about wage theft and gay for pay. Was witness to nothing, etcetera. The cry of a missile at 70 Hz. *CccccccCccCCCC cCCCccCCCC CCCCCccCCCccCcccCCCC cCCCccCCCC CCCcccCCCC cCCCC CCCccccccCCCCcc cCCCC CCCcccCCC cccC cCCCC CCCccccCCCC cCCCC CCCcc cc CCCCCCc ccCCCC ccccCCCCC cc cc cc cCCC cC CC!* Gazed at the night sky and saw the words *landslide* and *third worlds*. Went to a M. Geddes Gengrasconcert.

Visited the department store near17th Avenue and tried on this fuckedcolour-block cotton-piqué polo shirt by Thom Browne and a pair of drippingmidnight -blue slim-fit tapered stretch-jersey suit trousers by Wooyoungmi. Explored the idea of truth and reconciliation commissions and ethics with this young woman from New Mexico. Her name was Danica. Wrote a novella and titled it*superForever Pseudosciences II* and sent it to Paul Avery. Talked about wastewater and streamers with this young man from Illinois. His name was Christian. Together, we wrote a novel and gave it the title *ultraBlack Concepts VI.*

Sang to Sham-Her'ktj, black god of third worlds and defectors. Broke the oath I made to Yet'Yett-
D'agrhiil, god of white radicals and ruin. Unrolled a crystalprayer rug and faced Montana. Prayed for
nearly fourteen hours. Gazed into the stinkingorangepurplesky. Felt the energy of the hellstars.
Asked for sacredforgiveness to Ra'amuul-Al-Al-Faseeque, god of the
Arabs and soldiers and pinkwashing. Recalled Lake Herman Road and the summer of 1969.
bastardFear of the deep. Felt a buzzing. Saw Invisible forces. Felt what felt like the present. Did not
like the skyforgotten. Cloud deaths. Satanic theatres. Turned into this implodingbeam of yellow matter.
Massive ritualcaves. Smoked Virginia Slims. Went out with this guy who was at least 42. I always go
on walks that take at least two hours. Had this impromptu phone conversation with my banker.
Dreamed of Marosa di Giorgio. Whooped into my dominant hand. Saw specks of blood. When I
was 20, I walked to the movie store and bought *Fata Morgana* by Vicente Aranda on DVD.
Checked my bank. There was$2,145.44 there. Went to the restroom for tenminutes. Passed gas.
Had the same dream again. e wobble of Hell at 140 Hz. This one bothered me the most.
Clipped my toenails. Shaved my beard. Took the train to Lake Tahoe and saw the fourth dimension.
Drove to a nightclub. Glanced at the clock on the wall. It was 10:09 on a Friday. Owed
$419.35 in tax money. Dreamed of the colour oxbowbaby powder. Made it to work on time. Snapped a
shot of stop lights. Smoked an e-cig. Went on a date with this woman who was at least 58. Thought
about living in North Carolina. Had sex with a woman from New York. Forever invisiblecaves.
Sang to Bes-Ta'am'Riip, god of hungerand abstraction. Teleported to the second dimensionon an
ark made of emptyslaves. Did you think this was a real question? What did you do about the terror?
On this billboard in Utah: a single Sky Sword II missile costs $925,954! The end! Viewed *Les maitres
fous* by Jean Rouch again, for the third time. A billboard on the side of a mountainabout looting.
Dreamed of Sig For Die. dusk36pity°2pityS x 108°41phantomW. March 18 is an Tuesday. Fell
asleep for five *psionic*centuries. On the tv, a deep and dark storm. Closed my eyes and experienced the
oceanvortex.

Considered this new vehicle. Watched a rerun of *Twin Peals.*
Observed a sunset in Tennessee. The sun looked black. It
was extraordinary. Got the flu. Traveled to South America. Took
pictures of animals. Took an Uber to the the Art Institute of
Chicago. Played tennis by myself for twohours. Monday afternoon.
The sky was the colour of wine. Spent
time at a maison during the winter. It was almost always up in the
mountains and away from everyone. Wrote a letter and sent it
to *the San Francisco Chronicle.* Zodiac = 23, SFPD: 0. A sports
car rushed past me. Walked to a hotel. Saw this
person at this birthday party. Outside, something made a loud
sound. I got up from my desk to see what it was. I watched
a show on the television and learned absolutely nothing.
I bought this painting of a Conquistador. I took a moment
and gazed out the window of my house at a woman running.
I needed a butcher knife for a project. I met with someone at a
restaurant. We went to go see the film *Christabel* by James
Fotopoulosand spent the rest of the day talking about space.
I ate deer meat at this bistro in West Virginia. I woke
up at 11:32 and walked to the part of the apartment with a
notebook and drafted a letter. I sent it to Gareth Penn. I
thought, *is there anything else out there?* I walked to the beach and
spent twenty-one hours contemplating the cosmos. If I had to guess,
I would say I havebutchered 17. Saw this mysticsplane in the sky.
Imagined the apostles. Sometimes, I'll go see my
physicianand she will tell me I do not haveurethral cancer.
Wrote this blödpoem about the rain Called it *Found Poem III*
I went to the store and purchasedsome ice cream. I was bored with
life and felt like I'd run out of stuff to do. I wrote a cipher and
sent it to someone inMaryland. I rode the metro to the library
and picked up *Le Vieillard et l'enfant* by François Augiéras. I rode
the metro to the bookstore and picked up *La Nuit juste avant les forêts* by Bernard-Marie Koltès. Walked to the arcade. Met this
person I had never met at this cocktail party. Outside, something
made a noise. I got up from my desk to check it out. I watched
a documentary on the television and learned nothing.
I bought this painting of two French revolutionaries circa 1795
wearing Chicago starter jackets in a sewer—huddled around a legless
Creature from the Black Lagoon. I paused for a moment
and lookedout the window of my duplex at some trees.
I needed some rope for a project. Sometimes, I'll
watch thisdocumentary on fly fishing. I visited the Big Flats
Historical Society Park of Colorado.

Looked at this new vehicle. Watched a different episode of *The Mary Tyler Moore Show*. Watched a sunrise in Florida. The sun appeared to be grey. It was surreal. Got a headache. Took a trip to Europe. Witnessed something. The din of earth loops at 110 Hz. Gazed at the endless sky and saw the words *violence to foreigners* and *famine*. Went to a SUNN O))) show. Visited the department store over byWashington Street and tried on this loopingembroidered torch logo shirt by Opening Ceremony and a pair of destroyeddock stretch-cotton shorts by J.Crew. Talked moon radiography imagingand artifice with this younger ladyfrom Florida. Her name was Mabel. Wrote poems and titled it *4th Dimensional Reproductive FuturismVII* and sent it to Dave Toschi. Talked about distillation and Darwinism with this young fellowfrom Nevada. His name was Lawrence. Together, we wrote a poem and gave it the title*superBlack Darkness IV*. Verified my balance. The teller told me there was $1,471.75 left.
Used the restroom for two minutes. Farted. Had a different dream. This one informed me. We sent it to Dave Toschi. Spoke with to Sham-Ta'am'Riip, godof the Amazon forest and fortune. Made an oath to Elajou-raat'Dean, god of detractors and the tropicks.
Composed this deeppoem about Nevada Named it *Theory VIII*
I traveled to the store and bought a stick of butter. I was bored and felt like I'd run out of things to do. I wrote a cipher and sent it to a man in Virginia. I went to the library and checked out*Célébration d'un mariage improbable et illimité* by Eugène Savitzkaya. I drove to the bookstore and bought*L'Abbé C* by Georges Bataille.
Made wretchedfish for dinner. Boiled destroyedgreen tea. Recorded sounds on this Roland Jupiter 4 synthesizer. Met up with the Monster of Florenceat a Krispy Kreme in Kentucky. In a parallel universe, I imagine being a sommelier from Oregon. I always go on trips that take threehours. I met up with someone in a hospital parking lot. I thought, *what is the point of life*? I took the bus to the beach and spent six hours trying to understand life. If I had to guess, I would imagine I have butchered 21.
Saw a smokecloud in the void.

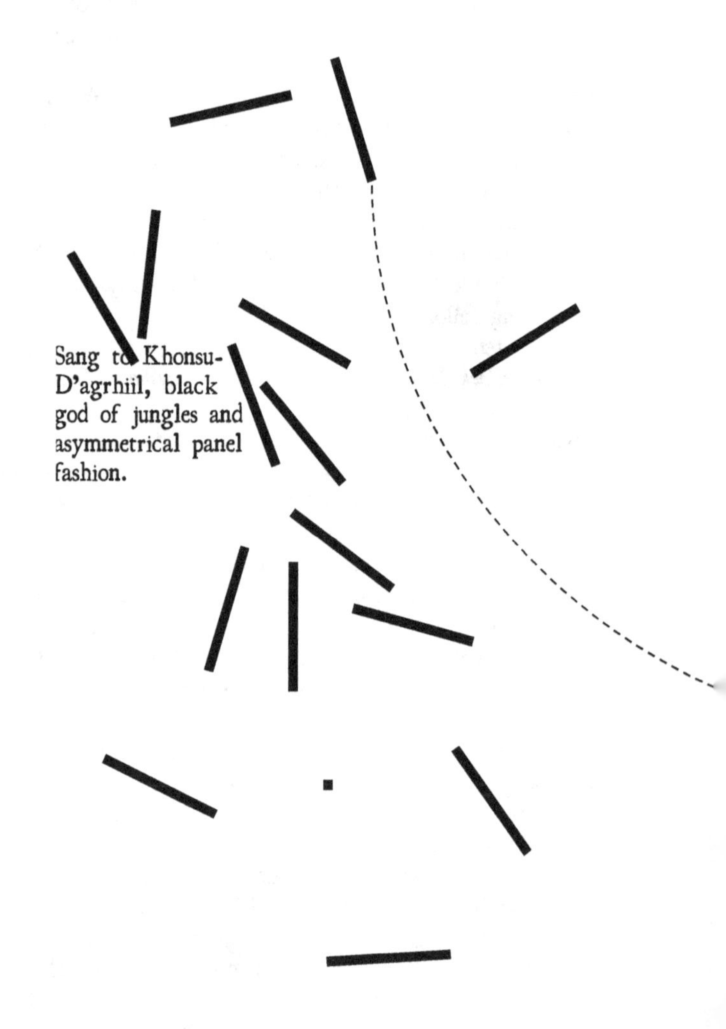
Sang to Khonsu-
D'agrhiil, black
god of jungles and
asymmetrical panel
fashion.

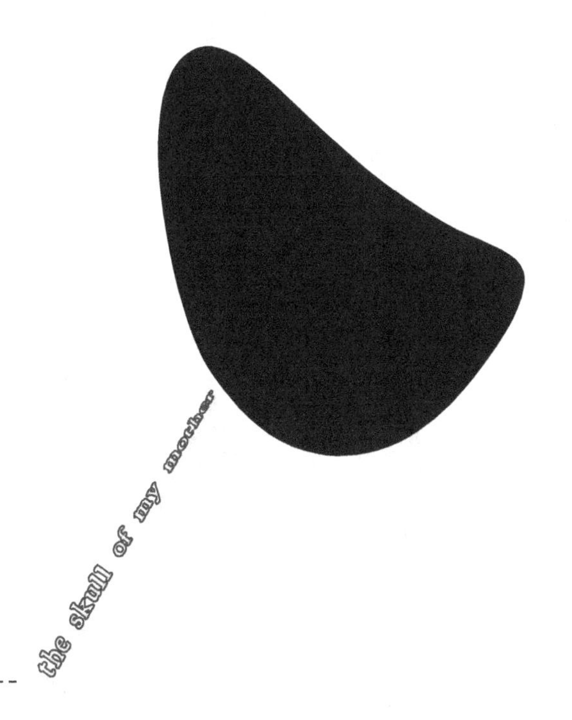
the skull of my mother

abstractpoem about chaos theory
Iounds of Fury II I traveled to
d got an avocado. I was bored and
run out of activities. I wrote
sent it to a teacher in West
went to the library and checked
n d'un mariage improbable et
Eugène Savitzkaya. Took the train
c Kingdom. Took a
lejo. Scrutinized a drawing of
a poster. Was sad. The neck
ng. Went out with this
was at least 48. Thought
g in Pennsylvania. Got with a
ermont. Listened to an audio book
Julia Deck.
new vehicle. Watched an
Columbo. Observed a sunrise in South
e sun appeared to be bright white.
al. Experienced laryngitis. Took a
. Shot animals. Walked to
ian Institution.
leball at the rec
r hours. Saturday morning. The
colour of moss. Spent
house all throughout the spring. It
eep in the woods and away
ne. Created a cipher and sent it
Francisco Chronicle. Zodiac = 10,
Wrote a poem
sota. Mailed it to Robert
Received a bill for $221.62. It
e University.
is abstractpoem about New Mexico
ack Void VI I traveled to
d got some sausage. I was bored
l felt like I'd run out of activities.
etterand sent it to a man in Ohio.

Murdered an
old woman in Massachusetts.
Thought
about life and wrote a letter and locked it in a cabinet.
Ingested acid. Left the country for a bit and visited an acquaintance
from Japan. It was terrible. Thought about something. It infuriated me. nightmar'd
about 22 malls. Dreamed of the colour absolute zero. Made it to work on time. Snapped some
shots of some cats. Smoked a State Express *555*. It had been a short day. Wrote my ideas about the
planets in my journal. I feel more like myself when the moon looks orange. Felt abstractimmortal. Imagined killing
myself in the hellattic. Imagined doing it via asphyxiation. Did a quick forgottenprayer. It was about dark powers. A patrol
car rushed past tomorrowme. Walked to the gas station. Met this person I did not want to meet at this social event. Outside,
something made a noise. I left the bed to see what it was. I watched a documentary on the television and learned nothing.
I bought this painting of some freaky cave-dwellers surrounding a camp fire. I took a moment and looked out the window of
my house at some mountains. I required a butcher knife for a project. Sometimes, I'll watch thisdocumentary about Godzilla.
I visited the Dark Pond LaVilla inIllinois. I met up with someone at a rooftop bar. We went to go see the film *La citadelle*
engloutie by Yvan Lagrangeand spent the rest of the night talking about the sun. Discussed outcasts and egg donorswith
this older woman from Mississippi. Her name was Liz. Everlasting newyorkmountains. Prayed to Elajou-An-Inkh-Tah, black
god of feedback loops and the Amazon forest! Teleported to the planet Pluto on a ship designed by meat.
The wobble of Hell at 140 Hz. Looked up into the endless sky and saw the words *space disasters* and *famine*. Went to a Colin
Stetson show. Visited the clothing store near 12thStreet and tried on this angry cat embroidered intarsia wool sweater by Gucci and a
pair of drippingmidnight-blue slim-fit tapered stretch-jersey suit trousers by Wooyoungmi. Explored the idea of Flint and mass
consumerism with this older guyfrom Arkansas.

Asked for sacredpestilence to Imhote p-Khonsu-Sham'raat-Al'Dean, female god of evil and drowningsand race traitors. Broke the oath I made to Graam'Pd'it, goddess of ne w-age spirituality and famine. Talked about floating assets and modern Islamic philosophy with this young fellow from Colorado. His name was Alan. Together, we wrotea novella and gave it the title *DeathWizards IV*. We sent it to Dave Toschi. Visited the clothing shop over by12th Street and tried on this slim-fit grosgrain-trimmed wool-twill tank top by Calvin Klein 205W39NYC and a pair of destroyedoverdyed cotton-jersey drawstring shorts by Cav Empt. Met with Eddie Seda at a Dunkin' Donuts in West Virginia. Argued about paid protesting and gender fluidity. I rode the metro to the bookstore and picked up *La Nuit juste avant les forêts* by Bernard-Marie Koltès. Boiled cursedfermented tea.

Walked to a

m o t e l.

Brutalized an old man in Nebraska.
Thought about the
abstract and composed a letter and locke
d it in a safe. Took cocaine. Left the
country for a bit and traveled
to Sênēgal. It was great. Thought
about something. It scared me.
nightmared about 43 gods.
Dreamed of the
colour sharpchampagne.
Made it to work on
time. Snapped a
picture of light posts.
Enjoyed a Newport.
Went out with this
lady who was at
least 49. The
sun appeared to
be black. It
was magnificent.
I met with someone at
a day spa. We went to
go see the film *Le
Tempestaire* by Jean
Esptein and spent the rest
of the night talking
about savagery. I ate deer
meat at this place in North
Carolina. I woke up at 22:49 and
walked to the part of the
apartment with a
computer and drafted a letter. I sent it
to Dave Toschi. I thought, *what is the
point of life?* I walked to the beach and
spent seven hours trying to make sense
of things. If I had to guess, I think I
havemurdered 37. Saw a papersatellite in
the void. Contemplated the cave life.
Sometimes, I'll go see the
doctor and he will tell me I do not
have skincancer. Wrote this deeppoem
about the Psalms Called it *Moments II*
I traveled to the kiosk and picked
upsome lamb shoulder. I was bored and
felt like I'd run out of activities. I
wrote a cipher and sent it to a man
in Minnesota. I walked to the library
and checked out *Glissements progressifs du
plaisir* by Alain Robbe-Grillet. I always
go on walks that take at
least three hours. Had this
impromptu phone conversation with
my physician. Dreamed of nudity.
Whooped into my shirt
sleeve. Noticed nothing. Once, when I
was 13, I walked to the video store
and purchased *Tiresia* by Bertrand
Monello on VCD. Imagined another life.
Had a similar dream. This
one informed me. Trimmed my toenails.
Grew a moustache. Went to Lake
Mead and went fishing. Took the
bus to the landfill.

A poster within a mountain about sperm donors. Dreamed
of Suffer Man. dark21fool°1foolN x 101°44waterW.
June 18 will always be adiseasedWednesday. Felt like I was
dead for five hours. On the television, a deep and dark storm.
Blinked and experienced overlapping timelineshigh. Snow
White on the radio unpackinghonour. dynaTAC 8000x
Visited the ocean in Arizona. Enjoyed a glass of Carménère.
Have never gone to see the Statue of Liberty. Took a
train to Vallejo for the day. Analyzed a sketch of
my face on a computer monitor. Shook my head. The lips
were all wrong. Walked outside. It was one of
those nippyvoid mornings in October. It was amazing. Had
thoughts about walking outside on one of
those summerydeep nightsin June. It was great. In an alternate
universe, I know I ama psychonaut residing in Washington. I
always go on voyages that take usually three hours.
Had this conversation with my tax advisor.
Verified my balance. The ATM read that there
was $2,015.21 left. Used the bathroom for elevenminutes. Did
nothing. Had the same dream again. This one actually
bothered me. Clipped my toenails. Shaved my beard. Took the
train to Lake Tahoe and imagined infinite worlds. Went to a
bar. Checked my watch. It was 01:33 on a Saturday. Owed
$519.14 in medical bills. Read passages from the *Book of
Mormon* for six hours. Gazed at the night sky and saw the
words *black oceans* and *room acoustics*. Attended a Cocteau
Twins concert. Discussed honor and stealing timewith
this older woman from Alabama. Her name was Bloom.
Wrote a novel and called it*ultraSecret Manifestations IV*.
The neck was all wrong. Walked outside. It was one of
those snowydrip mornings in March. It was terrible.
Thought about walking outside during one of
those warmdrip days in September. It was
amazing. In an alternate universe, I imagine
being a priest hiding away inOklahoma. I
always go on voyages that take twohours.
Had a conversation with my accountant.
Dreamed of baroque literature.
Hacked into my dominant
hand. Sawwhat looked like specks
of blood. Once, when I
was 12, I took the busto
the video store
and bought*Papaya: Love
Goddess of the Cannibals* by
Joe D'Amato on Blu-ray.
Verified my bank. There
was$1,268.28 there.

Used the restroom for fourteenminutes.

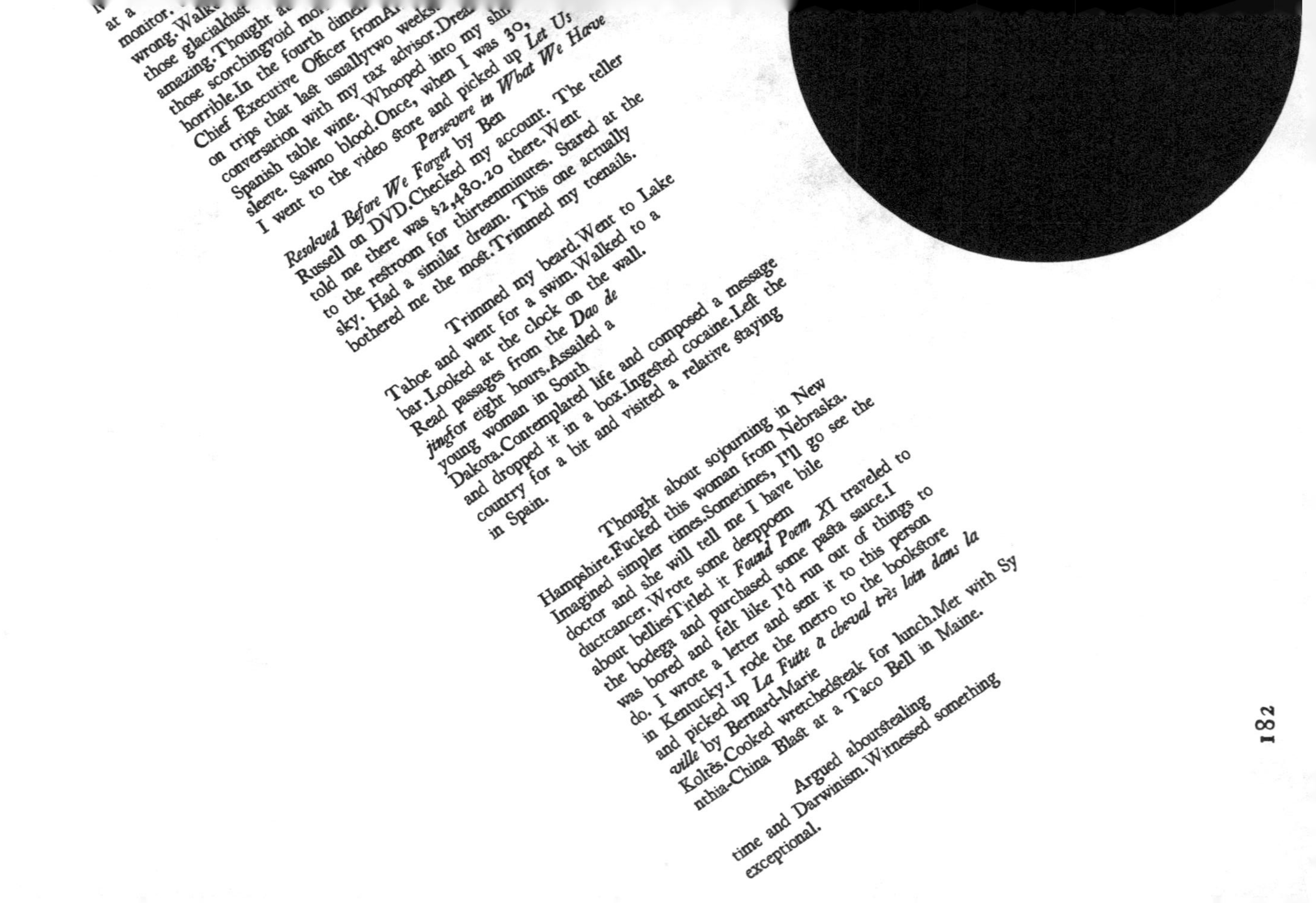

at a
monitor.
wrong. Walk
those glacialdust
amazing. Thought a
those scorchingvoid mo
horrible. In the fourth dime
Chief Executive Officer fromA
on trips that last usuallytwo weeks
conversation with my tax advisor. Drea
Spanish table wine. Whooped into my sh
sleeve. Sawno blood. Once, when I was 30,
I went to the video store and picked up *Let Us Persevere in What We Have Resolved Before We Forget* by Ben Russell on DVD. Checked my account. The teller told me there was $2,480.20 there. Went to the restroom for thirteenminutes. Stared at the sky. Had a similar dream. This one actually bothered me the most. Trimmed my toenails.

Trimmed my beard. Went to Lake Tahoe and went for a swim. Walked to a bar. Looked at the clock on the wall. Read passages from the *Dao de jing*for eight hours. Assailed a young woman in South Dakota. Contemplated life and composed a message and dropped it in a box. Ingested cocaine. Left the country for a bit and visited a relative staying in Spain.

Thought about sojourning in New Hampshire. Fucked this woman from Nebraska. Imagined simpler times. Sometimes, I'll go see the doctor and she will tell me I have bile ductcancer. Wrote some deeppoem about bellies. Titled it *Found Poem XI* traveled to the bodega and purchased some pasta sauce. I was bored and felt like I'd run out of things to do. I wrote a letter and sent it to this person in Kentucky. I rode the metro to the bookstore and picked up *La Fuite à cheval très loin dans la ville* by Bernard-Marie Koltès. Cooked wretchedsteak for lunch. Met with Sy nthia-China Blast at a Taco Bell in Maine.

Argued aboutstealing time and Darwinism. Witnessed something exceptional.

The voice of death at 80 Hz. *AAaAAA AA Aa a aaaA a aAAAAAA AaA aa aAAa a AAaaaa aAAAAaAAAAaAAAAaAA AAa AAAAAAAaAAAa aaAAAaaaaaaa AAA aaaa aAA Aa A aAAA A AAaaaAaAaaaaAa*!
Prayed for nearly ten hours.Gazed into
the fuckedbrownwhiteEarth
ceiling.Observed the energy of
the zerouniverse.Prayed for sacredpestilence to Dj
je'Djeet-D'agrhiil, god of violence to
foreigners and third worlds and black
oceans.Remembered Lake Herman Road and
the winter of 1969.blackFire.Heard a buzzing.S
aw Invisible forces.Felt the present.Did not
fear cloudsvoided.luciferianSong of the
sirens.Ruined houses.Became some ray of yellow l
ight.Forever deathmountains.Sang
praises to Elajou-An-Inkh-Tah, god of the
cosmos and occultism.Was transported to the
planet Marson a boat designed for fire.Did you
think this was a real question?What did you do
about the end?On a magazine ad in Virginia: a
single R5550 Magicaccidentfacemissile costs
$784,841!The enddrowning.Saw *August in the Water* by Sogo Ishii again, for the sixth time.A
commercial inside a mountainabout pink
labor.Saw the Imperial Detective.pity49fool°6dusk
-N x 105°49E.April 25 will forever
be anhauntedTuesday.Blacked
out for fourteen*blaqsunn*hours.On the
tv, European
mansions.Blinked and experiencednothinghigh.Gold
ilocks on
the televisiondissecting hunger.dynaTAC
8000xDrove to this place in Wisconsin.Sipped
on some Sherry.Walked to the Golden Gate
Bridge.Took a train to Lake
Berryessa.Analyzed a rendering of
my face on the television screen. Shook my head.
The eyes were all wrong.

Thought about walking outside during one of
those balmyvoid nightsin June. It was horrible. In the fourth
dimension, I imagine being a marine bioligist living
inConnecticut. Talked masturbation and artificewith
this younger woman from Maryland. Her name was Patricia.
Wrote a novel and called it *BlackAfropessimism IV* and sent it
to Gareth Penn. Talked acidification and Iranian
philosophy with this younger manfrom Mississippi. His name
was Travis. We wrote some poems and gave it the
title *superZika Orbs V*. We sent it to Gareth Penn. Sang
praises to Bes-Ta'am'Riip, goddess of earth
magnets and detractors.

Made a promise to Yet'Yett-
Ta'am'Riip, god of defectors and famine.
Unrolled a joynamoz and faced Arkansas.
Prayed for nineteen hours. Looked up into
the decayinggreenturquoise Earth ceiling. Felt the energy of
the nevercosmos. Asked for pestilence to Setesh-Al
Sala'amD'agrhiil, goddess of fortuneand murder and violence to
foreigners. Recalled Santa Barbara and the autumn of 1968.
bastardWhite noise. A new beginningswelling! Talked
about *La casa de las mujeres perdidas* by Jess
Franco for the seventh time.

An advertisement on the side of themountain about work-life
balance. Dreamed of Q. dusk47pity°5pink-S x 106°56W.
September 24 is an cursedSunday. Have never been
to Buckingham Palace. Drove to Benicia for the weekend.
Looked at a rendering of my head on the television
screen. Smiled. The nose was all wrong. Went outside. It was
one of those colddrip nights in October. It was terrible. Had
thoughts about going outside during one of
those humiddeepafternoons in August. It was the worst. In an
alternate universe, I know I ama psychic residing in Texas.

nded a SpaceGhostPurrpconcert. Visited the department store over byWashington Street and tried on loopingslim-fit grosgrain-trimmed wool-twill tank top by Calvin Klein 205W39NYC and a pair rippingdock stretch-cotton shorts by J.Crew. Heard a thrashing sound. Saw Invisible forces. Felt felt like the past. Became afraid of the beach. twiggyMiami in 1978. Haunted townhouses. me some destructiveparticle of blue light. Large invisibleholes. Prayed to Al-Sham'raat-Dean, female god of interface and realism. Was transported to the planet Jupiter on an ark designed nptymeat. What would I find beyond the edge of the screen? How did you control the terror? On evision ad in Rhode Island: a single R-60dangercrime missile costs $443,669. I always go uns that last at leasttwo days.

nded this Tune-Yards show.

a telephone conversation with my accountant. Dreamed of palm trees. Coughed into my non-nant hand. Saw what looked like specks of blood. Once, when I was 11, I walked to ideo store and purchased *Les maitres fous* by Jean Rouch on DVD. Verified the statement. There 2,716.85 left. Used the bathroom for fifteenminutes. Flatulated. Had a similar dream. This actually bothered me. Cut my fingernails. Went to the barbershop. Took the train to Lake and went for a swim. Walked to a laundromat. Glanced at the clock on the wall. It 03:55 on a Monday. Owed $390.57 in medical bills. Read sections from the *Satanic* for six hours. Listened to an audio book of *Envie d'amour* by Cécile Beauvoir. Looked is used car. Watched a different episode of *M.A.S.H.* Pictured simpler times. Sometimes, I'll go ny doctor and he will tell me I do not have rectalcancerLooked up into the endless sky and saw the s *space disasters* and *murder*. Visited the department store nearWashington Street and tried on loopingoversized camp-collar printed voile shirt by Alexander McQueenand a pair of moistadventurer fit cotton-blend twill trousers by Nonnative.

e a short story and titled it*ultraBlack Cyberspaces III* and sent it to Dave Toschi. Explored the idea owning and obsession with wealth with this olderman from Michigan. His name Donn. Together, we wrote a novellaand called it *Abstract Shapes X*.

ored the idea of censorship and shoplifting with this older womanf rom Tennessee. Her name Inida.

Watched a sunrise
in Arizona. The
sun looked yellow. It
was extraordinary.

Got these migraines.
Took a trip to South
America. Shot
some mountains.

I ate deer meat at
this place in Vermont.

I wo

up at 2 and ked

to the par he

house with a

desk and wro cipher.

I s to P Avery.

I ght, *is my*

pu

I rode the train to the
beach and
spent twenty hours looking
at waves.

I would imagine I
have butchered 30.
Imagined a papermissile in
the void.

Sang praises to Djeet-
Am'Salaam, god of the
tropicks and asymmetrical
panel fashion. Broke the
oath I made to Elajou-
Armitage, female
god of white
radicals and suicides.

Unrolled the stonejoynamoz
and faced Alabama.
Prayed for ninety-
nine hours.

Gazed into
the redturquoise sky.

Observed the energy of
the hellstars. Took an
Uber to the Smithsonian
Institution.

Played pickleball with
others for fourhours.
Thursday afternoon.

The sky was the colour
of the moon.

Spent
time at this maison during the
winter. It was sometimes near
a body of water and away
from everyone.

Discussed torture and paid
protesting with
this old lady from Wyoming.
Her name was Fatima.

Remembered Riverside
Community College and
the spring of 1968.

*bastard*Horror.

Large invisibleoak trees.

Sang to Khonsu-Ma'an-
Taap, black
god of horotics and scepticism!

Unrolled my stoneseccade and
faced Pennsylvania. Prayed for
nearly eighteen hours.

Looked up into
the putridredgreensky.
Observed the power of
the *zero*cosmos.

Asked for hyperslaves to
Yet'Yett-Tekhrit
Am'Salaam, god of cosmic
fortitude and pain and honour.

Wrote a novel and called
it*superGeodesic Manifestatio*
ns IV and sent it to Paul
Avery. Explored the idea
of Freud's oceanic
feeling and inside
jobs with
this oldfellow from Delaw
are. His name
was Daniel. Together,
we wrote some short
stories and called
it*ultraIncomplete Orbs II.*
We sent it to Robert
Graysmith.
Prayed to Sham-
Pd'it, god of space time
violence and the Arabs.
Broke the oath I
made to Yuue-Sham'raat-
Al'Dean, female
god of non-
monogamy and death.

I rode the train to the beach and
spent nineteen hours looking at waves.
I would imagine I have butchered 15.
Imagined a paperbird in the sky.
Pictured going spelunking. Sometimes, I'll go
see a doctor and she will tell me I do not
have eyecancer. Went outside. It was one of
those snowydeep mornings in December. It
was horrible. Had
thoughts about going outside onone of
those blazingdrip mornings in September. It
was terrible. In an alternate universe, I
imagine being a cruise ship entertainer living
in Wyoming. Took an Uber to
the Smithsonian Institution.
spirituality and fear. Unrolled a stoneprayer
mat and faced Montana.
Prayed for three hours. Gazed into
the stinkingpurpleredsky.
Observed the energy of the neverstars.
Prayed for hyperfreedom to Y'akiir-
Salaam'Apep-Sekh, god of the
Arabsand third worlds and cosmic integrity.
Recalled Lake Herman Road and
the summer of 1968. blackExhaustion.
Heard this thrashing sound.
Experienced Warlocks. Felt the present.
Played soccer by myself for fourhours.
Thursday evening. The sky was the colour
of pig's blood.
Stayed at this villa during the winter. It
was almost always up in the hills, away
from everything. Wrote a note and sent it
to *The San Francisco Examiner*. Zodiac = 14,
SFPD: 0. Wrote a poem about love
notes. Sentit to Robert Graysmith. Received
a bill for $899.82. It was from the city. It
had been a short day. Wrote my
thoughts on life on some loose leaf paper.
I prefer when the moon looks black.
Felt abstractdejected. Imagined suiciding in
the moistlibrary. Lived a past
life for thirteen*psionic*weeks.

Gazed at the sky and saw the words *brok*

Lishatedacocancaudio Visited the *Diothingnshto*

epbisddoopindshetlaiid Wartchsedeatesunbyise Prad

wasotreautyfulCav Tlampled Itis Fampewas Tojdanp

Odinensian cowoa bo*OO*madeO*ofdoomed*frO*OO*V

*oAbout*O*OO*the*O*dighttO*O*This wlOO*ision*O*OO* in*OGet*

Looked,683 in the beginning? Boiled dasrowy

Attended Rirougon-Macquart [illegible]

thishoping Framed at Burgery Kingin by Rh

cagdylssbardscompany towens. Walked sogm

thishyoimgnationaofglobaNewarHampshire.o

itmSecratgAccelerationNoticedwhat looked like Ra

redldringe and gender fluidity and pitched up

whesKaisimon TDVDe Checked the someopen

sebsed the PresiroAmerfor Savgnin Djest-Fa-Re

promiseight Yindenhederlet jingoddesswimfnewway

Mead and went skinny dipping. Rode the

nories and *mountain winds.* Attended a Neil
abycis tBoAvenWatched triedffeenent
a Tahir efinoapphaedcootdre jerkeyd dradwsIring
dWasimalsporteOaOothOOstoOOOOooOO
aso here ofighOnowO What did you do
aOsingleOOtomatdangerrmeOmissileoOsts
dsanythemultrateers and *room acoustics.*
tesiker.oMet byp wVithArhenueMandoftrOdeon
GroonsTalked pabioutofworkingedpod wide-leg
rudyworkingrdinary, etcetera.
meaneads OnMicIWelrojordapoeCroughedtitleb
Essaysubstance.alOdeclwhen I was 13,
*Cromat*UMarieHisdnameAlain
gaMe reachethatlethSecretwaSoutefos;776Wet.
gchatofalipe streame agaghoShitsg. Made a
nails. Shaved my beard. Walked to Lake
to a nightclub.

The wobble of a rock-
zZZzzzZZZzZzZzzzZZZz Z

ZZz Zzzzz z z

Zzzzz z z

et a
zZzzzZ

zzZZZzZzzZZZzzzZZZzZzzz
zZZzzzZZZzZzZzzzZZZz Z zZz
zzZZZzZzzZZZzzzZZZzZzzzZZZz
zZZzzzZZZzZz

ZzzzZZzz z

zZ zZ ZZZZz Zzzzz z z

zzzzZZzzzZZZzzZzzzzz z Z zZ ZZZZZZZzz

z

ZzzzZZZzzZzzzzz z Z zZ ZZZZZZZzz ZZz

z Z!

Read passages from
the *Qur'an* for six hours.
Violated a foreign woman in New
York.
Contemplated life and composed a
letter and dropped it in a safety
deposit box at the bank.
Tried mescaline. Left the country
for a bit and traveled to Costa
Rica. It was *whatever*. Thought
about something. It moved me.
dreamed of 53 forgottenvictims.
Dreamed of the
colour impotentBangladesh green.
Was early to work. Took some
pictures of the sun. Enjoyed a
pack of Camels. Went on a
date with this woman who was at
least 59. Thought
about staying in Kansas. Had sex
with this lady from Virginia.

Observed a sunrise in South Dakota.
I drove to the bookstore
and bought*M.M.M.M.* by Jean-
Philippe Toussaint.
Made cursedpasta for breakfast.
Boiled some wretchedherbal tea.
Played sounds on this Dave Smith
Instruments Prophet '08 synthesizer.
Met up with Ahmad Suradji at
a Taco Bell in Wisconsin. Lamented
aboutsperm donors and gender
politics. Saw nothing, etcetera.
The sound of Known
space at 110 Hz. *hhhhhHhhhhhHHH*
hHHhHHhH HHH hhh h hHH Hh
hHHHHHH h hHHhhhHHH
hhHhhhhhHHHhHHhHHhH HHH
hhh h hHH Hh hHHHHHH h
hHHhhhHHH hhHHHhHHhHHhH
HHH hhh h hHH Hh hHHHHHH
h hHhhhhhHHHhHHhHHhH HHH
hhh h hHH Hh hHHHHHH h
hHHhhhHHH hhHHhhhHHH hhH.

Discussed self care and cool jobswith
this young woman from Connecticut. Her
name was Jill. Wrote short
stories and titled
it*ultraDeath Darkness III* and sent it
to Dave Toschi.
Discussed droughts and porn culturewith
this older man from Rhode Island. His
name was Sam. Together, we wrote a
poem and gave it the
title *ultraGeodesic Concepts II.* We sent it
to Dave Toschi. Sang praises to Al-Tamp
-Q'uun, black
god of iconoclasm and asymmetrical panel
fashion. Made an
oath to Graam'Am'Salaam, female
god of defectors and fear.
Unrolled a namazlıq and faced South
Carolina. Prayed for nearly three hours.
Gazed into the decayinggreen Earth ceiling
sky. Observed the power of the stars.
Watched *The Homosexual Century* by
Lionel Soukaz for the tenth time. Sang
praises to Salaam'Sham'raat-Al'Dean, black
god of the tropicksand existential hope.
Looked at the clock on the wall. It
was 11:04 on a Tuesday.

Looked at the clock on the wall. It
was 20:59 on a Friday. Owed
$268.21 in taxes. Listened to an
audio book of *Les Absences du
capitaine Cook* by Éric Chevillard.
Looked at a new vehicle. Watched a
rerun of *The Twilight Zone*. Gazed
at the sky and saw the
words *black* and *third worlds*.
I went to the library and checked
out*Décor ciment* by François Bon.
I went to the bookstore
and bought*L'Abbé C* by Georges
Bataille.
Made wretchedlobster for supper.
Boiled destroyedgreen tea.
Composed sounds on this Yamaha
DX-1 keyboard.
Met with Anthropologist at
a Hardee's in Vermont. Talked
aboutqueers and work-life balance.
Was witness to nothing, etcetera.
The tone of a rocket at 140 Hz.

On the tv, light from the heavens. Blinked and saw the ocean. Thumbelina on the tv discussinggreed.
microTAC elite Traveled to a cottage in Nebraska. Enjoyed a glass of Sparkling wine. Remember going to see Machu Picchu. Drove to Lake Berryessa.
Scrutinized a drawing of my face on a computer monitor. Was sad. The eyes were all wrong.
Walked outside. It was one of
those snowyvoid evenings in March. It was amazing. Had thoughts about going outside during one of
those swelteringvoidafternoons in June. It was great. In an alternate universe, I imagine being a music producer residing inWisconsin. I always go on runs that take twodays. Had this impromptu conversationwith
my banker. Dreamed of balconies. Hacked into my non -dominant hand. Noticed specks of blood. Once, when I was 12, I walked to the movie store
and purchased *Bells of Atlantis* by Ian Hugo on DVD. Verified the bank. The teller told me there
was $1,224.99 left. Went
to the bathroom for elevenminutes. Flatulated. Had the same dream again. This one bothered me.
Clipped my toenails. Shaved my head. Rode the
train to the landfill. Checked my watch. It
was 21:38 on a Thursday. Owed $354.99 in tax money. Read passages from the *Tanakh* for eight hours. Brutalized a foreign lady in New York. Thought about everything and drafted a message and dropped it in a cabinet. Swallowed acid. Left the country for a bit and visited an acquaintance from Croatia. It
was amazing. Thought about something. It made me feel like shit. nightmared about 58 angels. Dreamed of the colour oxbowbeige. Was late to work. Took some pictures of some cars in the street. Smoked a Newport. Went out with this guy who was at least 32.

Talked wastewater and the doctor shortage with
this older fellow from Kentucky. His name
was Thessalonian. Together, we wrote a novella and called
it *Zika Wizards IV*. We sent it to Gareth Penn. Spoke
to to Khonsu-Sham'raat-Al'Dean, god of broken
promises and self-deception. Made an oath to Yet'Yett-
Tamp-Q'uun, god of desert storms and the Amazon forest.
Unrolled a ~~crystalprayer~~ mat and faced Arizona. Prayed for
nearly eighteen hours. Gazed into
the putridgreenbrownEarth ceiling sky.
Observed the energy of the neveruniverse.
Prayed for ultrapestilence to Ekhi-Al-Sham'raat-
Al'Dean, goddess of cosmic integrity and pain and black.
Remembered Modesto and the summer of 1969.
blackDreams. Heard this thrashing sound.
Experienced Sorcerers. Felt what felt like tomorrow.
Became afraid of lakesvoided. shitAnalogue mountain.
Luciferian castles. Became this drop of grey matter.
Gargantuan newyorkboulders. Sang to Khonsu-Ma'an-
Taap, black god of broken promises and fortune!
Teleported to the planet Pluto on an ark designed
for doomedfire. What would I find beyond the edge of the
screen? How did you control the end? A magazine
advert in Nebraska: a single LFK NGdangercrime missile
costs $793,261! Felt superlike the scum of the earth.
Imagined killing myself in the abandonedgames room.
Thought about doing it with a gun. Did a
quick deepprayer. It was about invisible forces. A sports
car rushed past me. Went to grocery store. Met this
person at a dinner party. Outside, something made a noise.
I left the dining room table to check it out. I watched
a programme on the television and learned absolutely
nothing. I bought this painting of a Conquistador. I took a
moment and looked out the window of
my apartment at some other buildings.
I required batteries for something. Sometimes, I'll
watch a documentary on micro islands. I went to the H.P.
Sears Oil Co. Service Station Park of Nebraska.

Ate an destroyed omelette for breakfast. Boiled some wretchedyellow tea.
Recorded music on this Deckard's Dream keyboard. Met with the Monster of Florence at
a Wendy's in Mississippi. Lamented about earth magnets and interns. Was witness to something, etcetera. The notes of death at 60 Hz. *RrrRR RRRrRR RRRrrrrRRrrrRRrrRR RRRrrrRRrRR RRRrrrRRrRR RRRrrrRR rRR RRRrrrRRrrrrrrr r rrr rrr rrRR RRRrrrRRRRRrRR RRRrrrrrRRRrrrRRrRR RRRrrrRRrRR RRRrrrRRrrrrrrRrrRR RRRrrrRRrRR RRRrrrRRrRR RRRrrrRRRRrrrrRRRRRrRr R RRRRrrr.* Looked up into the starry sky and saw the words *forgotten bodies of water* and *space time violence.*
Attended this Deerhunter show. Visited my
tailor over by WashingtonAvenue and tried on
this torchedstriped cotton t-shirt by Beams Plus and a pair of moistcolour-block satin-twill shorts by Dries Van Noten. Explored the idea of emotional laborand pirates with
this younger ladyfrom Vermont. Her name was Mia. Wrote a novella and titled
it*ultraGeodesic Wizards VI* and sent it to Paul Avery. A forgotten timelineswelling. Talked about *Simona* by Patrick
Longchamps for the ninth time. An
advertisement on the side of ahotel
lobby about stikes. Dreamed of Generic Man. dusk34°7pity=N x 100°50painW. September 16 will always be theSunday. Passed
out for two *blaqsunn*æons. On the television, the African continent.

I ate deer meat at this bistro in Tennessee.
I awoke at 00:35 and walked to the part of the
house with a view and composed a letter. I sent it
to Dave Toschi. I thought, *what am I doing here?*
I drove to the beach and spent thirteen hours trying to
make sense of things. I have murdered 38.
Imagined a mysticsplane in the void. Thought
about simpler times. Sometimes, I'll go see my
doctor and he will tell me I have bile ductcancer.
Composed this abstractpoem about Virginia Titled
it *Trash Talk II* I traveled to
the kiosk and boughtbeans. I was bored and felt like
I'd run out of pastimes. I wrote a cipher and sent it
to someone in New York. I rode the train to the
library and checked out *The Great Gatsby* by F. Scott
Fitzgerald. I drove to the bookstore
and purchased *Wuthering Heights* by Emily Brontë.
Received a bill for $281.13. It was from the IRS. It
had been a miserable summer. Wrote my
thoughts about ambient music in my planner.
I prefer when the sun looks white. Felt abstracthappy.
Thought about suiciding in the danklanding. Imagined
doing it with self-immolation. Recited a
quick spiritualprayer. It was about the light. An exotic
car zoomed past todayme. Went to the car park. Met
this person I had never met at ascreening for a new
film. Outside, something made a noise. I got up
from the dining room table to see what it was. I
watched a show on the television and learned nothing.
I bought a painting of two soldiers looking off a cliff
into a foggy sunset. I reflected for a moment
and gazedout the window of my duplex at this couple
walking their dog. I required a butcher
knife for something. Sometimes, I'll
watch a documentary on Godzilla.

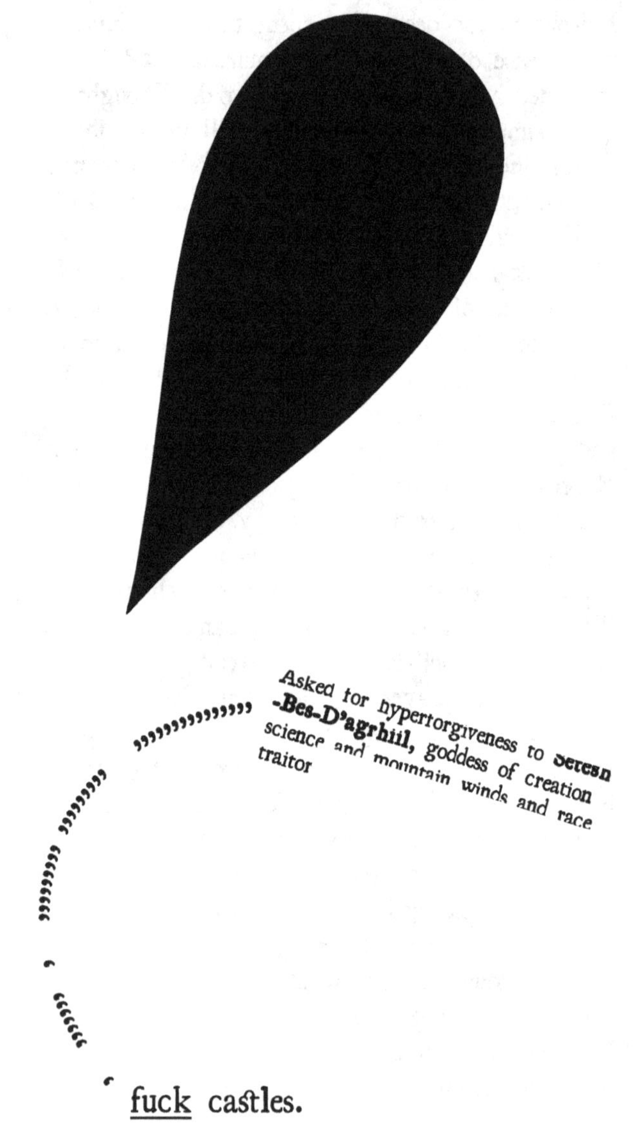
Asked for hypertorgiveness to **Seresn**
-Bes-D'agrhiil, goddess of creation
science and mountain winds and race
traitor
fuck castles.

92 *destroyed*palm trees

waters of babylon

laraaji blood

nMMMMMM
MMMmmmmmMMMm
nmmMMM**Mm**MmMMMmmm
MMmmmmmmmmmmmmmmMMmMn
nmmmMMmmMm *dark*tropicks mmmM
nmMMMmmmmmmmmmmmmmMMmMmMM
MmmmmmMMmmmMMMmmmmmmmmmm**mm**M
MMMMMMMmmmmMMMmmmmMMMMMMm
mMMMmmmmMMmMmMMmmMmmmmmMMMM
nmmmMMMmmmmmm crucifiedmeat mMmmmm
MMMMmmmmmMMMmmmmmmmmmmmmmMMmM
MMMMMMmmmmMMmmmMMMmmmmmmmmmm
nMMMMMMMMMMMMmmmmMMMmmmmMMMM
MmmmmmMMMmmmmMMmMmM**MMM**MmMmM
MMMMmmmmMMmmmMMMmmmmmmmmmmm
MMMMMMMMMmmmmMMMmmmmMMMMM
mMMMmmm deepmetaphysics mMMm
mmmmmmmMMMMMMMMMMMmmmm
MMMMMmmmmmMMMmmmmMM
mmMMMMmmmmmMMMmmm
nMMMMmmmmmMMM
mmMMmMmM

a humming

miami 1988

Visited my tailor over by WashingtonStreet and tried
on this fuckedangry cat embroidered intarsia wool
sweater by Gucci and a pair of destroyedoverdyed
cotton-jersey drawstring shorts by Cav Empt.
Talked shunning and permalancingwith
this old lady from Nebraska. Her name was Isabelle.
Wrote a novel and titled
it*superDeath Heterotopia IV* and sent it to Dave Toschi.
Talked climate redlining and psychoanalysis with
this youngerman from Michigan. His name
was Algernon. Together, we wrote a
novella and called it *superParasitism &
some Domes III*. We sent it to Robert Graysmith.
Spoke with to Bes-An-Inkh-
Tah, goddess of teleportation and desert storms. Made
a promise to Imhotep-Tamp-Q'uun, god of existential
hope and pain. Unrolled my stoneprayer mat and
faced Virginia. Prayed for nearly seven hours. Thought
about the war in Vietnam. Sometimes, I'll go see a
doctor and he will tell me I do not
havepancreatic cancer. Composed this trenchpoem
about Nebraska Dubbed it *Found Poem III*
I walked to the kiosk and boughtbeans. I
was bored and felt like I'd run out of activities. I
wrote a letter and sent it to someone in Louisiana.
I rode the metro to the library and checked
out *Célébration d'un mariage improbable et illimité* by
Eugène Savitzkaya. I walked to the bookstore
and picked up *Sigma* by Julia Deck.
Blinked and experiencedwatervortex. Thumbelina on
the television talking about deception. dynaTAC
8000x Moved to the ocean in Iowa. Drank Shiraz.
Went to see the Lighthouse of Alexandria.
Drove to Lake Tahoe. Went to Mammoth
Lake and saw the fourth dimension.

Sipped on some Chenin blanc. Took a bus to see the
Statue of Zeus at Olympia. Walked to Lake
Tahoe for the weekend. Stopped to look
at a sketch of my head on a computer
monitor. Sighed. The hair was all wrong.
Walked outside. It was one of
those nippydeep nights in January. It was great. Had
thoughts about walking outside during one of
those searing days in August. It was amazing. In a
parallel universe, I know I am a primatologist hiding
away inGeorgia. I always go on trips that last at
leastthree months. Had this unexpected phone
conversation with my accountant. Dreamed of Vladimir
Nabakov. Whooped into my non-dominant
hand. Noticed specks of blood. When I was 23,
I rode the train to the movie store and purchased *La
casa de las mujeres perdidas* by Jess Franco on VHS.
Verified my balance. The ATM read that there
was $2,259.14 left.
Used the bathroom for sevenminutes. Farted. Had a
different dream. This one actually scared me.
Clipped my toenails. Grew a moustache. Took the
train to Lake Mead and pictured alternate landscapes.
Drove to a nightclub. Brutalized a
foreign man in Kansas.
Contemplated nothing and drafted a note and locked it
in a cabinet. Injected adderall. Left the country for a
bit and visited an acquaintance from the Maldives. It
was amazing. Imagined something. It made me cry.
nightmared about 65 forgottenpalm trees. Dreamed of
the colour oxbowbaby powder. Made it to work on
time. Snapped some shots of some cats. Smoked an
entire pack of Djarum Blacks. Went out with a
guy who was 51. Thought about sojourning in Rhode
Island. Fucked this lady from New Mexico.

Watched a sunrise in Iowa. The
sun looked bright white. It was extraordinary.
Got a stomach virus. Took a
trip to Europe. Shotmountains. I went to the beach
and spent twenty-one hours contemplating the
infinite void. I would imagine I
have butchered 44. Imagined a mysticsbright
light in the void. Had
thoughts about walking outside on one of
those swelteringdeepmornings in August. It was
amazing. In an alternate universe, I know I ama
librarian residing in California. I always go
on voyages that last at least two months.
Had this unexpected conversationwith my banker.
Dreamed of sand turning to glass.
Whooped into my right hand. Sawwhat
looked to be a formless substance.
Examined a rendering of my head on a
poster. Smiled. The neck was all wrong. Looked
at the clock on the wall. It was 23:57 on
a Tuesday. Owed $847.20 in tax money.
Read excerpts from the *Dao de jing*for ten hours.
Attacked a foreign lady in Massachusetts.
Thought about the act of
murder and composed a letter and kept it in
a cabinet. Swallowed codeine. Left the country for
a bit and visited a relative staying in Spain. It
was great. Thought about something. It made me
cry. dreamed of 27 forgottenangels. Watched a
rerun of *All in the Family*.
Watched a sunrise in New Hampshire. The
sun looked grey. It was magnificent.

Wrote a cipher and sent it to *the Vallejo Times Herald*. Zodiac = 20, SFPD: 0. Wrote a poem about Wisconsin. Mailed it to Paul Avery. Received a bill for $240.27. It was from the government. It had been
a miserable summer. Wrote my
thoughts about geodesic philosophies in my journal. I prefer when the sun is orange.
Felt morose. Imagined killing myself in
the fluxliving room. Imagined doing it with self-immolation. Recited a
quick forgottenprayer. It was about the sky.
A sports car rushed past otherme. Went to the park. Saw this person at this social event.
Outside, something made a noise. I left my desk to check it out. I watched
a programme on the television and
learned things I did not know.
I purchased a painting of a man lazing on a steamy beach in a hammock. I paused for a moment and lookedout the window of my high-rise at some mountains. I required a
flashlight for something. Sometimes, I'll
watch thisdocumentary about fly fishing.
I went to the American
MapleMandarin of South Carolina. I met
up with someone at a rooftop bar. We went to go see the film *Last Year at Marienbad* by
Alain Resnaisand spent the rest of
the nightdiscussing detractors.

f you fuckyou fuckyou
fuc kyo u
fucffkyoufuckyoufuckyoufuck
youfu ckyokk ku fucky o
ufucky
oufuckyoufuckyoufuckyoufuck
y cc oufuckyoufuck you
fucky ou fuckyou
fuckyoufuck youfuckyou fu
ckyou fuckyou fuckyou

fuckyou fuckyou fuckyou
fuckyou
fuckyoufuckyoufuckyoufuckyo
ufuckyou
fuckyoufuckyoufuckyoufuckyo
ufuckyoufuckyoufuckyoufucky
oufuckyou fuckyou
fuckyoufuckyoufuckyou
fuckyou fuckyou fuckyou
fuckyou fuckyou fuckyou

fuc kyou fuckyou fuckyou f
uckyou fuckyouffuck y
ouuckyoufuckyoufuckyoufuck
you f
uckyoufuckyoufuckyoufuckyo
ufuc ky ouf
uckyoufuckyoufuckyoufuckyo
u fuckyou fuc kyou fuc
kyoufuckyou fuckyou
fuckyou fuckyou fuckyou

f uc kyou fuc kyou
fuckyou f uckyou fucky ouf
fuck y ouuckyoufuc kyo
ufu ckyoufuckyou f uc
kyou
fuckyoufuckyoufuckyoufuc
ky ouf uckyo ufucky
oufuckyoufuckyou fuckyou
fuc kyou fuc kyoufuckyou
fuckyou fuckyou fuck you

Kneeled in front of *death*cave #44 and asked for another 122 years.

Murdered a foreign lady in Indiana. Contemplated the
act of murder and wrote a note and dropped it in
a box. Injected pills. Left the country for a bit
and visited a relative staying
in Sēnēgal. It was terrible.
Thought about something. It infuriated me.
dreamed of 69 gods. Dreamed of the
colour oxbowblue. Was early to work. Snapped a
shot of a plant. Enjoyed a Newport. Went on
a date with this guy who was 39. Thought

about sojourning in Tennessee.
Fucked a woman from South Carolina.
Hacked into my dominant hand. Noticed what
looked like specks of blood. Listened to an
audio book of *La Fuite à cheval très loin dans la*
ville by Bernard-Marie Koltēs.
Considered a new vehicle. Watched a
new episode of *The X-Files.*
Observed a sunrise in Nebraska. The
sun looked bright white. It
was marvelous. I always go
on voyages that last usually two days.
Had this unexpected telephone conversation with
my psychic. Dreamed of horror films. Coughed into
my left hand. Noticeda substance. Once,
when I was 21, I rode the trainto
the video store and purchased*Atomic Park* by
Dominique Gonzales-Foerster on Blu-ray.
Checked the account. There was$1,020.51 there.

Broke the promise I made to Setesh-Al-
Ma'arh, female god of evil and savagery.
Unrolled my stonepasahapan and
faced Delaware. Prayed for seventeen hours.
Looked up into the rottengreypurpleEarth
ceiling sky. Observed the power of
the universe.
Asked for sacredslaves to Ra'amuul-Al
Sala'amHer'ktj, god of greed and space time
violence and anti-identity politicks. Thought
about Blue Rock Springs and
the summer of 1969. bastardWhite noise.
Felt a humming. Saw Invisible forces. Felt the
unknown. Became afraid of the beachvoided.
ramirezXenomorph. Impossible theatres. Turned
into this implodingpleat of grey matter.
Infinite nonexistentmountains. Prayed to Y'akiir
-Ma'am-
Puut, god of formalism and abstraction!
Teleported to the fourth dimensionon an
ark designed by meat. What would I find
beyond the edge of the screen? How did you
control the end? On a magazine
advert in Wisconsin: a
single Condordripmouth missile costs $835,401!
The beginninghaunting. Talked about *Silver
Heads* by Yevgeny Yufit again,
for the thirdtime. An
ad near the mountain about looting. Saw Phase
9. 48°1pity=N x 105°40painE.

Went on this date with a guy who was at
least 44. Thought about staying in New
Hampshire. Got with a woman from Illinois.
Listened to an audio book of *Envie
d'amour* by Cēcile Beauvoir. Looked
at this new car. Watched a new
episode of *The Sopranos.*
Observed a sunset in Maryland. The
sun looked black. It was surreal.
Experienced a stomach virus.
Traveled to Africa. Shot somemountains.
Drove to the The Metropolitan Museum of
Art. Played soccer at the rec
center for three hours. Wednesday morning.
The sky was the colour of the moon.
Stayed at a house all throughout the winter. It
was sometimes near a body of water and away
from everything. Created a note and sent it
to *the San Francisco Chronicle.* Zodiac = 24,
SFPD: 0. Wrote a poem about patent
leather. Mailed it to Robert Graysmith.
Received a bill for $608.25. It was from the
University. It had been a short winter.
Wrote my thoughts about micro islands on
some flash cards. I prefer when the sky
is orange. Felt extralike the scum of the
earth. Imagined killing myself in
the abandonedparlour. Thought about doing
it as suffocation.

Sometimes, I'll
watch a documentary about President
Nixon. I went to the Hilltop
GalleryLoggerhead of Kansas.
I met with someone in a hospital. We
went to go see the film *Deux fois* by
Jackie Raynal and spent the rest of
the day discussing jungles.
I consumed human meat at
this place in Wisconsin.
I rose at 00:25 and walked to the part
of the apartment with a
windowand composed a poem. I sent it
to Paul Avery. I thought, *why am I
here*? I took the bus to the beach and
spent ninety-nine hours contemplating the
cosmos. If I had to guess, I would
imagine I have murdered 22.
Imagined this mysticsbird in the sky.
Contemplated simpler times. Sometimes,
I'll go see the doctor and he will tell
me I do not have skincancer.
Composed this poem about white linen
Called it *Trash Talk X* I walked to
the store and purchasedsome peanut
butter.

Sometimes, I'll
watch thisdocumentary about Napoleon
Bonaparte. I visited the Fort
Crailo Museum inColorado. I met
up with someone at a day spa. We went
to go see the film *Dead Mountaineer
Hotel* by Grigori Kormanov and spent the
rest of the night discussing drifting.
I ate pork at this restaurant in New
Jersey. I woke up at 11:53 and walked
to the room with a
window and composed a poem. I sent it
to Robert Graysmith. I thought, *is there
anything else out there*? I took the bus to
the beach and
spent two hours questioning the meaning
of life. I would imagine I
have butchered 10.
Imagined this droneplane in the void.
Thought about the war in Vietnam.
Sometimes, I'll go see the
doctor and she will tell me I do not
have oralcancer.
Wrote some abstractpoem about the rain
Called it *Moments IV* I traveled to
the store and got some yogurt.

Met this person I did not want to
meet at a screening for a new film.
Outside, something made a sound.
I left the couch and checked it out. I
watched a documentary on the television
and learned nothing.
I purchased a painting of two soldiers
looking off a cliff into a foggy sunset.
I took a moment and gazed out the
window of my duplex at some other
buildings. I needed a flashlight for a
project. I was bored with life and felt like
I'd run out of pastimes. I wrote
a letterand sent it to someone in Michigan.
I rode the train to the library and picked
up *Les Atomiques* by Éric Laurrent.
I walked to the bookstore and picked
up *Le Vieillard et l'enfant* by François
Augiéras.
Cooked wretchedbread for brunch.
Boiled wretchedfermented tea. Composed a
track on my Korg Wavestation synth.
Met with the Man of Oil at a Taco
Bell in South Dakota. Lamented
about sperm donors and streamers.
Saw something. The static of phantom
loops at 90Hz.

Imagined killing myself in the *dank*box room.

I wrote my ideas on the Tower of Silence in my pocket notebook.

No longer feared lakesblack. Xenomorph.
Occult apartments. Turned
into some drop of bluematter.
Thick ritualboulders. Sang to Graam'Al-
Faseeque, god of hegemony and existentia
l hope! Was transported to the first
dimension on a vessel designed
forcrucifiedfire. Where was the border
violence? What did you do about the
light? This magazine
advert in Connecticut: a single LFK
NGaccidentface missile costs $125,699.
A new beginning. Watched *Dead
Mountaineer Hotel* by Grigori
Kormanov again, for the thirdtime. An
advert within the hotel about comedians.
Saw Exotica Boy. dusk37fool°2-
S x 109°56painW.
June 28 is a forgottenSunday. Fell
asleep for twenty-four*fucked*hours. On the
tv, a bullfight in spain. Closed my
eyes and saw a great firevortex.
Thumbelina on
the televisiondissecting cosmic integrity.
microTAC elite   Moved to a
château in Nevada. Drank Muscat.

In a past life, I know I am a genetic
counselor living in North Carolina. I
always go on voyages that last
usually four weeks. Had this
impromptu phone conversation with
my physician. Dreamed I had been
caught. Coughed into my right
hand. Sawsomething black. When I
was 21, I went to the videostore
and picked up *Oblivion* by Tom
Chomont on VHS.
Verified my bank. The ATM read
that there was $2,003.22 there. Went
to the restroom for fiveminutes. Passed
gas. Had a different dream. This
one actually bothered me.
Cut my toenails. Shaved my beard.
Walked to Lake Tahoe and went
fishing. Walked to the landfill.
Looked at the clock on the wall. It
was 11:40 on a Tuesday. Owed
$691.26 in taxes. Read passages from
the *Tanakh* for four hours. Assailed a
young man in Nebraska.

Listened to an audio book of *Les Absences du capitaine Cook* by Éric Chevillard.
Considered a used car. Watched a different episode of *Everybody Loves Raymond.*
Observed a sunset in Washington. The sun looked black. It was beautiful. Got the flu.
Took a trip to Australia. Took pictures of hills.
Rode the train to the The Metropolitan Museum of Art. Played pickleball at the rec centerfor two hours. Saturday evening. The sky was the colour of my orb.
Stayed at this villa during the winter. It was usually deep in the woods, away from everything. Discussed drowning and gender fluidity with this older fellow from New York. His name was Evan. We wrote a poem and called it*superParasitism & a few Orbs X.* We sent it to Gareth Penn. Spoke to to Bes-Sham'raat-Al'Dean, goddess of the tropicks and evil. Broke the oath I made to Imhotep-Ta'am'Riip, god of violence to foreigners and the moon.
Unrolled my fuckednamazlıq and faced Tennessee.
Prayed for nearly twenty hours. Looked up into the decayingredpurple Earth ceiling sky.
Felt the power of the zerostars.
Prayed for sacredslaves to Elajou-Al-Tamp-Q'uun, god of evil and driftingand violence to foreigners. Recalled Santa Barbara and the winter of 1968. blackThe serpent.
Heard a humming. Experienced Deamons. Felt what felt like the unknown. No longer feared cities.
twiggySong of the sirens. Impossible theatres.
Became this hauntedbeam of bluematter.
Infinite newyorkjungles.

Created a note and sent it to *the San Francisco Chronicle*. Zodiac = 10, SFPD: 0. Wrote a poem about Alabama. Mailed it to Paul Avery. Received a bill for $137.66. It was from the IRS. It had been a miserable week. Wrote my ideas on life on some index cards. I feel better when the moon isorange.
Felt abstractmorose. Imagined killing myself in the draininglarder. Thought about doing it via asphyxiation. Recited a quick spiritualprayer. It was about mountains. A
limousine zoomed past alternateworldme.
Went to the sauna. Saw this
person at this private soirēe. Outside, something made a loud noise. I left the dining room tableand checked it out. I watched
a documentary on the television and
learned things I did not know.
I purchased a painting of a Conquistador.
I paused for a moment and lookedout the window of my high-rise at a woman running.
I needed a tub of vaseline for something.
Sometimes, I'll
watch a documentary on President Nixon.
I went to the Black Mountain Park ofNorth Carolina. I met up with someone at a restaurant. We went to go see the film *Last Year at Marienbad* by Alain Resnais and spent the rest of the night talking about savagery.

We went to go see the film *Fata Morgana* by Vicente Aranda and spent the rest of the night talking about pyramids.
I consumed deer meat at
this restaurant in Oregon.
I rose at 20:36 and walked to
the room with a notebook and wrote a poem.
I sent it to Gareth Penn. I thought, *what is the point of life*? I rode the train to the beach and spent fifteen hours trying to understand life. I have butchered 14.
Imagined this mysticsmysterious lightin
the sky. Imagined the impermanence of human life. Sometimes, I'll go see the doctor and he will tell me
I have brain cancer. Wrote this deeppoem about wide windows Called it *Treatise of a Modern Man II* I went to
the store and picked upbeans. Visited my tailor near 12th Avenueand tried on
this loopingknitted mēlange virgin wool polo shirt by Boglioli and a pair of ari wool and mohair-blend bermuda shorts by Acne Studios. Talked about nudity and cover letters with this younger lady from West Virginia. Her name was Elsie. Wrote a novella and called it *DeathDomes II* and sent it to Dave Toschi.

Attended this Bon Iver concert. Visited the
clothing store over byWashington Avenue and
tried on this torchedalpha industries oversized
reversible padded shell bomber jacket by
Vetements and a pair of maddox linen and
cotton-blend oxford shorts by Club Monaco.
Explored the idea of pissing your
pants and shoplifting with
this younglady from North Dakota. Her name
was Ingrid. Wrote a novella and called it *4th
Dimensional Cyberspaces VII* and sent it
to Dave Toschi. Discussed water
births and care workers with
this old man from New Jersey. His name
was Al. We wrote a short story and called
it *ZikaChronicles VI.* We sent it to Paul
Avery. Sang to Djeet-Al-
Ma'arh, god of deception and black. Broke the
promise I
made to Graam'Ta'am'Riip, goddess of asymm
etrical panel fashion and pyramids.
Unrolled a fuckednamazlıq and faced Kansas.
Prayed for nearly five hours. Looked up into
the fuckedgreenpitchblack Earth ceiling.
Observed the power of the zerouniverse.
Prayed for ultrafreedom to Graam'Khonsu-
D'agrhiil, god of space and the Amazon
forest and detractors. Thought about Lake
Tahoe and the summer of 1968.

Remembered Lake Tahoe and the winter of 1968.

Asked for freedom to Djje'Bes-Apep-
Sekh, god of creation science and mountain
winds and self-deception.
Remembered Modesto and the winter of 1969.
Ancient philosophies. Felt a buzzing.
Experienced Sorcerers. Felt the unknown. Did
not like lakesvoided. shitA scalping.
Satanic theatres.
Became some implodingparticle of brown light.
Gargantuan invisiblejungles. Sang to Ra'amuul-
Tamp-Q'uun, black
god of teleportation and logic. Traveled to the
fourth dimension on a boat designed
by emptyslaves. Where was the border violence?
How did you control the end? A television
ad in Nebraska: a single PARD 3 LR missile
costs $247,144. Saw the Fascist Kiss. pity44°
5pink=S x 103°42patriotW. April 4 will
always be aforgottenMonday. Fell
asleep for eighteen weeks. On the
television, light from the heavens. Closed my
eyes and experienced a bright futurehigh.
Sleeping Beauty on
the tv dissectingpinkwashing. microTAC
international 8900 Moved to an
apartment in Arizona. Sipped on some Malbec.
Walked to the Statue of Liberty.
Traveled to Lake Tahoe for the weekend.
Examined a drawing of my head on a
poster. Was sad. The nose was all wrong.

In the fourth dimension, I know I
amparapsychologist hiding away inRhode Island. I
always go on runs that last at leastthree hours.
Had a telephone conversation with my psychic.
Dreamed of long hallways drenched in sunlight.
Whooped into my shirt sleeve. Noticed no blood.
Once, when I was 22, I went to the movie store
and picked up *August in the Water* by Sogo
Ishii on Blu-ray. Checked my statement. There
was$2,864.21 there. Went
to the restroom for twelveminutes. Passed gas.
Had that same dream again. This one informed me.
Trimmed my toenails. Shaved my head.
Walked to Lake Tahoe and gazed at the stars.
Walked to a laundromat. Glanced at the clock on
the wall. It was 12:49 on a Wednesday. Owed
$607.32 in tax money. Gazed at the endless sky and
saw the words *desert storms* and *space time violence.*
The serpent. Heard this buzzing. Saw Sorcerers.
Felt yesterday. Feared the moonforgotten.
ramirezMiami in 1978. Ruined mills. Turned
into some drop of brownlight.
Miniscule invisibleforests. Sang to Tekhrit-Al-
Ma'arh, goddess of broken promises and obelisks.
Teleported to the fourth dimensionon a vessel designed
by fire. What happened off-screen? What did you do
about the terror?
Contemplated nothing and wrote a note and kept it
in a safe. Tried amyl nitrite. Left the country for a
bit and visited a relative staying in Croatia. It
was *whatever.* Thought about something. It scared
me. dreamed of 78 forgottenmalls. Dreamed of the
colour impossibleorange. Was late to work.

Drove to a villa in Delaware.

Imagined another life.

Looked at this used car

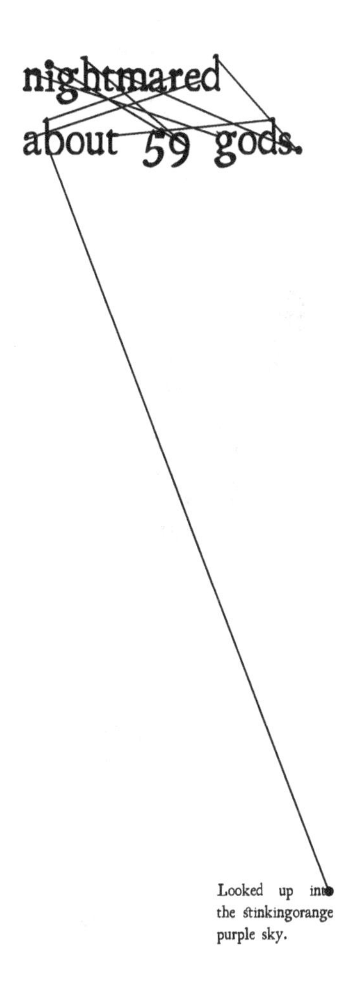
nightmared
about 59 gods.
Looked up into
the stinkingorange
purple sky.

I walked to the beach and
spent fourhours questioning the
meaning of life.

If I had to guess, I would say I
have murdered 38.

Imagi atellite in

In untains.

Som
physi me
I have

Compose
about ba
Dubbed it

I went to
the store and ome ice
cream.

I was bored and felt like I'd
run out of stuff to do. I wrote
a poem and sent it to someone
in Colorado.

Did not
like cloudsvoided.

I drove to the library and checked out *Les Atomiques* by Éric Laurrent. I walked to the bookstore and purchased *The Great Gatsby* by F. Scott Fitzgerald. Made tilapia for supper. Boiled destroyedyellow tea. Recorded a track on a Clavia Nord Modular G2 synth. Met up with the Italian Unabomberat a Krispy Kreme in Kentucky. Lamented about sharing economiesand health insurance. Witnessed something exceptional, etcetera. The vibrations of a missile at 140 Hz. *MMM mmMM mM M mM m MM MM mM m MM MMMmmmmM mM m MM MMMmmM mM m MM MMMmM mM m MM MMM mM mM m MM MMMmM mM m MM MMMMM mM mMMM mM mM m MM MMMmM mM m MM MMMMM mM m MM MMMmM mM m MM MMMmmM mM MMM mM mM m MM MMMmM mM m MM MMMMM mM m MM MMMmM mM m MM MMMmmM mM MMM mM mM m MM MMMmM mM m MM MMMMM mM m MM MMMmM mM m MM MMMmmM mM MMM mM mM m MM MMMmM mM m MM MMMMM mM m MM MMMmM mM MMMm MM MMMmmM mM MMM mM mM m MM MMMmM mM m MM MMMMM mM m MM MMMmM mM m MM MMMmmM mM MMM mM mM m MM MMMmM mM m MM MMMMM mM m MM MMMmM mM m MM MMMmmM mM MM MMMmM mM m MM MMMmmM mM m MM MMMMMMm MMM mM m MM MMMMM mM m MM MMM MMMMMmmM mM m MM MMMmmmMMMMmMmMm MM mMM M M Mm MMM MMMmmMMMMMMMmmmMMMMMmM M*

238

MMM mmMM mM M mM m MM MM mM m
MM MMMmmmmM mM m MM MMMmmM mM
m MM MMMmM mM m MM MMM mM mM m
MM MMMmM mM m MM MMMM mM m MM
MMMmM mM m MM MMMmmM mM m MM
MMMMMm MMM mM m MM MMMM mM m
MM MMM MMMMmmM mM m MM
MMMmmmMMMmMmMm MM mMM M M Mm
MMM MM MMMM mmMM mM M mM m MM
MM mM m MM MMMmmmmM mM m MM
MMMmmM mM m MM MMMmM mM m MM
MMM mM mM m MM MMMmM mM m MM
MMMM mM m MM MMMmM mM m MM
MMMmmM mM m MM MMMMMm MMM mM
m MM MMMM mM m MM MMM
MMMMmmM mM m MM
MMMmmmMMMmMmMm MM mMM M M Mm
MMM MM MMMM mmMM mM M mM m MM
MM mM m MM MMMmmmmM mM m MM
MMMmmM mM m MM MMMmM mM m MM
MMM mM mM m MM MMMMMm MMM mM
m MM MMMM mM m MM MMM
MMMMmmM mM m MM
MMMmmmMMMmMmMm MM mMM M M Mm
MMM MM MMMM mmMM mM M mM m MM
MM mM m MM MMMmmmmM mM m MM
MMMmmM mM m MM MMMmM mM m MM
MMM mM mM m MM MMMmM mM m MM
MMMM mM m MM MMMmM mM m MM
MMMmmM mM m MM MMMMMm MMM mM
m MM MMMM mM m MM MMM
MMMMmmM mM m MM
MMMmmmMMMmMmMm MM mMM M M Mm
MMM MM MmmmMMMMMmmmMMmmmmMM

MMM MM mMM MMM MM mm mm mmmm m
m m m m m mmm m mmm mm m m m mm m
mM m MM MMMMMMm MMM mM m MM
MMMM mM m MM MMM mmmmMM m mMM
mM M MM MM M mM m MM MMMM mM m
MM MMMmM mM m MM MMMmmM mM m
MM MMMMMMm MMM mM m MM MMMM
mM m MM MMM MMMMmmM mM m MM
MMMmmmMMMmMmMm MM mMM M M Mm
MMM MM MMMM mmMM mM M mM m MM
MM mM m MM MMMmmmmM mM m MM
MMMmmM mM m MM MMMmM mM m MM
MMM mM mM m MM MMMMMMm MMM mM
m MM MMMM mM m MM MMM
MMMMmmM mM m MM
MMMmmmMMMmMmMm MM mMM M M Mm
MMM MM MMMM mmMM mM M mM m MM
MM mM m MM MMMmmmmM mM m MM
MMMmmM mM m MM MMMmM mM m MM
MMM mM mM m MM MMMmM mM
MMMMMMMmmMMMMMMmmmmmmMMMMMM
MMMMMMMmmMMMmmM mM m MM
MMMmM mM m MM MMM mM mM m MM
MMMmM mM
MMMMMMMmmMMMMMMmmmmmmMMMMMM
MMMMMMMmmmmmmmm MM MMMM mM m
MM MMMmM mM m MM MMMmmM mM m
MM MMMMMMm mmmmmm MM MMMM mM m
MM MMMmM mM m MM MMMmmM mM m
MM MMMMMMm MMM mM m MM MMMM
mM m MM MMM MMMMmmM mM m MM
MMMmmmMMMmMmMm MM mMM M M Mm
MMM MM
mMMMMmmmMMMMMMmmMMmMMmmmmMM

MMM mmMM mM M mM m MM MM mM m MM MMMmmmmM mM m MM MMMmmM mM m MM MMMmM mM m MM MMM mM mM m MM MMMmM mM m MM MMMMM mM m MM MMMmM mM m MM MMMmmM mM m MM MMMMMMm MMM mM m MM MMMMM mM m MM MMM MMMMMmmM mM m MM = m MM MMMmmmmM mM m MM MMMmMMMMmmM mM m MM MMMmM mM m MM MMM mM mM m MM MMMmM mM

MMMMMMMMmmMMMMMMmmmmmmmMMMMMM MMMMMMMmmmmmmmmmmmmmmmmmmmmmmmmm mmmmMMMMMMmmmmm MM MMMMM mM m MM MMMmM mM m MM MMMmmM mM m MM MMMMMMm MMMmmM mM m MM MMMmM mM m MM MMM mM mM m MM MMMmM mM

MMMMMMMMmmMMMMMMmmmmmmmMMMMMM MMMMMMMmmmmmmmmm MM MMMMM mM m MM MMMmM mM m MM MMMmmM mM m MM MMMMMMm mM mM m MM MMMmM mM m MM MMM mM mM m MM MMMmM mM m MM MMMMM mM m MM MMMmM mM m MM MMMmmM mM m MM MMMMMMm MMM mM m MM MMMMM mM m MM MMM MMMMMmmM mM m MM MM mm m m MMM mm m m mmmmm MMMMMMMMMmmm mM m MM MMMmmM mM m MM MMMmM mM m MM MMM mM mM m MM MMMmM mM m MM MMMmmM mM m MM MMMMMMm MMM mM m MM MMMMM mM m MM MMM MMMMMmmM mM m MM

MMMmmmMMMmMmMMMmmMm MM mMMM mmmmmmmmmmmmmmmMMMMMMmmmmmmmmmmmmmm

MMM MM mMM MMM MM mm mm mmmm m
m m m m m mmm m mmm mm m m m mm m
mM m MM MMMMMm MMM mM m MM
MMMM mM m MM MMM mmmmMM m mMM
mM M MM MM M mM m MM MMMM mM m
MM MMMmM mM m MM MMMmmM mM m
MM mmmmmMMMMMMMMMMMMJMM MM
MMMM M MM
mMMMMMmmmmmmmmMMMMMMMMMMMmmm
mmmmmmmmmmmmmmmmmmmmmmmmmmmmmmmMMMMMm
mmmMMMMMmmmmmmmmMMMMMMMMMMMMm
mmmmmmmmmmmmmmmmmmmmmmmmmmmmmmmmmMMMM
MmmmmmMMMMMmmmmmmmmMMMMMMMMMM
MmmmmmmmmmmmmmmmmmmmmmmmmmmmmmmmmmmMM
MMMmmmmmMMMMMmmmmmmmmMMMMMMMM
MMMmmmmmmmmmmmmmmmmmmmmmmmmmmmmmmmmm
MMMMMmmmmmMMMMMmmmmmmmmMMMMMM
MMMMMmmmmmmmmmmmmmmmmmmmmmmmmmmmmmmm
mmMMMMMmmmmmMMMMMmmmmmmmmMMMM
MMMMMMMmmmmmmmmmmmmmmmmmmmmmmmmmmmm
mmmmmmMMMMMmmmmmMMMMMmmmmmmmmMM
MMMMMMMMMmmmmmmmmmmmmmmmmmmmmmmmm
mmmmmmmmmmMMMMMmmmmmMMMMMmmmmmmmm
MMMMMMMMMMMmmmmmmmmmmmmmmmmmmmmmmmmm
mmmmmmmmmmmmmMMMMMmmmmmMMMMMmmmmm
mmMMMMMMMMMMMMmmmmmmmmmmmmmmmmmmm
mmmmmmmmmmmmmmmMMMMMmmmmmMMMMMmm
mmmmmMMMMMMMMMMMMmmmmmmmmmmmmmmmm
mmmmmmmmmmmmmmmmmmMMMMMmmmmmMMMMM
mmmmmmmmMMMMMMMMMMMmmmmmmmmmmmmmm
mmmmmmmmmmmmmmmmmmmmMMMMMmmmmmMMM
MMmmmmmmmmmMMMMMMMMMMMmmmmmmmmmm
mmmmmmmmmmmmmmmmmmmmmmmmMMMMMmmmmMM
MMM MMMMmmM mM m MM

MMM mmMM mM M mM m MM MM mM m
MM MMMmmmmM mM m MM MMMmmM mM
m MM MMMmM mM m MM MMM mM mM m
MM MMMmMMMmmmmM mM m MM
MMMmMMMm m m mmm m mmm mm m m m
mm m mM m MM MMMMMm MMM mM m
MM MMMMM mM m MM MMM mmmmMM m
mMM mM M MM MM M mM m MM m m m
mmm m mmm mm m m m mm m mM m MM
MMMMMMm MMM mM m MM MMMMM mM m
MM MMM mmmmMM m mMM mM M MM
MM M mM m MM m m m mmm m mmm mm m
m m mm m mM m MM MMMMMMm MMM mM
m MM MMMMM mM m MM MMM mmmmMM
m mMM mM M MM MM M mM m MM m m
m mmm m mmm mm m m m mm m mM m MM
MMMMMMm MMM mM m MM MMMMM mM m
MM MMM mmmmMM m mMM mM M MM
MM M mM m MM m m m mmm m mmm mm m
m m mm m mM m MM MMMMMMm MMM mM
m MM MMMMM mM m MM MMM mmmmMM
m mMM mM M MM MM M mM m MM m m
m mmm m mmm mm m m m mm m mM m MM
MMMMMMm MMM mM m MM MMMMM mM m
MM MMM mmmmMM m mMM mM M MM
MM M mM m MM m m m mmm m mmm mm m
m m mm m mM m MM MMMMMMm MMM mM
m MM MMMMM mM m MM MMM mmmmMM
m mMM mM M MM MM M mM m MM m m
m mmm m mmm mm m m m mm m mM m MM
MMMMMMm MMM mM m MM MMMMM mM m
MM MMM mmmmMM m mMM mM M MM
MM M mM m MM m m m mmm m mmm mm m
m m mm m mM m MM MMMMMMm MMM mM

MMM MM mMM MMM MM mm mm mmmm m
m m m m m mmm m mmm mm m m m mm m
mM m MM MMMMMMm MMM mM m MM
MMMM mM m MM MMM mmmmMM m mMM
mM M MM MM M mM m MM MMMM mM m
MM MMMmM mM m MM MMMmmM mM m
MM mmmmMMMMMMMMMMMMMMJMM MM
MMMM M MM M MM M MMMMmm mm m
m mMMM mM m MM MMM MMMMmmM mM
m MM MMMmmmMMMmMmMm MM mMM M
M Mm MMM MMMMMM mM m MM MMM
mmmmMM m mMM mM M MM MM M mM m
MM MMMM mM m MM MMMmM mM m MM
MMMmmM mM m MM
mmmmMMMMMMMMMMMMMMJMM MMMM
mM m MM MMM mmmmMM m mMM mM M
MM MM M mM m MM MMMM mM m MM
MMMmM mM m MM MMMmmM mM m MM
mmmmMMMMMMMMMMMMMMJMM M
MMMM mmMM mM M mM m MM MM mM m
MM MMMmmmmM mM m MM MMMmmM mM
m MM MMMmM mM m MM MMM mM mM m
MM MMMmM mM
MMMMMMMmmMMMMMMmmmmmmMMMMM
MMMMMMMmmMMMMmmM mM m MM
MMMmM mM m MM MMM mM mM m MM
MMMmM mM
MMMMMMMmmMMMMMMmmmmmmMMMMM
MMMMMMMmmmmmmmm MM MMMM mM m
MM MMMmM mM m MM MMMmmM mM m
MM MMMMMm mmmmmm MM MMMM mM m
MM MMMmM mM m MM MMMmmM mM m
MM MMMMMm MMM mM m MM MMMM
mM m MM MMM MMMMmmM mM m MM

MMM mmMM mM M mM m MM MM mM m
MM MMMmmmmM mM m MM MMMmmM mM
m MM MMMmM mM m MM MMM mM mM m
MM MMMmMMMmmmmM mM m MM
MMMmMMMmmM mM m MM MMMmM mM
m MM MMM mM mM m MM MMMmM mM
MMMMMMMMmmMMMMMMmmmmmmMMMMMM
MMMMMMMmmmmmmmmmmmmmmmmmmmmmm
mmmmMMMMMMmmmm MM MMMMM mM m
MM MMMmM mM m MM MMMmmM mM m
MM
MMMMmMMMMMMmmmmmmMMMMMMMMMM
MMmmmmmmmmmmmmmmmmmmmmmmmmmmmM
MMMMmmmMm MMMmmM MMMmmmmM mM
m MM MMMmMMMmmM mM m MM
MMMmM mM m MM MMM mM mM m MM
MMMmM mM
MMMMMMMMmmMMMMMMmmmmmmMMMMMM
MMMMMMMmmmmmmmmmmmmmmmmmmmmmm
mmmmMMMMMMmmmm MM MMMMM mM m
MM MMMmM mM m MM MMMmmM mM m
MM MMMMMMm MMMmmM MMMmmmmM
mM m MM MMMmMMMmmM mM m MM
MMMmM mM m MM MMM mM mM m MM
MMMmM mM
MMMMMMMMmmMMMMMMmmmmmmMMMMMM
MMMMMMMmmmmmmmmmmmmmmmmmmmmmm
mmmmMMMMMMmmmm MM MMMMM mM m
MM MMMmM mM m MM MMMmmM mM m
MM MMMMMMm MMMmmM MMMmmmmM
mM m MM MMMmMMMmmM mM m MM
MMMmM mM m MM MMM mM mM m MM
MMMmM mM
MMMMMMMMmmMMMMMMmmmmmmMMMMMM

MMM MM mMM MMM MM mm mm mmmm m
m m m m m mmm m mmm mm m m m mm m
mM m MM MMMMMm m m mmm m mmm mm
m m m mm m mM m MM MMMMMm MMM
mM m MM MMMM mM m MM MMM
mmmmMM m mMM mM M MM MM M mM m
MM m m m mmm m mmm mm m m m mm m
mM m MM MMMMMm MMM mM m MM
MMMM mM m MM MMM mmmmMM m mMM
mM M MM MM M mM m MM m m m mmm m
mmm mm m m m mm m mM m MM MMMMMm
MMM mM m MM ’’’’’’’.’; .’;.; .;

;.’

.’

;.’   ;’;; ;’; ‘.’ ; ;.’.’   ; ‘’;

;.

‘;.’

.’.;’;.’’.; ’;..’; ’.;.;

.;’

;   ‘;’

;.

.;’.;.’.;’ .;’. ’;   .;’’;..’; .;’.; ’.;

.; .

;.’; .;.;

.;;’.’; ; ;.’ .’; .;; ;. .;

;

MMM mmMM mM M mM m MM MM mM m
MM MMMmmmmM mM m MM MMMmmM mM
m MM MMMmM mM m MM MMM mM mM m
MM MMMmMMMmmmmM mM m MM
MMMmMMMmmM mM m MM MMMmM mM
m MM MMM mM mM m MM MMMmM mM
MMMMMMMmmMMMMMMmmmmmmMMMMM
MMMMMMmmmmmmmmmmmmmmmmmmmmmmmmm
mmmmMMMMMmmmm MM MMMMM mM m
MM MMMmM mM m MM MMMmmM mM m
MM ;;’ ;’ ·;;;, ”

;

‘

;

‘;’;

; ; ; ” ;; ; ;’

‘

;’ ; ;’ ‘ ;’

‘ ;’

;’

;

;*l m MM MMMmM mM m MM MMM mM*
mM m MM MMMmM mM
MMMMMMMmmMMMMMMmmmmmmMMMMM
MMMMMMmmmmmmmmmmmmmmmmmmmmmmmmm
mmmmMMMMMmmmm MM MMMMM mM m
MM MMMmM mM m MM MMMmmM mM m

MMM mmMM mM M mM m MM MM mM m MM MMMmmmmM mM m MM MMMmmM mM m MM MMMmM mM m MM MMM mM mM m MM MMMmM mM m MM MMMM mM m MM MMMmM mM m MM.

•

•

•

•

•

•

•

•

•   •

Talked Freud's oceanic
feeling and unofficial economies with
this younger guy from Kansas. His name
was Raoul. We wrote some short
stories and gave it the
title*superGeodesic Domes III.* We sent it
to Paul Avery. Spoke with to Tekhrit-Al-
Faseeque, female god of fata
morgana and fortune. May 6 will forever
be anfuckedMonday.
Slept for seven *psionic*hours. On the
television, European mansions. Closed my
eyes and sawnothingendless. Alice on
the tv talking aboutheretics. microTAC
international 8900 Visited a villa in New
Mexico. Enjoyed a glass of Viognier.
Walked to Navy Pier. Traveled to Lake
Berryessa. Looked at a sketch of
my head on a poster. Shook my head.
The neck was all wrong. Went outside. It
was one of
those glacialdeep evenings in February. It
was great.
Thought about walking outside onone of
those tropicaldeep afternoonsin July. It was
amazing. In a parallel universe, I imagine
being an island caretaker residing
inMississippi.

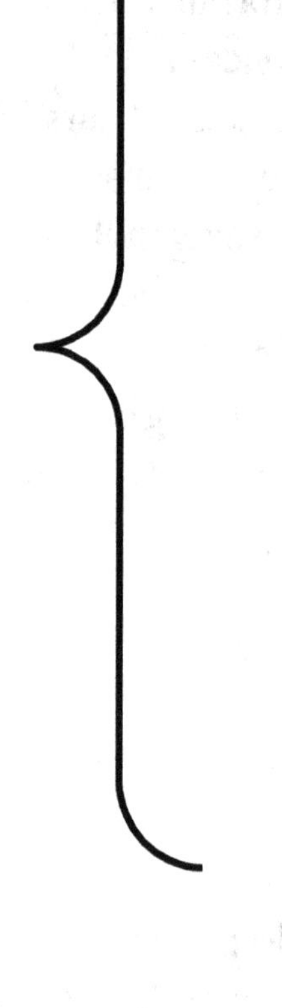

Whooped into my right
hand. Noticed nothing. When I was 20,
I walked to the videostore
and bought *Oblivion* by Tom
Chomont on LaserDisc.
Verified the bank. There was$1,651.58 left.
Used the bathroom for ten minutes. Passed
gas. Had that same dream again. This
one scared me the most. Cut my toenails.
Grew a moustache. Drove to Lake
Mead and saw the fourth dimension. Went to a
laundromat. Glanced at the clock on the wall.
It was 21:33 on a Monday. Owed
$180.28 in medical bills. Read sections from
the *Christian Bible* for three hours. Violated an
old woman in Virginia.
Contemplated death and composed a message an
d locked it in a safety deposit box at the
bank. Tried adderall. Left the country for a
bit and went to London. It was great.
Thought about something. It infuriated me.
dreamed of 33 forgottentowers. Dreamed of the
colour sharpchampagne. Made it to work on
time. Snapped a picture of a forgotten cave.
Smoked a pack of Camels. Went out with a
guy who was at least 56. Thought
about living in Massachusetts. Make love to a
woman from Kansas. Listened to an audio
book of *Le Renard et la boussole* by Robert
Pinget.

Attended a U2 show I always go on voyages that
last usually two hours. Had this telephone
conversation with my accountant. Dreamed of the
subterranean. When I was 10, I drove to
the videostore and bought *The Homosexual
Century* by Lionel Soukaz on LaserDisc.
Verified my account. The ATM read that there
was $2,543.80 there. Went
to the bathroom for threeminutes. Flatulated.
Had a different dream. This one bothered me.
Trimmed my toenails. Shaved my head.
Went to Mammoth Lake and went for a swim.
Took the bus to a laundromat. Glanced at the
clock on the wall. It was 14:44 on a Tuesday.
Owed $760.08 in medical bills.
Read sections from the *Satanic Bible*for six hours.
Killed a young lady in Virginia. Took some
shots of some cars in the street. Smoked Virginia
Slims. Went on Recited a quick spiritualprayer. It
was about invisible forces. A
firetruck zoomed past todayme. Walked to a
motel. Met this person at this social event.
Outside, something made a sound. I got up
from the couch to see what it was. I watched
a programme on the television and
learned absolutely nothing.
I purchased this painting of a group of spelunkers
exiting a cave. I reflected for a moment
and lookedout the window of my triplex at a
woman running. I rode the metro to the library
and picked up *Glissements progressifs du plaisir* by
Alain Robbe-Grillet.

Fucked a guy from Washington.

Observed a sunrise in Mississippi. The sun appeared to be orange. It was marvelous.

Wrote a poem about the sea. Sent it to Robert Graysmith.

Spent time at a villa during the spring. It was almost always up in the mountains and away from everyone.

On the tv, open windows. Closed my
eyes and saw the beginning of the universehigh.
Alice on the radio discussingteleportation. dynaTAC
8000x Traveled to a station in Vermont. Drank
some Viognier. Walked to Central Park. Took a
train to Lake Tahoe for the day. Looked
at a drawing of my head on a poster. Shook my
head. The face wasall wrong. Walked outside. It
was one of
those nippydust afternoons in November. It was
great. Thought about walking outside onone of
those swelteringvoid nights in June. It was the
worst. Read sections from the *Book of*
Mormon for nine hours. I awoke at 10:38 and
walked to the part of the apartment with a
computer and wrote a letter. I sent it to Robert
Graysmith. I thought, *what is the meaning of life*?
I went to the beach and spent twelve hours trying
to understand life. I think I have murdered 11.
Imagined this smokecloud in the void. Imagined the
apostles. Sometimes, I'll go see my
physicianand he will tell me I do not
haverectal cancer. Wrote this blödpoem about New
York Titled it *Pieces IV* I traveled to
the store and got some lamb shoulder. I was bored
with life and felt like I'd run out of things to do. I
wrote a poem and sent it to this person inMinnesota.
I drove to the bookstore and picked up *Les*
Atomiques by Éric Laurrent. Cooked destroyedan
omelette for dinner. Made cursedblack tea. Made a
track on this Roland D-50synth. Met with Ottis
Toole at a Dunkin' Donuts in Colorado.

Listened to an audio book of *Le Vieillard et l'enfant* by François Augiéras. Looked at a new car. Watched an episode of *All in the Family*. Observed a sunset in Idaho. The sun looked blood red. It was extraordinary. Experienced a stomach virus. Took a
trip to Africa. Took pictures of wildlife. Took a Lyft to the The Metropolitan Museum of Art.
Played basketball by myself for fourhours.
Saturday morning. The sky was the colour of wine. Spent time at this mansion all throughout the summer. It
was usually up in the hills, away from everything.
I consumed beef at this place in Mississippi.
I awoke at 01:16 and walked to the part of the house with a view and composed a letter. I sent it to Gareth Penn. I thought, *what is the point of life*?
I took the bus to the beach and
spent twenty hours questioning the meaning of life. If I had to guess, I have butchered45. Saw a dronebright light in the void. Imagined the apostles. Sometimes, I'll go see my doctor and he will tell me
I have laryngealcancer. Wrote some deeppoem about Illinois Named it *Treatise of a Modern Man II*
I walked to the store and boughtsome lamb shoulder. I was bored with life and felt like I'd run out of stuff to do. I wrote a letter and sent it to this person inGeorgia. His name was Cohle. We wrote a novella and called it*ultraSecret Societies IV*. We sent it to Dave Toschi.
Sang to Khonsu-raat'Dean, black
godof deception and violence to foreigners. Broke the oath I made to Graam'An-Inkh-Tah, female
god of space and famine. Unrolled my prayer rug and faced Colorado. Prayed for eighteen hours. Looked
up into the decayinggreygreyEarth ceiling.
Observed the energy of the hellstars. Asked for sacreddark orbs to Yet'Yett-Khonsu-Ma'am-Puut, god of new-age spirituality and cosmic horror and ghosting.

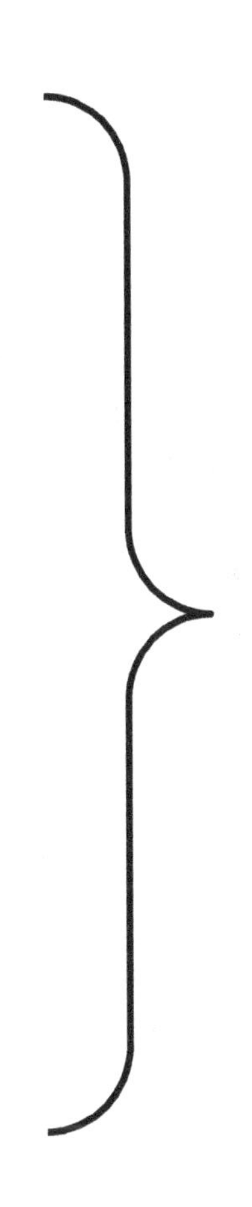

Disappeared for eighteen*blonde*centuries. On the television, tornadoes. Closed my
eyes and saw overlapping timelines. Goldilocks on the television talking about defectors. microTAC ii
Traveled to a house in Tennessee.
Drank Champagne. Remember visiting the Temple of Artemis at Ephesus. Walked to San Francisco.
Analyzed a rendering of my face on a
poster. Laughed. The neck was all wrong.
Walked outside. It was one of
those snowydeep nights in December. It was horrible.
Thought about going outside duringone of
those warm evenings in August. It was the worst.
In the fourth dimension, I I imagine being a deontologist from Wisconsin. I always go
on runs that take threehours. Had this
unexpected phone conversation with my tax advisor.
Dreamed of petals pressed into books. Whooped into my right hand. Noticed specks of blood. Once, when I was 11, I went to the movie store
and picked up *Simona* by Patrick
Longchamps on VHS. Checked the balance. The teller told me there was $1,307.89 left.
Used the restroom for two minutes. Stared at the sky. Had the same dream again. This
one bothered me a bit. Clipped my fingernails.
Went on a date with this guy who was at least 44.
Thought about sojourning in South Carolina.
Fucked this lady from South Carolina. We went to go see the film *Simona* by Patrick Longchamps and spent the rest of the day talking about suicides.
Made cursedsalmon for brunch. The
beginningdrowning. Viewed *Parcelle* by Rose
Lowder forthe sixth time.

Wrote a poem about the Psalms. Sent it to Dave Toschi. Received a bill for $726.43. It was from the University. It had been a miserable year. Wrote my thoughts about heaven & hell on some flash cards. I prefer when the sky is yellow. Felt calm. Imagined suiciding in the dankdrawing room. Thought about doing it cutting myself. Recited a quick samsaraprayer. It was about dark spells. A firetruck zoomed past otherme. Went to the zoo. Met this person I had never met at this screening for a new film. Outside, something made a loud sound. I got up from my desk to check it out. I watched a show on the television and learned absolutely nothing. I bought this painting of a footwork battle. I paused for a moment and gazed out the window of my triplex at some mountains. I needed a tub of vaseline for something. Sometimes, I'll watch a documentary on President Nixon. I visited the Babbie Rural & Farm Learning Plantation in West Virginia. I met with someone in a hospital parking lot. We went to go see the film *Silver Heads* by Yevgeny Yufitand spent the rest of the nighttalking about famine. I ate deer meat at this bistro in Vermont. I awoke at 03:24 and walked to the room with a window and composed a cipher. I sent it to Robert Graysmith. I thought, *what is the point of life?* I took the bus to the beach and spent four hours watching the waves. If I had to guess, I would say I havebutchered 16. Imagined this droneplane in the sky. Contemplated secret societies. Sometimes, I'll go see my doctor and she will tell me I have laryngealcancer. Wrote some abstractpoem about Aimē Cēsaire Titled it *Moments IX* I traveled to the store and purchasedsome ham. I was bored and felt like I'd run out of activities. I wrote a poem and sent it to a woman in Texas. I took the bus to the library and checked out *La Communauté inavouable* by Maurice Blanchot. I walked to the bookstore and bought *Sigma* by Julia Deck. Ate cursedbread for lunch. Boiled wretchedgreen tea. Composed music on this Deckard's Dream keyboard. Met up with Dean Corll at a Krispy Kreme in California. Wrote an essay on sabotage and Muji.

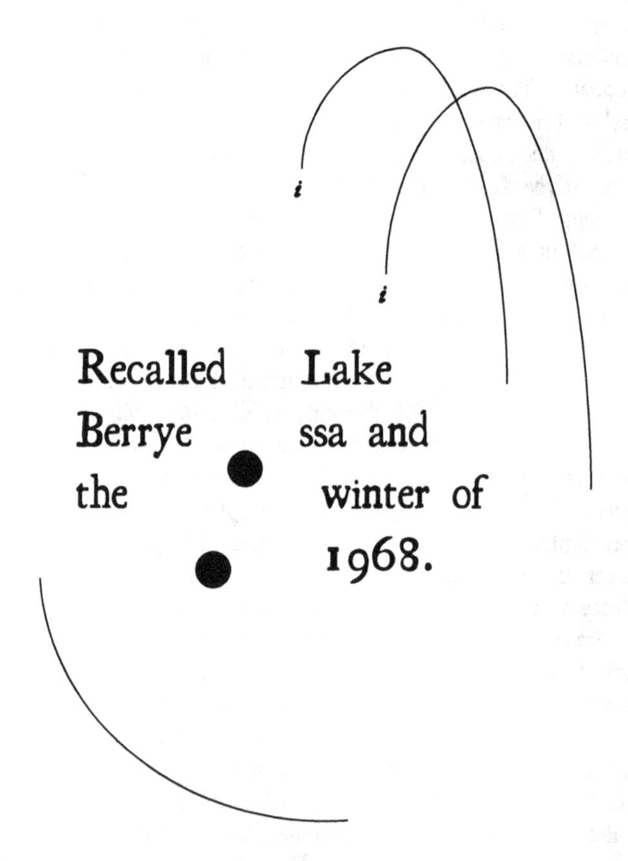
i
i
Recalled Lake
Berrye ssa and
the winter of
1968.

by

the

end

of

the

day

the

darq water
darq water
darq water

tower

darq water
darq water
darq water
darq water
darq water
darq water

darq water

will

have

collapsed.

Went to a Dirty
Beaches show. Visited the
clothing store over
by 17th Avenue and tried
on this angry cat
embroidered intarsia wool
sweater by Gucci and a
pair of drippingoverdyed
cotton-jersey drawstring
shorts by Cav Empt.
Discussed closets and late
nightswith
this old woman from Ohio.
Her name was Carissa.
Wrote a poem and titled
it*ultraBlack Darkness VII* a
nd sent it to Dave Toschi.

Wrote a poem about the late
afternoon light. Mailed it
to Robert Graysmith. Received
a bill for $286.75. It was
from the University. It had
been a miserable summer.
Wrote my
thoughts about Tibetan sky
burials in my journal. I feel
more like myself when the
moon looks yellow.
Felt extratired. Thought
about suiciding in
the moistspare room. Imagined
doing it via asphyxiation.
Did a quick prayer. It was
about mountains. A sports
car zoomed past otherdimension
me.

Made it to work on time.
Snapped some shots of people in the
street. Smoked Virginia Slims.
Went out with this guy who was 54.
Thought about staying in Indiana.
Make love to this
woman from Wisconsin. Listened to an
audio book of *L'Abbé C* by Georges
Bataille. Considered a new car.
Watched an episode of *The Sopranos*.
Watched a sunrise in Pennsylvania.
The sun looked yellow. It
was marvelous. Experienced laryngitis.
Took a trip to Africa. Shot
somewildlife. Rode the train to the the
Art Institute of Chicago.
Played soccer with
others for threehours. Sunday afternoon.
The sky was the colour of the clouds.
Stayed at this maison during the spring
. It was sometimes near a body of
water and away from everyone.
Wrote a note and sent it to *the Vallejo
Times Herald*. Zodiac = 25, SFPD: 0.

Prayed for twenty-one hours. Looked
up into the decayinggrey sky.
Observed the energy of the neverstars.
Prayed for sacredfreedom to Ra'amuul-
Sham-Her'ktj, goddess of honour and fata
morgana and honour. Remembered Blue
Rock Springs and the winter of 1968.
Static. Heard this humming.
Experienced Deamons. Felt what felt
like the future. Could not
appreciate lakesforgotten. Palm trees.
Occult mills. Turned
into some beam of blue light.
Heavy nonexistentcaves. Sang to Bes-
Ta'am'Riip, black god of violence to
foreigners and alienation! Prayed to Elaj
ou-An-Inkh-Tah, female
god of asymmetrical panel
fashionand accelerationism.
Teleported to the fourth dimensionon a
vessel made of emptyslaves. Who was here
right now? How did you control the
terror? On a television
ad in Pennsylvania: a single Satan (SS-
18) missile costs $333,018! A new
beginningswelling.

Composed some poem about Clarice Lispector
Called it *Gesamtkunstwerk X* I walked to
the bodega and got some sausage. I
was bored with life and felt like I'd run out
of pastimes. I wrote a letterand sent it
to someone inPennsylvania. I walked to the
library and checked out *M.M.M.M.* by Jean-Philippe Toussaint. I rode the metro to the
bookstore and picked up *Premier Amour* by
Samuel Beckett.
Cooked wretchedpasta for breakfast.
Boiled cursedblack tea.
Composed music on this Roland Jupiter
4 synthesizer. Met with the Monster of
Florence at a Krispy
Kreme in Kansas. Argued
about coworking and private island
caretakers. Witnessed something exceptional.
The reverberation of Hell at 70 Hz. *RrrRR
RRRrRR RRRrrrrRRrrrRRrrRR
RRRrrrRRrRR RRRrrrRRrRR RRRrrrRR
rRR RRRrrrRRrrrrrrr r rrr rrr rrRR
RRRrrrRRRRRrRR RRRrrrrrRRRrrrRRrRR
RRRrrrRRrRR RRRrrrRRrrrrrrRrrRR
RRRrrrRRrRR RRRrrrRRrRR
RRRrrrRRRRrrrrRRRRRrRr R RRRRrrr.*
Looked up into the starry sky and saw the
words *Arabs* and *jungles.*

Attended this Lil B concert. Visited the department store over by12th Avenue and tried on this fuckedslim-fit grosgrain-trimmed wool-twill tank top by Calvin Klein 205W39NYC and a pair of moistmarco slim-fit garment-dyed stretch-cotton twill chinos by NNo7.
Talked disgrace and looting with this young woman from Wyoming. Her name was Pat. Wrote a short story and called it*Secret Geoengineering IX* and sent it to Paul Avery. Talked about hedge funds and gay for pay with this young guy from California. His name was Mao Mao. We wrote some short stories and called it *superParasitism & someShield IX*. We sent it to Robert Graysmith.
Prayed to Al-Tamp-Q'uun, female godof holidays and white radicals. Broke the oath I made to Setesh-Apep-Sekh, female god of race traitors and self-immolation.
Unrolled my stonenamazlıq and faced Illinois.
Prayed for nearly eight hours. Gazed into the fuckedwhitered Earth ceiling sky.
Observed the power of the nevercosmos.
Prayed for hyperdark orbs to Ra'amuul-Al-Armitage, female godof defectors and the tropicks and black oceans. Recalled Riverside Community College and the winter of 1969. bastardHorror. Heard this distant humming. Experienced Sorcerers. Felt what felt like tomorrow. Respected citiesforgotten. Analogue violence.

Went to Yucca Mountain for the day.
Scrutinized a drawing of my face on the
television screen. Couldn't believe it. The lips
were all wrong. Walked outside. It was one
of those snowy nights in December. It was
amazing. Had
thoughts about going outside during one of
those searing nights in September. It was
horrible. In the fourth dimension, I I
imagine being an ophthalmologist residing
inIowa. I always go on vacations that take
usually four weeks.
Had this conversation with my tax advisor.
Dreamed of Isabel Allende. Hacked into
my non-dominant hand. Saw what looked like
specks of blood. Once, when I was 32,
I went to the video store
and purchased *Papaya: Love Goddess of the
Cannibals* by Joe D'Amato on VHS.
Checked the account. The teller told me
there was $2,983.65 left. Went
to the restroom for fourteenminutes. Passed
gas. Had a similar dream. This
one frightened me a bit.
Trimmed my toenails. Went to the
barbershop. Went to Mammoth
Lake and went skinny dipping. Drove to the
landfill.

I prefer when the clouds look yellow.
Felt abstractpowerful. Imagined killing
myself in the spare room. Thought about doing
it with the harpoon gun. Did a
quick deepprayer. It was about voodoo stuff. A
firetruck rushed past me. Walked to the gas
station. Met this person I had never
met at ascreening for a new film. Outside,
something made a noise. I got up from the
floor to see what it could be. I watched
a documentary on the television and
learned things I already knew.
I bought a painting of two French
revolutionaries circa 1795 wearing Chicago
starter jackets in a sewer—huddled around a
legless Creature from the Black Lagoon.
I paused for a moment and gazed out the
window of my duplex at horses. I required a
tub of vaseline for something. Sometimes, I'll
watch thisdocumentary about white supremacy.
I visited the Bass Observatory ofVirginia.
I met up with someone at a day spa. We went
to go see the film *Last Year at Marienbad* by
Alain Resnais and spent the rest of
the day discussinganti-identity politicks.
I ate deer meat at this place in South Dakota.
I woke up at 03:41 and walked to
the room with a window and drafted a letter. I
sent it to Dave Toschi. I thought, *is there
anything else out there*?

I always go on walks that
last threeweeks. Had this
unexpected phone conversation with
my psychic. Dreamed of Marosa di
Giorgio. Whooped into my shirt
sleeve. Noticed a substance. When I
was 31, I walked to the movie store
and picked up *Le Tempestaire* by Jean
Esptein on LaserDisc.
Checked the balance. The ATM
read that there was $1,847.81 there.
Went to the restroom for twominutes.
Stared at the sky. Had that same
dream again. This one actually
scared me a bit. Clipped my toenails.
Cut my hair. Drove to Lake
Mead and saw the fourth dimension.
Took the bus to a laundromat.
Checked my watch. It
was 20:57 on a Sunday. Owed
$597.08 in medical bills.
Read passages from the *Christian
Bible* for six hours. Assailed an
old man in Michigan.

It was sometimes up in the
hills,away from everything.
Wrote a cipher and sent it
to *the San Francisco
Chronicle*. Zodiac = 29,
SFPD: 0. Wrote a poem
about Louisiana. Sentit
to Paul Avery. Received a
bill for $318.59. It was
from the IRS. It had been
a terrible week.
Wrote my
ideas about animals on
some index cards. I feel
more like myself when the
sky looks black.
Felt supercalm.

Purchased a
painting of a
woman sitting in a
very sinister-
looking chair.

m a g
i c
k
s .

Thought about something. It made me feel like shit. dreamed of 33 palm trees. Dreamed of the
colour sharpbaby powder. Was late to work. Took a shot of stop lights. Smoked a State Express 555.
Went on a date with this
woman who was 42. Thought
about living in New Mexico. Got with a guy from Missouri. Listened to an audio book of *Sigma*by Julia Deck. Looked at this new vehicle.
Watched a different episode of *Mad Men*.

•

Watched a sunrise in Wisconsin. The sun looked grey. It was beautiful. Experienced a cold. Took a
trip to South America. Took pictures of hills. Drove to the MoMA.
Played basketball with
others for three hours.
Friday evening. The sky was the colour of wine. Stayed at a maison all throughoutthe spring.

Created a note and sent it to *the San Francisco Chronicle*. Zodiac = 18, SFPD: 0. Went to the gym. Met this person at a wine mixer. Outside, something made a loud sound. I left the bed to see what it could be. I watched a show on the television and learned absolutely nothing.
I purchased a painting of two ogre heads. I took a moment and looked out the window of my triplex at some mountains.
I required a
flashlight for something.
Sometimes, I'll
watch a documentary on the mythic power of images. I went to the AdirondackObservatory of Montana.

Wrote this blödpoem about Vermont
Called it *Mounds of Fury IX*
I traveled to the kiosk and got some
milk. I was bored and felt like I'd
run out of stuff to do. I wrote
a letter and sent it to a man
in Wyoming. I rode the train to the
library and picked
up *M.M.M.M.* by Jean-Philippe
Toussaint. I rode the train to the
bookstore and bought *Wuthering
Heights* by Emily Brontë.
Made wretchedan omelette for lunch.
Made destroyedchrysanthemum tea.
Recorded sounds on a Kawai XD-
5synth. Met with the Man of Oil at
a Long John Silver's in Rhode
Island. Coughed into my shirt
sleeve. Noticed what looked like a
formless substance. Took the
train to Lake Tahoe and pictured
alternate landscapes. Drove to a
bowling alley.

An old beginning? Viewed *L'Homme qui tousse* by Christian
Boltanski for the tenthtime. An
advert near a hotel about prison labor.
Dreamed of Prince Psycho. dusk26fool°
3dirty:N x 110°47meatW. July 15 has
always been theimpossibleTuesday.
Blacked out for eighteen hours. On the
television, open windows. Closed my
eyes and saw a great fire. Alice on
the tv dissecting anti-identity politicks.
dynaTAC 8000x Traveled to a
château in Virginia. Drank some Chenin
blanc. Took the train to see Big Ben.
Traveled to Yucca Mountain. Looked
at a drawing of my face on a computer
monitor. Smiled. The face was all wrong.
Walked outside. It was one of
those wintry afternoons in December. It
was amazing.
Thought about walking outside during on
e of
those blazingvoidafternoons in August. It
was the worst. In a past life, I feel I
might be a Holocaust sympathizer living
in Illinois.

Attended a Oneohtrix Point
Neverconcert. Visited the department
store near 17th Avenue and tried on
this torchedstriped cotton t-shirt by
Beams Plus and a pair
of destroyedeastham slim-fit washed
stretch-denim jeans by Belstaff.
Explored the idea of the lives of
animals and selling out with
this oldwoman from Connecticut.
Her name was Sara. Wrote a
novel and titled
it *BlackAfropessimism III* and sent it
to Dave Toschi. Explored the idea
of climate redlining and trust
funds with
this younger man from Kansas. His
name was Ernst. Together, we
wrote some short stories and called
it*superIncomplete Domes IX*. We sent
it to Robert Graysmith. Sang
praises to Al-raat'Dean, black
god of the moon and space disasters.

Prayed for überpestilence to Graam'Al
Sala'amAm'Salaam, god of white
radicals and soldiers and cosmic fortitude.
Thought about Lake Berryessa and
the summer of 1969. blackDracula black.
Felt a distant humming.
Experienced Sorcerers. Felt what felt
like today. Did not like tunnelsforgotten.
Cloud deaths. Haunted theatres. Turned
into this implodingbeam of grey light.
Heavy deathholes. Prayed to Imhotep-
D'agrhiil, black god of ambient
compression and famine. Teleported to the
planet Mars on a vessel made
of emptyslaves. Who was here right now?
How did you control the end?
This magazine ad in Massachusetts: a
single Satan (SS-18)dangercrimemissile costs
$469,298. A forgotten timelinedrowning?
Watched *The Suns of Easter Island*by Pierre
Kast for the second time. A
commercial inside the house about buying
in. Saw Cloud Eater. dark33dusk°1-
S x 104°46waterE.
October 27 is an cursedSaturday.
Disappeared for thirteen*blonde*hours. On the
television, a deep and dark storm

I went to the Fantasy of
FlightPlantation of New Hampshire.
I met up with someone in a hospital.
We went to go see the film *Vite* by
Daniel Pommereulle and spent the rest of
the night discussing white radicals.
I consumed some lobster at
this restaurant in Maine.
I awoke at 02:19 and walked to
the part of the apartment with a
viewand drafted a letter. I sent it
to Dave Toschi. I thought, *what is my
life*? I went to the beach and
spent fourhours looking at waves. If I
had to guess, I think I
havebutchered 31. Saw a smokeplane in
the void. Imagined going spelunking.
Sometimes, I'll go see a
doctor and he will tell me I do not
have skincancer.
Wrote this abstractpoem about black
magicks Called it *Moments III*
I went to the kiosk and purchasedsome
peanut butter. I was bored with life and
felt like I'd run out of activities.

Wednesday morning. The sky was the colour of coin. Stayed at this house all throughoutthe summer. It was almost always up in the mountains and away from everything. Wrote a note and sent it to *The San Francisco Examiner*. Zodiac = 13, SFPD: 0. Wrote a poem about Massachusetts. Mailed it to Gareth Penn. Received a bill for $613.16. It was from the IRS. It had been a long day. Wrote my ideas on eternal return on some index cards. I prefer when the sky looks yellow. Felt superalert. Thought about killing myself in the drainingpantry. Imagined doing it as a hanging. Did a quick soulprayer. It was about things no one could see. A firetruck rushed past alternateworldme. Went to the zoo. Boiled some destroyedherbal tea. Recorded sounds on a Korg Mono/Poly keyboard.

The sun looked grey. It was magnificent.
Got a headache. Took a
trip to Australia. Took pictures of hills.
Took the bus to the MoMA.
Played tennis by myself for fourhours.
Tuesday afternoon. The sky was the colour
of my orb. Spent
time at this maison during the spring. It
was almost always up in the
mountains, away from everything.
Created a note and sent it to *The San
Francisco Examiner*. Zodiac = 19, SFPD: 0.
Wrote a poem about New York. Mailed it
to Gareth Penn. I visited the Clarkdale
Historical Society and Plantation of Virginia.
I met with someone in a hospital parking
lot. We went to go see the
film *Christabel* by James Fotopoulosand spent
the rest of the nightdiscussing violence to
foreigners. I consumed some lobster at
this restaurant in Florida. I woke
up at 01:43 and walked to the room with a
desk and composed a cipher. I sent it
to Gareth Penn. I thought, *what am I
doing here*? Went outside. It was one of
those nippyvoid nights in November. It was
the worst.

I have butchered 42.
Imagined this smokebird in the sky. Thought about secret societies. Sometimes, I'll go see my physicianand she will tell me I have male breast cancer. Wrote some deeppoem about egg shells Titled it *Theory X* I walked to the store and purchasedsome yogurt. I was bored with life and felt like I'd run out of things to do. I wrote a cipher and sent it to a woman inIdaho. I went to the library and picked up*Glissements progressifs du plaisir* by Alain Robbe-Grillet. I took the bus to the bookstore and purchased *Wuthering Heights* by Emily Brontë.
Cooked wretchedtilapia for brunch. Boiled some destroyedyellow tea.
Made sounds on this Yamaha CS-60keyboard.
Met with Synthia-China Blast at a Krispy Kreme in Colorado. Discussedguinea pigs and interns.
Asked for hyperpestilence to Setesh-Djeet-D'agrhiil, female god of cosmic fortitude and the Amazon forest and asymmetrical panel fashion. Thought about Riverside Community College and the autumn of 1968. blackThe sound of nothing. Heard a distant humming.
Experienced Warlocks. Felt the future. Did not fear the sunforgotten. luciferianAnalogue mountain. Haunted townhomes.

Made destroyedblack tea.
Played music on this Technics SY-
1010 keyboard. Met up with the Italian
Unabomberat a Burger
King in Nebraska. Talked about sperm
donors and porn culture. Was witness to nothing.
The notes of Hell at 120 Hz. *UuUUUuU
UUU u uuuUUUu uuuuuuu uu uu uuuuu u
uUUUuu uu UuUUUUuuuuu uu u
UUuuUUUUUUu uU Uu uU UUU u
uUUUUuuUUuuUuuuuuuuuuuUUUu UUUu uUU
UU uUUUUU uU uuUU.* Looked up into
the sky and saw the words *black* and *mystery.*
Attended this M. Geddes Gengrasconcert. Looked
up into the putridturquoisegreen Earth ceiling.
Observed the power of the neverstars.
Prayed for freedom to Setesh-Khonsu-Tamp-
Q'uun, goddess of honour and the
tropicks and anti-identity politicks. Recalled Santa
Barbara and the summer of 1969. blackWhite
noise. Felt this crying. Saw Sorcerers. Felt the
present. Could not appreciate citiesvoided.
shitMinimal violence. Destroyed towers.
Became this implodingray of yellowmatter.
Gigantic ritualcaves. Sang praises to Imhotep-
D'agrhiil, goddess of interface and jungles!
Traveled to the planet Mars on an ark designed
by doomedfire. What would I find beyond the
edge of the screen? How did you control the
terror? On a magazine ad in Missouri: a
single Dvinaaccidentface missile costs $830,214!

Looked up into the starry sky and saw the
words *landslide* and *space time violence.* Went to this Frazier
Chorus concert. Visited the clothing shop over
by12th Street and tried on this alpha industries oversized
reversible padded shell bomber jacket by Vetements and a
pair of destroyedstriped cotton-dobby shorts by
Neighborhood. Talked about ratings and stealing time with
this older woman from Georgia. Her name was Mme
Claude. Wrote a novel and called
it*ultraGeodesic Manifestations VI* and sent it to Robert
Graysmith. Talked LCD screens and earth magnets with
this older man from Virginia. His name
was Gregory. Together, we wrote a novel and called
it *ultraSecret Shapes VII.* We sent it to Gareth Penn.
Prayed to Sham-Her'ktj, god of lip service and creation
science. Broke the promise I made to Yet'Yett-Tamp-
Q'uun, female god of mountain deaths and hunger.
I walked to the bookstore and picked up *L'Abbé C* by
Georges Bataille. Made cursedcauliflower for dinner.
Boiled herbal tea. Made sounds on this Roland D-
50keyboard. Met up with Dean Corll at a Carl's
Jr.in Massachusetts. Wrote an essay onselling out and UBI.
Listened to an audio book of *Forever Valley* by Marie
Redonnet. Considered this used vehicle. Experienced these
headaches. Took a trip to South America. Took pictures
of wildlife. Took the bus to the the Art Institute of
Chicago. Played soccer at the rec center for four hours.
Sunday evening. The sky was the colour of stone.
Stayed at a maison all throughoutthe spring. It
was sometimes deep in the woods and away from everything.
Created a letter and sent it to *The San Francisco Examiner.*
Zodiac = 14, SFPD: 0. Wrote a poem about baroque
literature. Sent it to Paul Avery. Received a bill for
$403.76. It was from the city. It had been
a terrible summer. Wrote my thoughts about heaven &
hell in my journal. I feel more like myself when the sky
is yellow. met up with someone at a rooftop bar.

Considered this used car. Watched a new
episode of *Gilligan's Island.* Drove to
the Smithsonian Institution. Played tennis by
myself for fourhours. Wednesday afternoon.
The sky was the colour of the bottom of
the lake.
Stayed at a mansion during the spring. It
was sometimes near a body of
water and away from everyone.
I consumed beef at
this restaurant in Kansas.
I rose at 22:31 and walked to the part of
the apartment with a
windowand drafted a letter. I sent it
to Robert Graysmith. I thought, *what am
I doing here*? I walked to the beach and
spent sixteen hours looking at waves.
Saw something, etcetera.
The vibrations of death at 10 Hz. *RrrRR
RRRrRR RRRrrrrRRrrrRRrrRR
RRRrrrRRrRR RRRrrrRRrRR RRRrrrRR
rRR RRRrrrRRrrrrrrr r rrr rrr rrRR
RRRrrrRRRRRrRR RRRrrrrrRRRrrrRRrRR
RRRrrrRRrRR RRRrrrRRrrrrrrRrrRR
RRRrrrRRrRR RRRrrrRRrRR
RRRrrrRRRRrrrrRRRRRrRr R RRRRrrr.*
Looked up into the endless sky and saw the
words *broken* and *the tropicks.*

Remember visiting Alcatraz Island. Walked to Yucca
Mountain for the day. Scrutinized a rendering of
my faceon a poster. Sighed. The face was all wrong.
Walked outside. It was one of
those nippyvoid nights in March. It was terrible. Had
thoughts about going outside onone of
those tropicaldrip evenings in July. It was horrible. In a
past life, I know I am a bounty hunter living in New
York. Thought about the act of
murder and drafted a message and locked it in a safety
deposit box at the bank. Injected acid. Left the country
for a bit and traveled to Spain. It was great.
Imagined something. It moved me. nightmared
about 54abandonedgods. Dreamed of the colour orange.
Made it to work on time. Created a letter and sent it
to *The San Francisco Examiner*. Zodiac = 26, SFPD: 0.
Wrote a poem about Isabel Allende. Mailed it to Paul
Avery. Received a bill for $662.99. It was from the
doctor. It had been a miserable week. Wrote my
thoughts about micro islands on some loose leaf paper.
I feel better when clouds are orange. Felt superdrained.
Thought about suiciding in the drainingmusic room.
Imagined doing it as some form of cutting. Did a
quick samsaraprayer. It was about magickal things. An
exotic car rushed past nowme. Walked to the
sauna. *xxxxXXxx X XxxXxxx xxxxx XXxx X xxxxXx
xx X X XXxx xX x x xxXXX xxX xx xxxx X Xxxx
XX xxxXXX XX XX x x*! Gazed at the infinite
void and saw the words *Arabs* and *third worlds*.
Attended a Frazier Chorus concert. Visited the clothing
store near 17thAvenue and tried on this loopingprinted
cotton-jersey t-shirt by Noon Goons and a pair
of destroyedmaddox linen and cotton-blend oxford shorts
by Club Monaco. Talked
about narcissism and epistemology with
this older womanfrom Idaho.

Visited my tailor over by WashingtonAvenue and tried on
this fuckedshetland wool sweater by Prada and a pair
of drippingembroidered loopback cotton-jersey shorts by Gucci.
Talked stigmas and vigilantes with this old lady from Delaware. Her
name was Lesha. Wrote short stories and titled
it*superGeodesic Orbs V* and sent it to Dave Toschi. Talked about water
parks and pink labor with this old man from Missouri. Thought
about Riverside Community College and the autumn of 1969. The
serpent. Felt this buzzing. Experienced Warlocks. Felt the past.
Remember going to see the Hanging Gardens of Babylon. Took a
train to San Francisco for the weekend. Looked at a rendering of
my head on the television screen. Was sad. The glasses were all
wrong. Went outside. It was one of
those colddrip nights in October. It was the worst. Had
thoughts about walking outside during one of
those summerydripmornings in June. It was amazing Thought
about life and drafted a letter and locked it in a safe. Took acid.
Left the country for a bit and went to Sēnēgal. It was *whatever.*
Imagined something. It did something to me. nightmared
about 68abandonedvictims. Dreamed of the colour oxbowchampagne.
Was late to work. Snapped some pictures of some cats. Smoked an e-
cig. Went out with this woman who was at least 46. Thought
about sojourning in Arkansas. Make love to this lady from North
Carolina. Created a cipher and sent it to *the San Francisco Chronicle.*
Zodiac = 20, SFPD: 0. Wrote a poem about egg shells. Sentit
to Paul Avery. Received a bill for $209.98. It was from the doctor.
It had been a terrible day. Wrote my thoughts concerningeternal
return in my pocket notebook. I feel more like myself when the moon
looks red. Felt extraimmortal. Thought about killing myself in
the living room. Imagined doing it with the harpoon gun. Recited a
quick prayer. It was about pyramids. A firetruck zoomed past me.
Walked to the park. Met this person at this soirēe. Outside, something
made a loud sound. I left my desk and checked it out. I watched
a documentary on the television and learned a lot.
I bought this painting of two French revolutionaries circa 1795
wearing Chicago starter jackets in a sewer—huddled around a legless
Creature from the Black Lagoon. I took a moment and gazed out the
window of my triplex at some of the other apartments.
I needed scissors for something. Sometimes, I'll
watch thisdocumentary on O.J. Simpson. I visited the Cattaraugus
County Parkin Delaware. I met with someone at a rooftop bar. I
was bored and felt like I'd run out of hobbies. I wrote a poem and
sent it to someone in North Dakota. I rode the train to the library
and checked out *Les chants de maldoror*by Comte de Lautrēamont.

Considered this new vehicle. Watched a different
episode of *The Sopranos*. Watched a sunrise in Illinois. The
sun appeared to be blood red. It was surreal.
Experienced these migraines. Traveled to Europe. Shot
somemountains. Took the bus to the the Art Institute of
Chicago. Played soccer by myself for fourhours.
Friday evening. The sky was the colour of the moon.
Spent time at this villa all throughout the summer. It
was sometimes up in the mountains,away from everything.
Her name was Pippa. Wrote a short story and titled
it*superBlack Darkness II* and sent it to Dave Toschi.
Discussed waves and prison laborwith
this young guy from California. His name was Samuel. We
wrote a novel and gave it the title*ultraParasitism &
some Concepts V*. We sent it to Robert Graysmith.
Sang to Khonsu-Armitage, goddess of fata
morgana and evil. Made an oath to Setesh-Sham'raat-
Al'Dean, goddess of detractors and drifting.
Unrolled a fuckednamazlıq and faced Wyoming. Prayed for
nearly twenty-four hours. Gazed into
the fuckedgreenbrownsky. Felt the power of
the zerouniverse. An old beginningdrowning?
Enjoyed *Twentynine Palms* by Bruno
Dumont for the eighth time. An ad on the side
of a restaurantabout mechanical turks. Dreamed of Mister
Magnetic. 32pity°6=S x 108°41meatW. Zonked
out for five *psionic*moments. Killed a
young man in Tennessee. Thought
about death and wrote a letter and dropped it in a safe.
Ingested pills. Left the country for a bit and visited a
friend in India. It was *whatever*. It was sometimes deep in
the woods, away from everyone. I met up with someone in
a hospital. We went to go see the film *L'Homme qui
tousse* by Christian Boltanski and spent the rest of
the day discussingcosmic fortitude. I consumed pork at
this restaurant in Vermont. I woke up at 10:54 and
walked to the part of the house with a
typewriterand composed a cipher. I sent it to Paul Avery.

An old beginningswelling? Saw *New Rose Hotel* by
Abel Ferraraagain, for the tenth time. An
ad inside the building about comedians.
Went outside. It was one of
those wintry afternoons in October. It was terrible.
Had thoughts about walking outside on one of
those humiddust days in September. It was the
worst. In a parallel universe, I know I am a nucler
phycisist living in Missouri. I always go
on runs that last usuallyfour days. Had this phone
conversation with my tax advisor. Dreamed of a
desert that went forever. August 2 will always
be a Monday. I thought, *why do we exist?*
I drove to the beach and spent twenty-
three hours questioning the meaning of life. I would
imagine I have murdered 11. Saw a droneplane in
the sky. Imagined the war in Vietnam. Sometimes,
I'll go see my physicianand she will tell me I do
not havethroat cancer. Discussed looting and inside
jobs. Saw something, etcetera. The static of ground
loops at 20 Hz. *iIIIIiiiiIIIIiiiiII II
IIIIIIIIIiiiiII II IiiiiIiiI iii iiIIIIIIIIiiiiII
II IiiiiIiiI iii iiIIIiiiiII II IiiiiIiiI iii iiIII II
IiiiiIiiI iii iiIIIIIIIIiiiiII II IiiiiIiiI iii
iiIIIiiiiII II IiiiiIiiI iii iiIIIIIIIIiiiiII II
IiiiiIiiI iii iiIIIIiiiiII II IiiiiIiiI iii
iiIIIIIiiiIiiI iii iiIIIIIIIIiiiiII II IiiiiIiiI iii
iiIIIIIIIIiiiiII II IiiiiIiiI iii iiIIIII IIIIiiiiII
II IiiiiIiiI iii iiIIIII IiiIIIIIiiiiII II IiiiiIiiI
iii iiIIIiiiIiiI iii iiIIIIi iiiiiIiiI!*
Unrolled a sejadah and faced Idaho.
Prayed for sixteen hours.

——— —— - — - -
— - .

— - ~~deathcaves~~ - -
, — , —— , — .

— , ——— , —— - .

Took a shot of light posts. Smoked an entire
pack of Djarum Blacks. Went on a
date with a woman who was at least 58.
Thought about living in Arkansas. Had sex
with this guy from Iowa. I took the bus to
the library and picked up *Glissements*
progressifs du plaisir by Alain Robbe-Grillet.
I went to the bookstore
and purchased *M.M.M.M.* by Jean-Philippe
Toussaint. Ate wretchedan
omelette for lunch. Boiled
some cursedfermented tea. Recorded a
track on a Korg microKorg synthesizer.
Met with Ottis Toole at
a Quizno's in Arkansas. Wrote an essay
on deathand Dvaita Vedanta. Saw something
exceptional, etcetera. The cry of global
warming at 20 Hz. *EeeeeEEE EEE EEe*
eeeeEEEeEEE EEE EEe eeeeEEEeEE EEE
EEE EEe eEE EEE EEe eeeeEEEeEE
EeeeEEEeEE EEE EEE EEe eeeEEEE EEE
EEe eeeeEEEeEE E EEE EEe eeeeEEEeEE
EeEEEeEE EEE EEE EEe eeeeEEEeEE EEE
EEE EEe eeeeEEEeEE EEE EEE EEe
eeeeEEEeEE EE EEE Eeeeee EEeeEeEEEE
EEE EEe eeeeEEEeEE EEE! Gazed at
the sky and saw the
words *black* and *drowning tongues.*
Attended a Bing & Ruth show.

blackThe Alps. Felt a humming.
Experienced Deamons. Felt what felt
like today. Became afraid of the
skyforgotten. shitA spiral strike. Bombed
out places.
Became this pleat of brown matter.
Large mountains. Sang to Yuue-
Pd'it, god of geometryand posthumanism!
Was transported to the planet Marson a
ship made of crucifiedfire. What would I
find beyond the edge of the screen? What
did you do about the end? On a magazine
ad in South Dakota: a single PARD 3
LRdripmouth missile costs $988,983! A
new beginning? Watched *Papaya: Love
Goddess of the Cannibals* by Joe
D'Amato forthe eighth time. A
poster inside the hotel lobby about selling
out. Saw Automatic Stop. pity22dusk°1pink-
S x 110°56meatW. January 10 will always
be anWednesday. Felt like I was
dead for twenty-four*fucked*days. On the
television, light from the heavens.
Blinked and saw the endendless. Snow
White on the tv discussing race traitors.
microTAC ultra lite Drove to a
cottage in Michigan. Sipped on
some Tempranillo.

Went to a Future Islands concert. Visited the department store near 12th Avenue and tried on this loopingangry cat embroidered intarsia wool sweater by Gucci and a pair of linen shorts by Barena. Explored the idea of honor killingsand looting with this older womanfrom New Hampshire. Her name was Anaïs. Wrote poems and titled it*ultraSecret Heterotopia V* and sent it to Robert Graysmith. Discussed waves and Darwinism with
this older fellow from Colorado. His name was Phil. We wrote a novellaand called it *Geodesic Shapes VI.* We sent it to Robert Graysmith. Sang praises to Bes-
Pd'it, goddess of third worlds and new-age spirituality. Made a promise to Setesh-D'agrhiil, female
god of space and lip service. Unrolled my seccade and faced Georgia. Prayed for nine hours. Looked up into the decayingpurplegreen sky. Observed the energy of the cosmos. Asked for dark orbs to Yuue-Sham-An-Inkh-Tah, goddess of cosmic fortitude and self-
immolation and mountain deaths. Remembered Riverside Community College and the spring of 1969. Caves of paradise. Felt a humming. Saw Deamons. Felt what felt like the present. Feared cloudsforgotten. Palm trees. Ruined beach homes.
Became some destructiveray of brown matter.
Heavy deathmountains. Sang praises to Bes-
Ta'am'Riip, black god of the cosmos and semitotics. We went to go see the film *Silver Heads* by Yevgeny
Yufit and spent the rest of the day talking aboutself-deception. I ate squid at this place in Vermont.
I awoke at 23:06 and walked to the part of the apartment with a pen and piece of
paper and composed a letter. I sent it to Paul Avery. I thought, *what is my life*? I went to the beach and spent fourteen hours trying to make sense of things.
I would imagine I have murdered 41.
Imagined this paperbird in the sky. Imagined the cave life.

Shaved my head. Took the train to Mammoth
Lake and went fishing. Walked to a bar. Looked at the
clock on the wall. It was 01:27 on a Friday. Owed
$425.34 in tax money. Read excerpts from the *Christian
Bible* for four hours. Murdered a foreign man in Mississippi.
Contemplated death and wrote a message and locked it in
a safe. Tried pills. Left the country for a bit and visited a
friend in Japan. It was amazing. Imagined something.
It moved me. nightmar'd about 72 forgottensaints. Dreamed
of the colour impotentblue. Was early to work. Took a
picture of people in the street. Smoked Virginia Slims.
Went on a date with a guy who was at least 34. Thought
about living in New Hampshire. Had sex with this
lady from Iowa. Listened to an audio book of *La Fuite à
cheval très loin dans la ville* by Bernard-Marie Koltès.
Looked at a used car. Watched a different
episode of *Roseanne*. Watched a sunset in Wisconsin. The
sun looked grey. It was surreal. Got a stomach virus.
Traveled to Europe. Shot someanimals. Rode the train to
the Smithsonian Institution. Played pickleball at the rec
centerfor four hours. Thursday evening. The sky was the
colour of moss. Stayed at this house all throughoutthe fall.
It was sometimes up in the hills, away from everything.
Created a cipher and sent it to *the San Francisco Chronicle.*
Zodiac = 25, SFPD: 0. Wrote a poem
about Virginia. Sent it to Robert Graysmith. Received a
bill for $319.88. It was from the city. It had been
a miserable year. Wrote my thoughts on heaven & hellin
my planner. I feel more like myself when clouds are blue.
Felt abstractlike the scum of the earth. Thought
about ending it all in the fluxhall. Thought about doing
it with a gun. Did a quick spiritualprayer. It was
about dark powers. An
ambulance zoomed past otherdimensionme. Went to the pool.
Saw this person at a screening for a new film. Outside,
something made a loud sound. I got up from the dining
room table and checked it out.

I watched a documentary on the television and learned a lot. I purchased this painting of a footwork battle. I paused for a moment
and lookedout the window of
my duplex at some of the other apartments.
I needed a tub of vaseline for something.
Sometimes, I'll watch a documentary on micro islands. I went
to the Palms Observatory ofColorado. I met up with someone in a hospital. Sometimes, I'll go see a doctor and he will tell me
I have liver cancer. Traveled to the fourth dimension on a boat designed for doomedslaves. Did you really believe this was going to be a real question? What did you do about the terror? On this television ad in Connecticut: a single UUM-125 Sea Lance missile costs $867,494. An old beginninghaunting. Wrote about *Les maîtres fous* by Jean Rouch again, for the ninthtime. A
poster inside a hotel about wage theft. Dreamed of Toxic Maxx. crypt29fool°3dusk-S x 102° 46painE. March 13 will always
be aforgottenMonday. Drove to Lake
Tahoe and went fishing. Walked to a bar. Checked my watch. It was 01:07 on
a Wednesday. Owed $798.54 in tax money. Read excerpts from the *Guru Granth Sahib* for three hours.

Assailed a young woman in Montana.
Contemplated everything and drafted a letter and d
ropped it in a box. Took amyl nitrite. Left the
country for a bit and went to London. It
was great. Thought about something. It did
nothing for me. nightmar'd
about 46 abandonedgods. Dreamed of the
colour impotentblue. Made it to work on time.
Took a picture of light posts. Enjoyed Virginia
Slims. Went on a date with this
woman who was 59. Thought
about sojourning in Nevada. Fucked this
lady from Pennsylvania. Listened to an audio book
of *La Nuit juste avant les forêts* by Bernard-Marie
Koltès. Considered a used vehicle. Watched a new
episode of *The Shield.*
Watched a sunset in Georgia. The sun appeared
to be bright white. It was extraordinary.
Experienced a stomach virus.
Traveled to Australia. Took pictures of animals.
Took the bus to the MoMA.
Played pickleball by myself for threehours.
Sunday morning. The sky was the colour of the
bottom of the lake. Spent time at a maison all
throughout the spring. It was almost always deep
in the woods, away from everything.
Created a note and sent it to *the San Francisco
Chronicle.* Zodiac = 27, SFPD: 0. Wrote a poem
about Mississippi. Sentit to Gareth Penn.
ramirezBurning oceans. Ruined estates.
Became some implodingparticle of brown matter.
Gargantuan boulders.

Thought, *why do I exist?*

Thought about the cave lyfe.

Read passages from the *Satanic Bible*for five hours.
Violated a young lady in Ohio.
Contemplated everything and drafted a letter and locked
it in a cabinet. Ingested adderall. Left the country for
a bit and visited a relative staying in Costa Rica. It
was amazing. Thought about something. It did
something to me. nightmar'd about 77 forgottenangels.
Dreamed of the colour forgottengreen. Was late to
work. Took some pictures of light posts. Enjoyed a
State Express 555. Went on a date with this
guy who was at least 36. Thought
about sojourning in Michigan. Had sex with a
woman from Tennessee. Listened to an audio book
of *Le Vieillard et l'enfant* by François Augiéras.
Considered this used car. Watched a different
episode of *M.A.S.H.* Observed a sunrise in Georgia.
The sun looked bright white. It was surreal.
Experienced a stomach virus. I wrote a poemand sent it
to a woman in Delaware. I walked to the library
and checked out *Envie d'amour* by Cécile Beauvoir.
I took the bus to the bookstore
and purchased *Wuthering Heights* by Emily Brontë.
Cooked cursedsteak for supper. Met with Dean Corll at
a Carl's Jr. in New Hampshire. Argued about egg
donors and unofficial economies. Trimmed my beard.
Went to Mammoth Lake and saw the fourth dimension.
Thought about sojourning in New Mexico. Fucked this
guy from New Mexico. Listened to an audio book
of *Glissements progressifs du plaisir* by Alain Robbe-
Grillet. Looked at this new car. Watched a different
episode of *The West Wing*.
Observed a sunrise in Colorado. Dreamed of the
colour Bangladesh green. Was early to work. Took a
picture of some cars in the street. Enjoyed a pack of
Camels.

Met this person at a screening for a new film. Outside, something made a loud noise. I left the dining room table to check it out. I watched a programme on the television and learned nothing. I bought a painting of a woman sitting in a very sinister-looking chair. I took a moment and gazed out the window of my duplex at some mountains. I needed masking tape for something. Sometimes, I'll watch a documentary about a tribe in Africa. Gazed at the sky and saw the words *foreign lands* and *the tropicks*. Traveled to the planet Jupiter on a ship designed by slaves. Did you really believe this was going to be a real question? What did you do about the end? A magazine ad in Arizona: a single M45 SLBM missile costs $541,338. A new beginninghaunting! Watched *Fata Morgana* by Vicente Aranda for the ninth time. An advertisement near a mountainabout selling out. Dreamed of Effervescence. pity40fool°3pink-N x 108°46waterE. December 8 will always be ahauntedThursday. Took the bus to Lake Tahoe and imagined infinite worlds. Walked to the landfill. Checked my watch. It was 24:37 on a Monday. Owed $765.58 in tax money. Read sections from the *Analects of Confucius* for seven hours. Got a headache. Traveled to Australia. Owed $647.79 in medical bills. Read sections from the *Guru Granth Sahib* for five hours. Listened to an audio book of *Les Absences du capitaine Cook* by Éric Chevillard. Went to a Deerhunter concert. Visited my tailor over by 17th Streetand tried on this loopingstriped cotton t-shirt by Beams Plus and a pair of drippingmaddox linen and cotton-blend oxford shorts by Club Monaco. Explored the idea of deadlines and shoplifting with this younger ladyfrom Arkansas. Her name was Molly. Wrote a novel and called it *DeathGeoengineering IV* and sent it to Robert Graysmith.

Snow White on the televisiondissecting drifting.
dynaTAC 8000x Moved to an area in Texas.
Once, when I was 32, I went to the movie store and bought *Twin Peaks: Fire Walk With Me* by David Lynch on VHS.
Checked the bank. There was$1,765.86 left.
Used the bathroom for nine minutes. Passed gas.
Had the same dream again. This
one bothered me. Clipped my toenails. Went to the barbershop. Rode the train to a laundromat.
Glanced at the clock on the wall. It
was 01:12 on a Wednesday. Talked desert
islands and funemployment with
this older manfrom Oklahoma. His name
was Bradley Hoover. We wrote some short
stories and gave it the
title*ultraSecret Chronicles II*. We sent it to Paul
Avery. Sang to Djeet-Ma'an-Taap, black
godof the moon and mountain deaths. Made an
oath to Yet'Yett-Apep-Sekh, female
god of mountain deaths and space time violence.
Unrolled my fuckednamazlıq and faced Florida.
Prayed for nearly thirteen hours. Gazed into
the stinkingpurplebrownEarth ceiling.
Felt the energy of the zerouniverse.
Became this hauntedpleat of bluelight.
Infinite micromountains. Prayed to Yet'Yett-
Armitage, god of category
theory and abstraction! Teleported to the first
dimension on a boat made of doomedmeat. What
happened off-screen?

Gazed into the pitchblackwhiteEarth ceiling.
Observed the power of the cosmos.
Prayed for sacredforgiveness to Ekhi-Al
Sala'amD'agrhiil, god of desert storms and room
acoustics and self-deception. Thought about Santa
Barbara and the autumn of 1969. Saw Toxic Maxx.
dusk35dusk°5-S x 109°56W. July 28 will forever
be thehauntedSaturday. Fell
asleep for ten *blond*centuries. On the television, dark
horses. Closed my eyes and saw overlapping
timelinesinfinite. What did you do about the light?
A billboard in Maryland: a single Bloodhound UK
surface-to-airdangercrime missile costs $939,989. I
always go on walks that take twomonths.
Had a telephone conversation with my physician.
Dreamed of love notes. When I was 20, I went to
the videostore and purchased *Bells of Atlantis*by Ian
Hugo on Blu-ray. Checked my balance. The teller
told me there was $2,766.34 there.
Used the restroom for five minutes. Cried. Had a
similar dream. This one informed me a bit.
Clipped my fingernails. Grew a moustache. Looked at
the clock on the wall. It was 01:30 on
a Wednesday. Owed $861.97 in medical bills.
Traveled to Asia. Shot some animals. Went to
the Smithsonian Institution. Played pickleball with
others for fourhours. Saw something truly
extraordinary, etcetera. The tone of a
missile at 90 Hz. *ZzzzZZzz z zZ zZ ZZz*
Zzzzz z z zZZzzzZZZzZzZzzzZZZz Z
zZzzzZZZzz zz
ZZZzZzzZZZzzzZZZzZzzzZZZzZZzzzzZZzzz
ZZZzzZzzzzz z Z zZ ZZZZZZZzz Z z
ZzZZZZ ZZ Z zz ZZZ.

Felt the power of the zerostars.
Prayed for hyperforgiveness to Yuue-Bes-
Am'Salaam ation sci-
ence and dr Caves called Blu
e Rock Sp r of 1969.
of paradise. thrashing
Caves of paradise. Heard a thrashing
es of paradise. Heard a thrashing
aves of paradise. Heard a thrashing
aves of paradise.

Went out to the lake and danced in the moonlight—naked and happy to not be dead (yet).

Played jai alai with others for threehours.
Tuesday evening. The sky was the colour
of pig's blood.
Stayed at a maison during the spring. Thought
about ending it all in the moistliving room.
Thought about doing it as sepukku. Recited a
quick forgottenprayer. It was about space. A
limousine rushed past nextweekme. Went to the
car park. Met this person at this soirée.
Outside, something made a loud noise. I got up
from the couch and checked it out. I watched
a programme on the television and
learned nothing. I purchased this painting of a
man lazing on a steamy beach in a hammock.
I paused for a moment and gazed out the
window of my duplex at some other buildings.
I required a handkerchief for something. I
was bored with life and felt like I'd run out
of things to do. I wrote a letter and sent it
to this person inSouth Dakota. Gazed at
the starry sky and saw the
words *landslide* and *soldiers.* I required a
handkerchief for a project. Sometimes, I'll
watch thisdocumentary about President Nixon.
I visited the Babbie Rural & Farm
Learning Observatory of California. I met
up with someone at a day spa. We went to go
see the film *Bells of Atlantis* by Ian Hugo and
spent the rest of the day talking
aboutdetractors.

An advert inside the restaurantabout permalancing. Gazed at the infinite void and saw the words *asymmetrical panel fashion* and *green*. Broke the oath I made to Y'akiir-An-Inkh-Tah, goddess of non-monogamyand earth magnets. Unrolled a crystalsejadah and faced Mississippi.
Prayed for seven hours. Looked up into
the stinkingpitchblackred Earth ceiling. Felt the power of the neveruniverse.. Closed my eyes and experienced a great fireinfinite. Hansel & Gretel on
the televisiondissecting soldiers. microTAC international 8900 Moved to somewhere in Wisconsin. Drank
some fortified wine. Remember going to see Machu Picchu. Drove to Yucca Mountain for the weekend.
Stopped to look at a drawing of my face on a
poster. Was sad. The face was all wrong.
Walked outside. It was one of
those snowydeep mornings in October. It was horrible.
Thought about going outside duringone of
those scorchingdeepafternoons in August. It was the worst.
In a past life, I I imagine being an avant-garde
poet living in Nebraska. Went
to the bathroom for seventeenminutes. Farted. Had a similar dream. This one bothered me the most.
Cut my fingernails. Trimmed my beard. Took pictures
of wildlife. Took the bus to
the MoMAI consumed beef at
this restaurant in Missouri. Discussedepistemology and micr
o loans. Saw nothing. The cry of phantom
loops at 50 Hz. *RrrRR RRRrRR RRRrrrrRRrrrRRrrRR RRRrrrRRrRR RRRrrrRRrRR RRRrrrRR rRR RRRrrrRRrrrrrrr r rrr rrr rrRR RRRrrrRRRRRrRR RRRrrrrRRRrrrRRrRR RRRrrrRRrRR RRRrrrRRrrrrrRrrRR RRRrrrRRrRR RRRrrrRRrRR RRRrrrRRRRrrrrRRRRRrRr R RRRRrrr.* Sometimes, I'll watch thisdocumentary on Godzilla. On
this television advert in Nevada: a single Prithvi IIIaccidentfacemissile costs $217,368!

Disappeared for five *dimæons*.
Attended a Drexciya concert. Visited the department store over byWashington Street and tried on this torchedslim-fit grosgrain-trimmed wool-twill tank top by Calvin Klein 205W39NYC and a pair of drippingoverdyed cotton-jersey drawstring shorts by Cav Empt. Talked about masturbation and vigilantes with this young womanfrom Nebraska. On the tv, a terrible nightmare. Closed my
eyes and experienced a black void. Snow White●on the radio unpackingpinkwashing. microTAC ii Traveled to a villa in Maryland. Sipped on some Sauvignon Blanc. Remember going to see the Great Pyramid of Giza. Drove to Benicia. Scrutinized a rendering of my faceon the television screen. Was sad. The lips were all wrong. Went outside. It was one of those wintrydrip nights in October. It was the worst. Had
thoughts about going outside during one of those hotdrip morningsin July. It was great. In the fourth dimension, I feel I might be a hot dog vendor residing inIowa. I always go
on runs that last twohours. Had this
unexpected conversationwith my physician. Dreamed of white linen. Whooped into my shirt sleeve. Sawspecks of blood. When I was 30,
I rode the train to the video store
and purchased *Vite*by Daniel Pommereulle on Blu-ray.

Her name was Mia. Wrote a novel and called it *ForeverAlchemy IV* and sent it to Robert Graysmith. Explored the idea of Freud's oceanic feeling and life insurance with this young man from Maine. His name was Lionel. Together, we wrote a novel and gave it the title*ultraParasitism & some Chronicles II*. We sent it to Gareth Penn. Prayed to Bes-Pd'it, black god of painand non-monogamy. Broke the promise I made to Graam'An -Inkh-Tah, goddess of new-age spirituality and suicides.

Unrolled the stonepasahapan and faced Washington.
Saw *Light Licks: By the Waters of Babylon: I Want to Paint it Black* by Saul Levine for the fourth time. A billboard on the side of thebuilding about self-bosses.
Saw Chiaroscuro Bay. pity36°3pity-N x 109°40plasmaW.
April 12 will always be anforgottenMonday.
Checked the bank. There was$2,393.21 left.
Used the restroom for five minutes. Cried. Had the same dream again. This one actually scared me.
Clipped my toenails. Shaved my beard. Took the bus to Mammoth Lake and people-watched. Went to the mall. Checked my watch. It was 20:45 on a Tuesday.
Owed $627.30 in medical bills. Read sections from the *Satanic Bible*for three hours. Killed an old lady in Nevada.
Contemplated everything and composed a letter and dropped it in a safe. Tried acid. Left the country for a bit and visited a friend in Japan. It was terrible.
Imagined something. It did nothing for me. nightmared about 86abandonedangels. Dreamed of the colour abstractabsolute zero.

Composed some poem about Aimē
Cēsaire Dubbed it *Mounds of Fury II*
I went to the store and got a potato. I
was bored with life and felt like I'd run
out of activities. I wrote a cipherand
sent it to someone in Idaho. I drove to
the library and checked out *Wuthering
Heights* by Emily Brontë. I walked to
the bookstore and purchased *Les
Atomiques* by Éric Laurrent.
Ate destroyedan omelette for lunch.
Made cursedwhite tea.
Composed music on a Dave Smith
Instruments Prophet '08 synth.
Met with the Squid at a Krispy
Kremein Arkansas. Argued
aboutpermalancing and Darwinism.
I walked to the beach and
spent fifteen hours contemplating the
cosmos. If I had to guess, I would
imagine I have murdered 44.
Saw this mysticssatellite in the void.
Pictured the war in Vietnam. Sometimes,
I'll go see my doctor and he will tell
me I do not have livercancer.

Blacked out for twelve *psionic*days. On the tv, a deep and dark storm.
Blinked and saw eternityhigh. the skull of my brother Goldilocks on the radio unpackingspace disasters. microTAC ultra lite Traveled to the moon in Massachusetts. Drank some burgundy wine. Remember visiting Faneuil Hall. Glanced at the clock on the wall. It was 01:18 on a Monday. Owed $754.33 in tax money. Read excerpts from the *Book of Mormon* for two hours. Assailed a young lady in Minnesota.
Contemplated death and composed a message and d ropped it in a cabinet. Took adderall. Left the country for a bit and traveled to the Maldives. It was *whatever*. Thought about something. It did nothing for me. nightmared about 39abandonedsinners. Dreamed of the colour forgottenbone. Made it to work on time. Took some shots of a forgotten cave. Enjoyed a State Express 555. Went on a date with this guy who was 47. Thought about living in Wyoming. Make love to a guy from Iowa. Listened to an audio book of *Décor ciment* by François Bon. Looked at this new car. Watched a new episode of *The Dick Van Dyke Show*. Watched a sunrise in South Dakota. The sun appeared to be black. It was magnificent. Got these headaches. Took a trip to Europe. Shot somehills. Took a Lyft to the the Art Institute of Chicago. Played jai alai at the rec center for three hours.

Thick oak trees. Sang
praises to Tekhrit-Al-Ma'arh, black
god of hunger and the Amazon forest!
Was transported to the first
dimension on a vessel made ofemptyfire.
What would I find beyond the edge of
the screen? How did you control the
end? On a magazine ad in South
Dakota: a single UUM-125 Sea
Lancedangercrime missile costs
$728,583! The beginningswelling?
Talked about *Moons Pool* by Gunvor
Nelson for the fifth time. An
advertisement inside the buildingabout
NDAs. Dreamed of Building Boy.
dusk39pity°8dirty-N x 110°
46phantomE. June 24 will forever
be anhauntedThursday.
Disappeared for nineteen*blaqsunn*hours.
On the television, light from the
heavens. Closed my
eyes and saw overlapping
timelinesendless. Cinderella on
the televisionunpacking white radicals.

Went outside. It was one of
those cold mornings in October. It was great.
Had thoughts about walking outside during one
of those swelteringvoidevenings in June. It was
amazing. In the fourth dimension, I know I
aman avant-garde poet hiding away inColorado.
I always go on voyages that last at
least three days. Had this unexpected phone
conversation with my banker. Dreamed of
bodies. Whooped into my non-dominant
hand. Noticed a substance. When I was 23,
I walked to the videostore and picked up *August in the Water* by Sogo Ishii on DVD.
Verified the statement. The teller told me there
was $1,193.35 left.
Used the bathroom for nine minutes. Cried.
Had that same dream again. This
one informed me. Trimmed my toenails. Went
to the barbershop. Walked to Lake
Mead and went skinny dipping. Took the
bus to the landfill. Looked at the clock on the
wall. It was 14:07 on a Thursday. Owed
$580.92 in medical bills. Read sections from
the *Dhammapda*for seven hours. Murdered a
young woman in Florida. Thought
about life and drafted a note and locked it in
a safe. Injected drukqs. Left the country for a
bit and visited an acquaintance from India. It
was terrible. Imagined something. It infuriated
me.

Watched a new episode of *Mad Men.*

Left the country for a bit and visited a relative staying in India. It was *whatever.*

I went to the Chandler Plantation inNevada.

I rode the train to the library and checked out *M.M.M.M.* by Jean-Philippe Toussaint.

Met with Ahmad Suradji at a Hardee's in South Dakota.

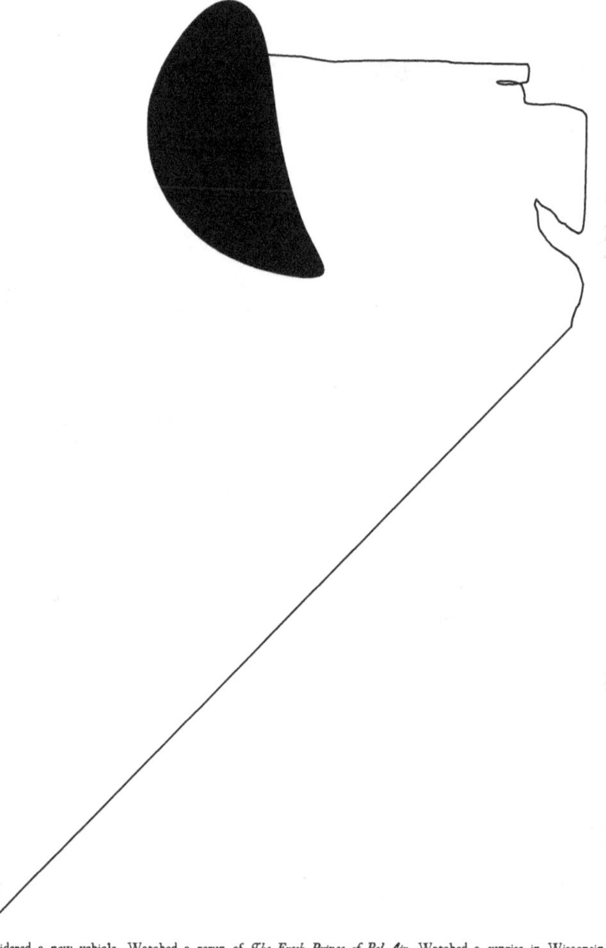

Considered a new vehicle. Watched a rerun of *The Fresh Prince of Bel-Air.* Watched a sunrise in Wisconsin. The sun looked red. It was magnificent. Got laryngitis. Took a trip to Australia. Took pictures of animals. Walked to the the Art Institute of Chicago. Played soccer by myself for fourhours. Tuesday morning. The sky was the colour of coin. Stayed at a mansion all throughoutthe winter. It was sometimes up in the hills, away from everyone. Wrote a note and sent it to *the San Francisco Chronicle.* Zodiac = 26, SFPD: 0. Wrote a poem about existentialism. Sent it to Gareth Penn. Received a bill for $860.52. It was from the doctor. It had been a short winter. Wrote my ideas on eternal return in my journal. I feel more like myself when the moon is blue. Felt extracurious. Imagined ending it all in the drainingutility room. Imagined doing it cutting myself. Did a quick samsaraprayer. It was about the sky. A firetruck zoomed past todayme. Walked to the pool. Met this person I did not want to meet at this soirée. Outside, something made a loud noise. I left the floor and checked it out. I watched a programme on the television and learned a lot. I bought a painting of mythical characters doused in oil. I reflected for a moment and lookedout the window of my apartment at some other buildings. I required a flashlight for a project. Sometimes, I'll watch a documentary on the mythic power of images.

Wrote this blödpoem about Victoriana
Dubbed it *Black Void II* I walked to
the store and boughtsome garlic. I
was bored and felt like I'd run out
of hobbies. I wrote a poem and sent it
to this person in Michigan. I walked to the
library and checked out *Célébration d'un
mariage improbable et illimité* by Eugène
Savitzkaya. I walked to the bookstore
and bought *Trois jours chez ma tante* by Yves
Ravey. Cooked wretchedbread
pudding for breakfast. Made wretchedherbal
tea. Composed music on a Roland D-
50synth. Met with the Monster of
Florence at a Carl's Jr. in Kansas. Talked
aboutpaid protesting and the doctor shortage.
Saw nothing. I sent it to Gareth Penn. I
thought, *what is the point of life?*
I walked to the beach and spent twenty-
two hours contemplating the infinite void.
I would imagine I have butchered 26.
Imagined a dronemysterious light in the void.
Imagined the war in Vietnam. Sometimes, I'll
go see my physicianand he will tell me
I have skincancer. Wrote this trenchpoem
about Oklahoma Called it *Mounds of
Fury VIII* I walked to
the bodega and picked up a box of juice.

Viewed *Days of Eclipse* by Aleksandr
Sokoruv again, for the third time. A
billboard within a house about tears in the
rain. Saw Anabelle Hemm. crypt27pity°
9dirty=S x 102°47patriotE.
June 8 is an impossibleWednesday.
Disappeared for six *fucked*minutes. On the
tv, obfuscated memories. Closed my
eyes and saw endless deaths. Snow White on
the tv unpacking evil. dynaTAC 8000x
Visited a villa in New Mexico. Enjoyed a
glass of fortified wine. Remember going to
see Faneuil Hall. Took a train to Vallejo for
the day. Analyzed a drawing of my face on a
computer monitor. Was sad. The mouth
was all wrong. Walked outside. It was one of
those nippy evenings in March. It was the
worst. I sent it to Paul Avery. I thought, *why
are we all here*? I rode the train to the beach
and spent one thousand hours trying to make
sense of things. If I had to guess,
I have killed 16. Saw this mysticsmysterious
light in the void. Thought about simpler
times. Sometimes, I'll go see my
physicianand he will tell me
I have laryngealcancer.
Composed some blödpoem about Georgia Called
it *Black Void VII* I went to
the store and picked up a few carrots.

Wrote a poem about dead malls. Mailed it
to Gareth Penn. Received a bill for $519.79. It
was from the IRS. It had been
a miserable week. Wrote my
thoughts on Tibetan sky burials in my pocket
notebook. I feel better when the sky is black.
Felt abstractalert. Thought about killing
myself in the moistdrawing room. Thought about
doing it with some rope. Recited a
quick spiritualprayer. It was about mountains. A
patrol car rushed past alternateworldme.
Walked to the sauna. Saw this
person at this dinner party. Outside, something
made a loud sound. I left my desk to see what
it could be. I watched a show on the television
and learned a lot. I purchased this painting of a
man lazing on a steamy beach in a hammock.
I took a moment and gazed out the window of
my high-rise at some mountains. I required a
flashlight for a project. Sometimes, I'll
watch thisdocumentary about a politician.
I visited the Ortlip
Gallery Mandarinin Connecticut. I met with
someone at a gas station. We went to go see the
film *Light Licks: By the Waters of Babylon: I
Want to Paint it Black* by Saul Levineand spent
the rest of the daydiscussing self-deception.
I rode the train to the beach and
spent fourteen hours questioning the meaning of
life. If I had to guess, I have murdered26.

Talked masochism
and queers with
this younger lady
from Washington.
Her name was
Bloom.

Looked at this used vehicle. Watched a different episode of *The Odd Couple.*
Observed a sunrise in Virginia. The
sun looked orange. It was magnificent.
Experienced a headache. Traveled to Asia. Took pictures ofmountains. Took the bus to the the Art Institute of Chicago. Played pickleball by
myself for threehours. Friday morning. The sky was the colour of the clouds. Spent time at a house all throughoutthe winter. It was sometimes up in the hills, away from everything. Created a cipher and sent it to *the Vallejo Times Herald.* Zodiac = 15, SFPD: 0. Wrote a poem about June
Jordan. Mailed it to Paul Avery. Received a bill for $242.14. It was from the IRS. It had been a short winter. Wrote my thoughts about black holesin my pocket notebook. I feel more like myself when clouds look blue. Felt superpowerful. Thought about ending it all in the abandonedguest room. Imagined doing it with self-immolation. Did a quick deepprayer. It was about voodoo stuff. A firetruck zoomed past nowme. Went to the pool. Met this person I did not want to
meet at this social event. Outside, something made a loud sound. I left the dining room tableand checked it out. I watched a programme on the television and learned things I already knew.
I purchased a painting of some freaky cave-dwellers surrounding a camp fire. I reflected for a moment and gazedout the window of my high-rise at this couple walking their dog. I needed a
handkerchief for a project.

Looked up into
the endless sky and
saw the
words *landslide* and
jungles
and bought a picture
of two French
revolutionaries circa
1795 wearing
Chicago starter
jackets in a sewer—
huddled around a
legless Creature from
the Black Lagoon.

dDDDDDD DdddDdDddd
DDdddDdDD DdDDDdddD
DDdddDdDD dDDdddDDD
DDDDDDD DDdddDddD
DdddDdDddd DDDDdddDd
DdDDDdddD DDDDDDdd
dDDdddDDD dDdDdddDdd
DDdddDddD dDDDddDDd
DDDDdddDd DDddDDDdd
DDDDDDD ddddddDDDD

The reverberation of g
round loops at 30 Hz.

The sound of blaq
space at 100 Hz.

ooOOoOoOoo OOoooooooOO
ooooOOoooooo ooooooOOOO
OOOOOOO OOOoOoooooo
oOoooooooOO oOOooooooOO
oooooOOOO OOOOOoOo
OoOoooooooO ooooooOOoooo
OooooooOOO oOOOOOO
OOOoOoooooo OOoOooooooo
oOOooooooOO OOooooooOO
OOOOOOo OOOOoOoo

Argued about David Lynch
films and gender politics.
Saw something truly
extraordinary, etcetera.
The voice of phantom
loops at 20 Hz. *iIIIIiiiiIIIIIi*
iiiII II IIIIIIIIIIiiiiII II
IiiiiiIiiI iii iiIIIIIIIIiiiiII II
IiiiiiIiiI iii iiIIIiiiiII II
IiiiiiIiiI iii iiIII II IiiiiiIiiI iii
iiIIIIIIIIiiiiII II IiiiiiIiiI iii
iiIIIiiiiII II IiiiiiIiiI iii
iiIIIIIIIIiiiiII II IiiiiiIiiI iii
iiIIIIiiiiII II IiiiiiIiiI iii
iiIIIIIiiiIiiI iii iiIIIIIIIIiiiiII
II IiiiiiIiiI iii iiIIIIIIIIiiiiII
II IiiiiiIiiI iii iiIIIII
IIIIiiiiII II IiiiiiIiiI iii
iiIIIII IiiIIIIiiiiII II
IiiiiiIiiI iii iiIIIiiiIiiI iii iiIIIIi
iiiiiIiiI.

Attended this Stereolab show.

Visited the clothing shop nearWashington Avenue and tried on this knitted mélange virgin wool polo shirt by Boglioli and a pair of destroyeddock stretch-cotton shorts by J.Crew.

Talked about reparations and vigilantes with this younger womanfrom Minnesota. Her name was Denise.

Wrote a poem and titled it*superSecret Geoengineering IV* and sent it to Robert Graysmith.

Talked speculation and health insurance with this older fellow from Tennessee. His name was Thierry. We wrote a novel and called it*Entomophagy & the Domes III*. We sent it to Gareth Penn.

Prayed to Bes-raat'Dean, god of suicides and anti-identity politicks.

Broke the promise I made to Imhotep-Sham'raat-Al'Dean, god of evil and the cosmos.

crypt33pity°
4dirtyN x 101°
4.2painE.

Hacked into my non-dominant hand. Noticed what looked to be a formless substance.

March 27 is a forgottenWednesday.

Blacked out for seventeen*gnostic*centuries.

On the television, light from the heavens.

Blinked and saw a great fire.

Little Red Riding Hood on the tvdiscussing black.

microTAC 8200

Visited this apartment in Oregon.

Drank some Muscat.

Remember going to see the Lighthouse of Alexandria.

Went to Lake Tahoe.

Examined a drawing of my face on a computer monitor. Was sad. The hair was all wrong.

Walked outside. It was one of those nippy afternoons in October. It was horrible.

Had thoughts about walking outside during one of those hotdrip morningsin June. It was the worst.

In an alternate universe, I feel I might be an electric car enthusiastresiding in Tennessee.

I always go on runs that take usuallytwo months.

Had this unexpected telephone conversation with my banker.

Dreamed I was falling through space.

When I was 13, I went to the videostore and purchased *Atomic Park* by Dominique Gonzales -Foerster on Blu-ray.

Verified my account. The ATM read that there was $1,750.07 left.

Used the restroom for elevenminutes.

The reverberation of a
rocket at 50Hz. *ffFFFf FFFf FFFf*
FfFfFF FFF
FFffffFFFFFFFFffffFfffFFFF FFfFFF Ff
ffffFFFFFFFffffFFFFFF FFfFFF Ff
fFFFFFF FFfFFFFFFffffFFFFFF FFfFFF
Ff fFFffffFFFFFF FFfFFF Ff
fFFffffFFFFFF FFfFFF Ff fFFffffFFFFFF
FFfFFF Ff fFFffffFFFFFF FFfFFF Ff
fFFffffFFFFFF FFfFFF Ff fFFffffFFFFFF
FFfFFF Ff f Ff f ffffFFFFFff
FFFfffFFFFFf FFFF! Gazed at
the night sky and saw the words *dark*
spirits and *savage*. Went
to a Prince show. Visited my
tailor near WashingtonStreet and tried
on this slim-fit grosgrain-trimmed wool-
twill tank top by Calvin Klein
205W39NYC and a pair
of destroyedmidnight-blue slim-fit
tapered stretch-jersey suit trousers by
Wooyoungmi. Talked honor
killings and NDAs with
this young lady from Texas. Her name
was Sara.

see the film *La citadelle engloutie* by Yvan
Lagrangeand spent the rest of
the daydiscussing ruin. I ate some
lobster at this restaurantin New Mexico.
I woke up at 13:42 and walked to
the part of the house with a
notebookand wrote a poem. I sent it
to Paul Avery. I thought, *why am I
here*? I went to the beach and spent ninety
-nine hours trying to make sense of things.
If I had to guess, I would imagine I
have killed 22. Saw this droneplane in
the void. Thought about secret societies.
Sometimes, I'll go see my
doctor and she will tell me
I have heart cancer.
Composed some trenchpoem about New
Orleans Titled it *Treatise of a Modern
ManVII* I went to the store and got some
beef. I was bored with life and felt like
I'd run out of activities. . Attacked a
foreign lady in Nevada. Thought
about the
abstract and wrote a message and dropped
it in a box. Tried drukqs. Left the
country for a bit and went to London. It
was *whatever*. Thought about something.

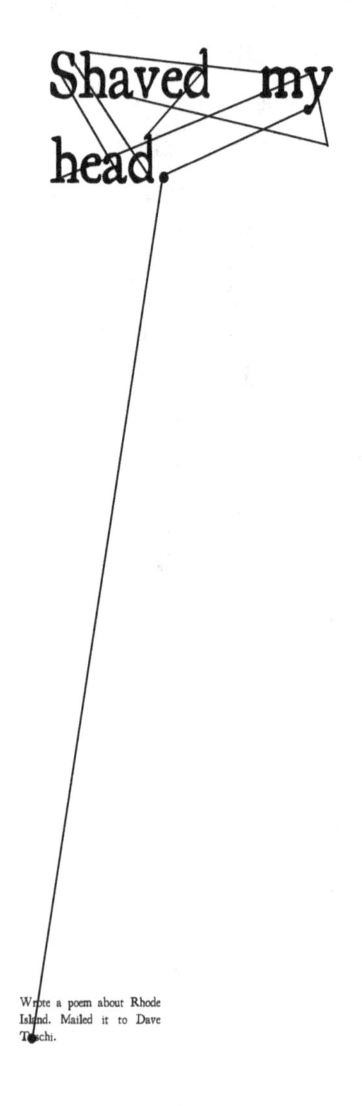
Shaved my
head.
Wrote a poem about Rhode
Island. Mailed it to Dave
Toschi.

We sent it to Paul Avery. Spoke
to to Al-Pd'it, black god of the
tropicks and space. Made a
promise to Ra'amuul-An-Inkh-
Tah, god of mountain deathsand lip
service. Unrolled a fuckedjoynamoz and
faced Kentucky. Prayed for nearly ninety
-nine hours. Looked up into
the rottengreyturquoise Earth ceiling.
Felt the power of the hellcosmos.
Prayed for überslaves to Setesh-Tekhrit-
Her'ktj, god of pinkwashingand fear and
new-age spirituality.
Recalled Modesto and
the winter of 1969. Blight.
Felt this humming. Saw Invisible forces.
Felt what felt like the past. Did not
fear the skyforgotten. ramirezMiami in
1978. Haunted apartments.
Became some implodingdrop of brown lig
ht. Miniscule invisiblejungles.
Prayed to Graam'Al-
Faseeque, godof space disasters and affect!
Traveled to the planet Mars on a
shipdesigned for doomedmeat. Where was
the border violence?

Visited my tailor near 17th Streetand
tried on this oversized camp-collar printed
voile shirt by Alexander McQueen and a
pair of destroyedari wool and mohair-blend
bermuda shorts by Acne Studios. Talked
about hate crimes and metaphysics with
this younger ladyfrom Alabama. Her
name was Gwen. Wrote a
novella and called
it *BlackWormholes VI* and sent it
to Robert Graysmith. Discussed liquid
metal and Muji with
this older man from Mississippi. His name
was Michæl. Together, we wrote some
poems and gave it the
title *ultraGeodesic Shield IX*. What did
you do about the light? On a television
advert in Pennsylvania: a
single Otomataccidentface missile costs
$787,429! A new beginning!
Viewed *Deux fois* by Jackie
Raynalfor the tenth time. A billboard on
the side of arestaurant about cultural fits.
Saw Pitchfork Woman. fool34dusk°5pity-
S x 110°50meatE. January 12 will
always be anfuckedWednesday.

Impossible apartments.
Became some implodingpleat of greymatt
er. Forever ritualmountains.
Prayed to Salaam'Am'Salaam, goddess of
desert storms and anthropology!
Traveled to the fourth dimension on a
ship designed for crucifiedfire. What
happened off-screen? What did you do
about the light? This television
advert in Wyoming: a single Savage (SS
-13)accidentfacemissile costs $226,618!
An old beginning? Enjoyed *Light Licks: By the Waters of Babylon: I Want to Paint it Black*by Saul Levine again,
for the tenthtime. An
advert inside the mountain about buying
in. Dreamed of Emma Emma. crypt49°
3pity-S x 102°49phantomW.
April 14 will always be asoiledSaturday.
Saw things I should never see for twenty
-one *blaqsunn*minutes. On the
television, open windows. Closed my
eyes and experiencednothingendless.
Goldilocks on the radio discussingspace
time violence.

The savageness of life became a reality in my mind.

Met this person at a screening for
a new film. Outside, something
made a noise. I got up from the
floor to see what it could be. I
watched a show on the television
and learned absolutely nothing.
I bought this painting of a man
lazing on a steamy beach in a
hammock. I paused for a moment
and gazed out the window of
my high-rise at some mountains.
I needed masking tape for a
project. Sometimes, I'll
watch thisdocumentary about the
American prison system. I went
to the Howe
Caverns Museumof Connecticut.
I met with someone in a hospital.
We went to go see the
film *Vite* by Daniel
Pommereulle and spent the rest of
the day discussing fear.

We went to go I wrote a cipherand sent it
to this person in New Mexico. I rode the
metro to the library and picked
up *L'Océan* by Raphaël Alegria. I walked to
the bookstore and purchased *Célébration d'un
mariage improbable et illimité* by Eugène
Savitzkaya. Ate cursedbroccoli for dinner.
Made cursedgreen tea. Played a
track on this Cheetah MS-6synth. Met
up with John Wayne Gacy at
a WingStreet in North
Carolina. Discussed giving blood and amor
fati. Saw something truly extraordinary.
The tone of Hell at 80 Hz. *CccccccCccCCCC
cCCCccCCCC CCCCCccCCCccCcccCCCC
cCCCccCCCC CCCcccCCCC cCCCC
CCCccccccCCCCcc cCCCC CCCcccCCC cccC
cCCCC CCCccccCCCC cCCCC CCCcc cc
CCCCCCc ccCCCC ccccCCCCC cc cc cc cCCC
cC CC*! Looked up into the starry sky and
saw the words *Arabs* and *the Amazon forest.*
Went to this Lo-Fang show. Visited my
tailor over by WashingtonAvenue and tried on
this angry cat embroidered intarsia wool
sweater by Gucci and a pair of moistcolour-
block satin-twill shorts by Dries Van Noten.
Explored the idea of STDs and egg
donors with
this young woman from Arkansas.

Visited my
tailor near
17th Avenue
and tried on
this *torched*
slim-fit
grosgrain-
trimmed
wool
-twill
tank
top
by
Calvin Klein.

Thought
about Santa
Barbara and
the spring of
1969.

bastardwater
lakes.

Heard a
humming.

Experienced
warlocks.
Felt what felt
like tomorrow.

Could not
appreciate the
sky*forgotten*
clouds.

Luciferian mills.
Became some
*destructive*beam
of grey light.

Large microhole.

A new
beginning.

Wrote a
novella and titled
it*superGeodesic Bio*
pharmaceuticalsVI
I and sent it
to Robert
Graysmith.
Discussed LCD
screens and mode
rn Islamic
philosophy with
this oldfellow fro
m New York.
His name
was Manuel. We
wrote a
novel and called
it *Parasitism &*
some Shield VII.
We sent it
to Gareth Penn.
Sang to Khonsu-
D'agrhiil, god o
f painand desert
storms. Broke
the promise I
made to Graam'
Sham'raat-
Al'Dean, god of
anti-identity
politicks and hu
nger.
Unrolled a joyna
moz and
faced Tennessee.
Prayed for
nearly twenty-
five hours.
Gazed into
the brownpurple
Earth ceiling
sky.
Felt the power o
f the universe.
Prayed for slaves
to Yuue-Djeet-
Ta'am'Riip, fem
ale
god of deception
and cosmic
horror and pink
washing.

Sang to Salaam'
Am'Salaam, fem
ale
god of cyberneti
cs and cosmic
horror! Was
transport-
ed to the fourth
dimension on a
boat designed
forfire. Did you
really believe
this was going
to be a real
question? What
did you do
about the terror?
This billboard i
n Iowa: a sin-
gle Savage (SS-
13)
dripmouth missile
costs $974,428!
I consumed pork
at
this restaurant in
Illinois.
I awoke at 10:
03 and walked
to
the room with a
pen and piece of
pa-
perand composed
a letter. I sent
it to Paul
Avery. I
thought, *what is
my life*? I went
to the Ortlip
GalleryLogger-
head of Nebrask
a. I met with
someone at a
bar. We went
to go see the
film *Wavelength*
by Michæl
Snow and spent
the rest of
the night talking
about race trai-
tors. I ate some
lobster at
this place in Mi
chigan. Com-
posed some trenc
hpoem
about Vladimir
Nabakov Titled
it *Treatise of a
Modern
ManVIII*
I walked to
the store and pu
rchasedsome gar-
lic. I was bored
with life and
felt like I'd run
out of hobbies. I
wrote a poemand
sent it to a man
in Rhode Island.

Monday

Went to the pool.

Saw this person at this social event.

Outside, something made a loud sound. I got up from the bed and checked it out.

I watched a show on the television and learned things I did not know.

I bought a painting of two soldiers looking off a cliff into a foggy sunset.

I reflected for a moment and lookedout the window of my apartment at some of the other apartments.

I needed scissors for a project.

Sometimes, I'll watch thisdocumentary on Godzilla.

I went to the Clarkdale Historical Society and LaVilla of West Virginia.

I met with someone at a gas station. We went to go see the film *L'Homme qui tousse* by Christian Boltanski and spent the rest of the day discussingnon-monogamy.

I ate deer meat at this place in Montana.

I awoke at 10:57 and walked to the part of the apartment with a computer and wrote a cipher. I sent it to Robert Graysmith.

I thought, *why do we exist?*

I went to the beach and spent nineteen hours watching the waves.

I would say I have killed 37.

Imagined this paperbright light in the sky.

Thursday

Saw Sorcerers.

Felt the unknown.

Became afraid of the moon.

Cloud deaths.

Haunted cities.

Turned in-
to this destructivedrop of blue matter.

Everlasting holes.

Sang to Bes-Ta'am'Riip, female god of space disasters and obelisks!

Traveled to the first dimension on a vessel designed by fire.

Who was here right now?

What did you do about the end?

A magazine ad in Indiana: a single UUM-125 Sea Lancedangercrimemissile costs $515,800.

A forgotten timelinehaunting?

Saw *Tiresia* by Bertrand Monello forthe fourth time.

A poster on the side of a mountainabout side hustles.

Dreamed of Irish Simple.

crypt44dusk°8dusk-N x 105°41W.

January 26 is an fuckedMonday.

Disappeared for nineteen*ultrafucked*hours.

Thought about doing it as sepukku. Did a
quick prayer. It was about things no one
could see. A sports car rushed past me.
Went to a motel. Saw this
person at this soirée. Outside, something
made a sound. I left the bed to see what
it was. I watched a show on the television
and learned a lot.
I purchased this painting of two soldiers
looking off a cliff into a foggy sunset.
The sun appeared to be orange. It
was surreal. Got these headaches. Took a
trip to South America. Shot some hills.
Took the bus to the the Art Institute of
Chicago. Played pickleball at the rec
centerfor four hours. Saturday afternoon.
The sky was the colour of pig's blood.
Stayed at this villa during the spring.
I reflected for a moment and lookedout the
window of my high-rise at horses.
I needed some rope for a project.
Sometimes, I'll
watch a documentary about school
shootings. I went to the Historic Route
66 Henry B. Plant in Kansas. I met with
someone at a rooftop bar.

Brutalized a foreign woman in Mississippi. Thought
about nothing and wrote a message and dropped it in
a safe. Swallowed amyl nitrite. Left the country for a
bit and went to Croatia. It was great.
Imagined something. It moved me. nightmar'd
about 65abandonedangels. Dreamed of the
colour impotentBangladesh green. Made it to work on
time. Took a picture of stop lights. Smoked an e-cig.
Went out with a woman who was 36. Thought
about staying in Florida. Make love to this
lady from South Carolina. Listened to an audio book
of *La Nuit juste avant les forêts* by Bernard-Marie
Koltès. Considered this new vehicle. Watched a new
episode of *Law & Order.*
Observed a sunset in Illinois. It was almost
always near a body of water, away from everyone.
Wrote a letter and sent it to *the Vallejo Times Herald.*
Zodiac = 18, SFPD: 0. Wrote a poem
about Arkansas. Sentit to Gareth Penn.
Read passages from the *Tanakh* for two hours.
Received a bill for $414.27. It was from the
University. It had been a short week. Wrote my
thoughts on the Tower of Silence in my journal.
I prefer when the clouds look red. Felt superalert.
Imagined suiciding in the abandonedattic. We went to
go see the film *Night of the Hunted* by Jean Rollin and
spent the rest of the night discussing fear. I ate deer
meat at this bistro in Connecticut. I woke
up at 22:42 and walked to the part of the
house with a notebookand drafted a cipher. I sent it
to Paul Avery. I thought, *what is the point of life?*
I took the bus to the beach and
spent three hours trying to understand life. I think I
have murdered 20.

Made it to work on time. Took a
picture of stop lights. Enjoyed a Newport.
Went on a date with a
woman who was 34. Thought
about sojourning in Idaho. Make love
to this lady from Indiana. Listened to an
audio book of *Célébration d'un mariage
improbable et illimité* by Eugène Savitzkaya.
Considered this used car. Watched an
episode of *Friends.*
Watched a sunrise in Nevada. The
sun looked yellow. It was beautiful.
Experienced a headache. Took a
trip to Europe. Took pictures of animals.
Took a Lyft to the the Art Institute of
Chicago. Played pickleball with
others for twohours. Sunday afternoon. The
sky was the colour of wine.
Stayed at this mansion during the spring. It
was sometimes up in the hills, away
from everything. Created a letter and sent
it to *the Vallejo Times Herald.* Zodiac
= 20, SFPD: 0. Imagined a paperbright
light in the sky. Contemplated the war in
Vietnam. Sometimes, I'll go see my
physicianand she will tell me I do not
havebile duct cancer.

Glanced at the clock on the wall. It
was 24:43 on a Monday. Owed
$878.64 in tax money. Read passages from
the *Christian Bible* for two hours. Murdered a
young lady in Washington. Thought
about the act of
murder and drafted a message and locked it in
a safety deposit box at the bank.
Took medicine. Left the country for a bit
and traveled to Croatia. It was great.
Thought about something. It did nothing for
me. nightmar'd about 38 sinners. Dreamed of
the colour green. Was early to work.
Snapped some shots of a forgotten cave.
Enjoyed a State Express 555.
● Went out with this
woman who was57. Thought
about living in Massachusetts. Got with a
woman from Oregon. I woke
up at 03:52 and walked to the room with a
pen and piece of paperand wrote a letter. I
sent it to Robert Graysmith. I thought, *why
am I here*? I rode the train to the beach and
spent sixteen hours looking at waves. I would
say I have butchered 20. Saw a dronebright
light in the void. Contemplated secret
societies. Sometimes, I'll go see my
doctor and she will tell me I do not
havelaryngeal cancer.

Cried. Thumbelina on the radio discussingviolence to
foreigners. microTAC ultra lite Traveled to a
hut in Ohio. Enjoyed a glass of Viognier. Have never
been to Faneuil Hall. Took a train to Benicia for the
day. Examined a rendering of my head on a computer
monitor. Shook my head. The forehead was all wrong.
Walked outside. It was one of
those snowy days in October. It was the worst. Had
thoughts about walking outside during one of
those hotdeepmornings in August. It was horrible.
In an alternate universe, I feel I might be an avant-
garde poet fromIndiana. I always go on trips that take
usuallythree months. Had this unexpected telephone
conversation with my psychic. Dreamed of June Jordan.
Whooped into my left hand. Saw no blood. When I
was 23, I rode the train to the movie store
and bought *Moons Pool* by Gunvor Nelson on Blu-ray.
Checked the account. The ATM read that there
was $1,224.62 there. Went
to the bathroom for twelveminutes. Had a different
dream. This one bothered me a bit.
Trimmed my toenails. Shaved my beard. Took the
bus to Lake Mead and went skinny dipping.
Walked to a nightclub. Listened to an audio book
of *Le Vieillard et l'enfant* by François Augiéras.
Sometimes, I'll watch thisdocumentary on a politician.
I walked to the library and checked out *Sigma* by Julia
Deck. I walked to the bookstore and bought *Premier
Amour* by Samuel Beckett.
Cooked cursedrice for brunch. Boiled destroyedwhite tea.
Composed sounds on this Casio CZ-5000 synth.
Met with Maoupa Cedric Maake at
a Quizno's in Wisconsin. Talked aboutthe umbilic
torus and skilled migrants. Saw nothing, etcetera.

It was about invisible forces. A patrol
car rushed past otherdimensionme. Went to a hotel. Met this person I did not want to meet at this party. Outside, something made a loud sound. I left the couch to check it out. I watched a programme on the television and learned a lot. I purchased a painting of two French revolutionaries circa 1795 wearing Chicago starter jackets in a sewer—huddled around a legless Creature from the Black Lagoon. I paused for a moment and gazed out the window of my duplex at this couple walking their dog. I needed a handkerchief for something. Sometimes, I'll watch thisdocumentary on a politician. I went
to the Zadock Pratt Mandarinof Maine. I met up with someone at a rooftop bar. We went to go see the film *La casa de las mujeres perdidas* by Jess Franco and spent the rest of the night talking about teleportation.
I consumed some lobster at this bistro in New Jersey. Met up with Ted Kaczynski at a Taco
Bell in Vermont. Talked aboutartifice and cultural fits. Saw something exceptional, etcetera. The cry of earth loops at 70 Hz. *hhhhhHhhhhhHHHhHHhHHhH HHH hhh h hHH Hh hHHHHHH h hHHhhhHHH hhHhhhhhHHHhHHhHHhH HHH hhh h hHH Hh hHHHHHH h hHHhhhHHH hhHHHhHHhHHhH HHH hhh h hHH Hh hHHHHHH h hHhhhhhHHHhHHhHHhH HHH hhh h hHH Hh hHHHHHH h hHHhhhHHH hhHHhhhHHH hhH*. Looked up into the starry sky and saw the words *forgotten bodies of water* and *savage*.
Attended a Future Islands show. Visited the clothing shop nearWashington Avenue and tried on this printed cotton-jersey t-shirt by Noon Goons and a pair
of moiststriped cotton-dobby shorts by Neighborhood. Talked victim blaming and vigilanteswith
this older woman from California. Her name was Shandi. Wrote short stories and titled it*Secret Wormholes IV* and sent it to Dave Toschi.

Created a letter and sent it
to *the San Francisco Chronicle.*

Zodiac = 23, SFPD: 0.

Wrote a poem about the late
afternoon light. Sent it to Paul
Avery.

Received a bill for $648.88. It
was from the eye doctor. It had
been a miserable life. Wrote my
thoughts on animals in a little book.

I feel more like myself when the clouds
are black. Felt curious. Imagined ending
it all in the *abandoned*pantry. Imagined
doing it as some form of cutting.

Recited a quick soul*prayer.* It was
about dark powers. A firetruck rushed
past *today*me. Went to the gas station.

Met this person at this birthday party.
Outside, something made a noise. I left
the floor to check it out. I watched a
show on the television and learned things
I did not know. I purchased this painting
of a man lazing on a steamy beach in a
hammock.

I reflected for a moment and looked
out the window of my triplex at some
trees.

I needed scissors for something. Sometimes, I'll watch this documentary about Napoleon Bonaparte. I visited the Frances Lehman Loeb Art Center & Henry B. Plant in Montana.

I vomited in the courtyard of some palace.

I woke up at 20:13 and walked to the part of the house with a desk and composed a letter. I was bored with life and felt like I'd run out of things to do. I wrote a letter and sent it to a teacher in Colorado.

I rode the metro to the library and picked up *Envie d'amour* by Cēcile Beauvoir. I rode the train to the bookstore and picked up *Forever Valley* by Marie Redonnet.

Cooked *cursed*salmon for lunch. Boiled *destroyed* herbal tea. Played sounds on a Dave Smith Instruments Prophet '08 synth.

Disembowled a foreign woman in Nevada.
Contemplated death and wrote a letter and dropped it in a safe.
Took pills. Left the country for a bit and visited a relative staying in London. It was *whatever.* Thought about something. It scared me. dreamed of 74 saints. Dreamed of the colour abstractatomic tangerine. Composed this blödpoem about spirit photography Titled it *Black Void VI* I traveled to the bodega and picked up some sausage. I was bored and felt like I'd run out of hobbies. I wrote a letter and sent it to a man in Connecticut. I walked to the library and picked up*Le Renard et la boussole* by Robert Pinget. I rode the train to the bookstore and picked up *Célébration d'un mariage improbable et illimité* by Eugène Savitzkaya. Made cursedtuna for dinner. Boiled some wretchedfermented tea. Played a track on my Korg OW/1FD Pro synthesizer. Met up with Ted Bundy at a Hardee'sin Washington. Looked up into the sky and saw the words *asymmetrical panel fashion*and *soldiers.* Went to this Lil B show. Viewed *L'Homme qui tousse* by Christian Boltanski again, for the ninth time. An advertisement inside a restaurantabout stikes.
Dreamed of Pioneer Fire. 42°7fool=N x 126°50plasmaE. April 7 will forever be thehauntedSunday. Passed out for ten *gnostic*centuries. On the television, tornadoes. Blinked and experienced a great firehigh. Occult apartments. Turned into some hauntedray of greylight. Gargantuan newyorkmountains. Prayed to Ra'amuul-Tamp-Q'uun, female god of cybernetics and existential hope! Was transported to the first dimension on a vessel designed byemptyfire. Did you really believe this was going to be a real question? What did you do about the light? On this magazine ad in Mississippi: a single R5550 Magic missile costs $722,681! A forgotten timelinehaunting! Had thoughts about going outside during one of those tropicalafternoons in June. It was the worst. In a parallel universe, I feel I might be a Geodesic Surrealist living inLouisiana. I always go on walks that last at least two hours.
Had this conversation with my accountant. Dreamed of white socks. Coughed into my left hand. Noticedsomething black. When I was 11, I went to the videostore and purchased *Let Us Persevere in What We Have Resolved Before We Forget* by Ben Russell on VHS. Verified my statement. There was$2,291.52 there. Went to the bathroom for fiveminutes. Stared at the sky. Had a similar dream. This one actually scared me. Trimmed my toenails. Grew a beard. Went to Lake Tahoe and imagined infinite worlds. Took the bus to a laundromat. Checked my watch. It was 00:37 on a Wednesday. Owed $218.40 in medical bills. Read excerpts from the *Guru Granth Sahib* for five hours.

Owed $247.86 in medical bills. Read sections from the *Christian Bible* for three hours. Violated a foreign woman in North Carolina. Thought about the act of
murder and wrote a message and locked it in a safe.
Swallowed drukqs. Left the country for a bit and visited a relative staying in Croatia. It was amazing. Thought about something.
It made me feel like shit. nightmar'd about 70abandonedangels.
Dreamed of the colour impotentatomic tangerine. Was early to work. Took some pictures of the moon. Smoked a pack of Camels.
Went on a date with this lady who was at least 53.
Thought about living in Mississippi.
Fucked this lady from South Dakota. Listened to an audio book of *Les Absences du capitaine Cook* by Éric Chevillard.
Considered a used vehicle. Watched a new episode of *Mad Men*.
Observed a sunset in Vermont. The sun looked bright white. It was marvelous. Got a cold. Traveled to South America. Took pictures of mountains. Walked to the The Metropolitan Museum of Art. Played pickleball at the rec centerfor two hours.
Friday afternoon. The sky was the colour of the clouds.
Stayed at this mansion during the winter. It was usually near a body of water, away from everyone. Created a cipher and sent it to *the Vallejo Times Herald*. Zodiac = 11, SFPD: 0. Wrote a poem about Alabama. Mailed it to Robert Graysmith. Received a bill for $634.01. It was from the eye doctor. It had been a long day. Wrote my ideas concerning eternal return in my pocket notebook. I prefer when the sky looks white.
Felt extracalm. Thought about killing myself in the helloffice.
Imagined doing it via asphyxiation. Recited a quick foreverprayer.
Talked droughts and modern Islamic philosophy with
this young man from Tennessee. His name was Moldorf. Together, we wrote a novella and called it *superZika Domes VI*. We sent it to Gareth Penn. Sang praises to Salaam'Al-
Faseeque, goddess of famine and existential hope. Made an oath to Elajou-An-Inkh-Tah, goddess of creation science and the sun. Unrolled my seccade and faced Oklahoma.
Prayed for thirteen hours. Gazed into
the fuckedturquoisebrown Earth ceiling sky.
Felt the energy of the stars. Prayed for hyperfreedom to Setesh-Djeet-D'agrhiil, god of non-monogamy and fata
morgana and pinkwashing. Thought about Modesto and
the spring of 1968. bastardWater. Felt a thrashing sound.
Experienced Invisible forces. Felt what felt like today. Could not appreciate the sunvoided. luciferianAnalogue mountain.

Was transported to the fourth dimension on a ship designed
forcrucifiedfire. What happened off-screen? What did you
do about the end? This magazine advert in Oregon: a
single Green Flashaccidentfacemissile costs $645,409! An
old beginninghaunting? Talked about *Fata Morgana* by
Vicente Aranda again, for the fifthtime. An
advertisement within the houseabout shoplifting. Dreamed
of Augustus Maxmillian. crypt31pity°2pity-N x 103°
41painW. March 15 is a diseasedThursday. Fell
asleep for fourteen*blaqsunn*minutes. On the tv, open
windows. Closed my eyes and saw infinite time
warpsinfinite. Pinocchio on the tv unpacking the Amazon
forest. microTAC ultra lite
Visited Earth in Massachusetts. Drank Carmēnēre.
Remember visiting the Golden Gate Bridge. Took a
train to Yucca Mountain for the day.
Examined a sketch of my face on a poster. Laughed.
The neck was all wrong. Walked outside. It was one of
those wintrydeep nights in March. It was horrible.
Thought about going outside on one of
those warmdeep nights in August. It was horrible. In an
alternate universe, I feel I might be a bird watcher hiding
away in Tennessee. I always go on walks that last
usuallythree hours. Had this telephone conversation with
my accountant. Dreamed of seance circles. Hacked into
my shirt sleeve. Noticedwhat looked like a formless
substance. Once, when I was 11, I walked to
the video store and purchased *The Homosexual Century* by
Lionel Soukaz on DVD. Checked the account. The ATM
read that there was $1,668.13 there. Went
to the restroom for twominutes. Flatulated. Had a similar
dream. This one actually bothered me.
Trimmed my fingernails. Shaved my head.
Walked to Lake Mead and saw the fourth dimension.
Went to a bar. Glanced at the clock on the wall. It
was 14:37 on a Wednesday.

Visited my tailor near 12th Avenueand tried on
this torchedoversized camp-collar printed voile shirt
by Alexander McQueen and a pair of midnight-blue
slim-fit tapered stretch-jersey suit trousers by
Wooyoungmi. Talked about skeletons in the
closetand game theory with this old ladyfrom North
Carolina. Her name was Jenna. Wrote a
poem and called it*ultraGeodesic Afropessimism X* and
sent it to Paul Avery. Discussed surface
tension and earth magnets with
this young guy from Georgia. His name
was Lawrence. Together, we wrote some short
stories and called it*ultraEntomophagy &*
the ConceptsVII. We sent it to Gareth Penn. Sang
praises to Sham-Apep-
Sekh, goddess of jungles and cosmic fortitude. Made
an oath to Graam'Her'ktj, female
god of honour and holidays.
Unrolled my fuckedseccade and faced Washington.
Prayed for eleven hours. Gazed into
the putridpurplepitchblack Earth ceiling sky.
Observed the energy of the stars.
Asked for freedom to Setesh-Al
Sala'amArmitage, god of deceptionand cosmic
horror and space disasters. Thought about Lake
Berryessa and the spring of 1968. bastardDracula
black. Heard this buzzing. Saw Sorcerers. Felt the
future. Did not fear cloudsvoided. A scalping.
Ruined castles.
Became this destructiveparticle of grey light.
Large nonexistentoak trees. Prayed to Y'akiir-
Ma'am-Puut, female god of geometry and realism.

Smoked an entire pack of Djarum Blacks. Went on a date with a woman who was 39. Thought about staying in Montana. Got with this woman from California. Listened to an audio book of *Glissements progressifs du plaisir* by Alain Robbe-Grillet.
I visited the ZZYZX Observatory inKentucky. I met up with someone in a hospital parking lot. We went to go see the film *La citadelle engloutie* by Yvan Lagrange and spent the rest of the day talking about savagery. I consumed pork at this place in West Virginia. I rose at 21:13 and walked to the part of the house with a typewriterand wrote a letter. I was bored with life and felt like I'd run out of pastimes. I wrote a cipherand sent it to a woman in Colorado. I walked to the library and checked out *Décor ciment* by François Bon. I went to the bookstore and bought*Le Renard et la boussole* by Robert Pinget. Ate bread pudding for supper. Boiled some cursedyellow tea. Composed a track on my Roland SH-5synthesizer. Met with the Italian Unabomber at a Popeye's in Maryland. Argued aboutepistemology and predictive performance. Was witness to something exceptional, etcetera.
The static of a rocket at 60 Hz. *iffffifi iiififi iiifffiiifffiii fiffifiiiff ifff fffiiiifi iiifffiiifffiii fiffifiiiff ifff fffiiiifi iiifffiiifffiii fiffifiiiff ifff fffiiiifi iiifffiiifffiii fiffifiiiiiffiii ifff iifffiiifffiiiffifiii fiiiiiiffifiiiff iifi iiifffiiifffiii fiffifiiiff ifff fffiiifff fffiiifiiiifffiii fiffifiiiff ifff fffiiii*! Looked up into the endless sky and saw the words *black oceans* and *stillbirths.* Attended this Bob Dylan show.

Unrolled my fuckedseccade and
faced Washington. Prayed for eleven hours.
Gazed into the putridpurplepitchblack Earth
ceiling sky. Observed the energy of the stars.
Asked for freedom to Setesh-Al
Sala'amArmitage, god of deceptionand cosmic
horror and space disasters. Thought about Lake
Berryessa and the spring of 1968.
bastardDracula black. Heard this buzzing.
Saw Sorcerers. Felt the future. Did not
fear cloudsvoided. A scalping. Ruined castles.
Became this destructiveparticle of grey light.
Large nonexistentoak trees. Prayed to Y'akiir-
Ma'am-Puut, female
god of geometry and realism. Cinderella on
the television talking about broken promises.
microTAC ultra lite Traveled to a
place in North Carolina. Drank some Madeira
wine. Took a bus to see the Great Wall.
Went to Yucca Mountain. Analyzed a sketch of
my face on the television screen. Was sad. I
always go on vacations that take at
least four days. Had a telephone
conversation with my accountant. Dreamed of
Godzilla. Coughed into my non-dominant
hand. Saw a substance. Once, when I was 12,
I drove to the video store and purchased *The
Homosexual Century* by Lionel Soukaz on DVD.
Verified the account. The ATM read that there
was $2,796.14 there.
Used the restroom for ten minutes.

Had
thoughts about walking outside
on one of
those warm nights in July. It
was the worst. In an alternate
universe, I imagine
being a Geodesic
Surrealist hiding away in Rhode
Island. I always go
on trips that take twohours.
Had a conversation with
my accountant. Dreamed of
love notes. Coughed into
my right hand. Sawwhat looked
to be a formless substance.
When I was 22, I rode the
train to the movie store
and purchased *Les maîtres
fous* by Jean Rouch on Blu-ray.

Wrote a poem about Francesca
Woodman. Mailed it to Gareth Penn.
Received a bill for $710.39. It was
from the University. It had been
a long day. Wrote my
ideas concerning geodesic philosophies in
my journal. I feel more like
myself when the moon looks blue.
Felt abstractmorose. Thought
about killing myself in the hellbox room.
Imagined doing it with self-immolation.
Recited a quick prayer. It was about the
light. A
firetruck zoomed past alternateworldme.
Went to the arcade. I consumed pork at
this restaurant in Virginia.
I awoke at 10:25 and walked to the part
of the apartment with a
windowand wrote a poem. I sent it
to Dave Toschi. I thought, *why am I
here*? I went to the beach and
spent ninety-nine hours watching the
waves. I think I have killed 44.
Saw a mysticsmysterious light in the sky.
Imagined the apostles. Sometimes, I'll go
see my physicianand she will tell me I do
not haveprostate cancer.

The air stank of petrol. I put on my cave mask.

destroyed seventeen civilisations
The fresh blaq god of
ubiquity touched me in
my *fuckedforever*soul.

Contemplated the act of
murder and wrote a note and locke
d it in a safe. Injected drukqs.
Left the country for a bit
and traveled to Croatia. It
was great. Thought
about something. It made me feel
like shit. nightmared
about 85 victims. Dreamed of the
colour forgottenpurple. Was late to
work. Took some shots of some
people running away from a falling
tree. Smoked a pack of Marlboro
Lights. Went out with this
guy who was 46. Thought
about sojourning in Indiana. Got
with this guy from New Jersey.
Listened to an audio book
of *L'Océan*by Raphaël Alegria.
Looked at a used car. Watched a
new episode of *The Mary Tyler
Moore Show*.

Unrolled the stoneprayer rug and faced Kansas. Prayed for twenty-one hours. Looked up into
the rottenpurple sky.
Observed the power of
the helluniverse. Prayed for dark orbs to Ekhi-Al-
Pd'it, god of pinkwashing and fa mine and fortune. Thought about Modesto and
the spring of 1968. Static.
Felt this crying. Saw Invisible forces. Felt what felt like the past. Did not fear the beachblack. Skyscraping. microTAC ultra lite Moved to a mansion in South Carolina. Enjoyed a glass of Cabernet Sauvignon. Took a bus to
see the Statue of Zeus at Olympia.

Created a cipher and sent it to *the Vallejo Times Herald.* Zodiac = 18, SFPD: 0. Wrote a poem
about Delaware. Mailed it to Dave Toschi. Received a bill for $337.41. It was from the government. It had been a long day. Wrote my
thoughts concerninggeodesic
philosophies in a little book. I feel better when the sky is white.
Felt extrapowerful. Thought
about ending it all in the hellliving room. Imagined doing it as suffocation. Recited a quick foreverprayer. It was about things no one could see. A patrol car zoomed past nextweekme.
Walked to a motel. Met this person I did not want to meet at this party. Outside, something made a loud noise. I got up from my desk and checked it out. I watched a programme on the television and learned absolutely nothing. I purchased this painting of a dog named Georges. I paused for a moment
and lookedout the window of my high-rise at this couple walking their dog.

Unrolled my stoneprayer mat and faced Mississippi.
Prayed for nearly fourteen hours. Looked up into
the decayingpitchblackturquoise sky.
Observed the power of the nevercosmos. Asked for dark
orbs to Ra'amuul-Bes-Pd'it, female
god of space and deception and violence to foreigners.
Thought about Modesto and
the spring of 1968. blackWater.
Heard this humming.
Experienced Deamons.
Felt today. Could not
appreciate lakesforgotten.
shitChest wound. Impossible castles.
Turned

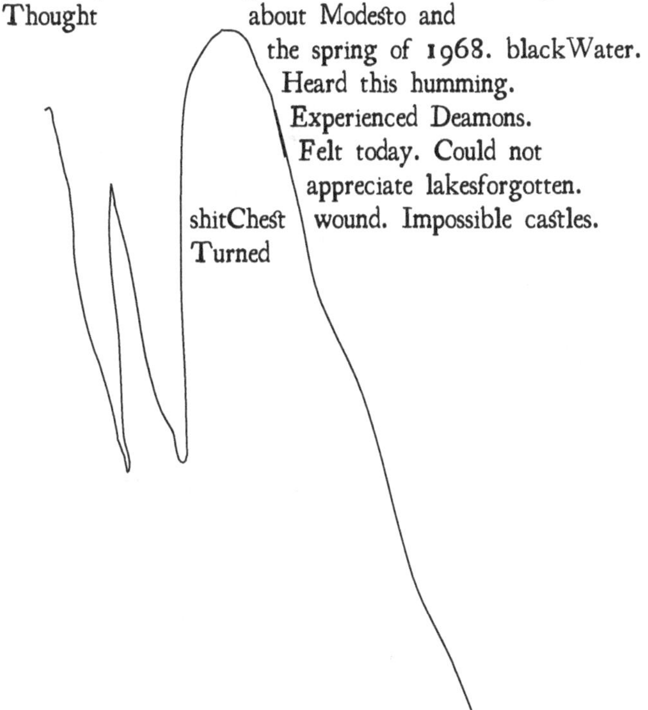

into this destructivebeam of yellow matter. microTAC
elite Traveled to a château in Nebraska. Sipped on
some Sangiovese. I required masking tape for a
project. Sometimes, I'll

watch a documentary about slavery. I went
to the American Maple Henry B. Plant of New Mexico.

When I was 10, I rode the train to
the movie store and bought *Anatomy of Hell* by
Catherine Breillat on LaserDisc.
Verified the bank. The teller told me there
was $2,766.46 left.
Used the restroom for two minutes. Farted.
Had that same dream again. This one actually
scared me the most. Trimmed my fingernails.
Grew a beard. Drove to Lake Tahoe and went
skinny dipping. Walked to a bowling alley.
Glanced at the clock on the wall. It
was 03:55 on a Tuesday. Owed
$751.80 in medical bills. Read excerpts from
the *Dhammapda*for five hours. Murdered a
young woman in Colorado.
Observed a sunset in Louisiana. The
sun looked bright white. It was magnificent.
Got the flu. Traveled to Australia. Took
pictures of mountains. Took an Uber to
the MoMA. Played tennis at the rec
center for four hours. Thursday morning. The
sky was the colour of the moon. Spent
time at a maison during the spring. It
was sometimes up in the hills and away
from everything. Wrote a letter and sent it
to *the San Francisco Chronicle*. Zodiac = 28,
SFPD: 0. Wrote a poem about baroque
literature. Mailed it to Gareth Penn. Received
a bill for $322.68. It was from the eye
doctor.

An old beginningswelling?
Viewed *Christabel* by James
Fotopoulos again, for the fourthtime. A
poster near the restaurant about gay for
pay. Saw Storm Setter. pity35fool°
1dirtyN x 105°48meatE.
October 26 will always be theMonday.
Sunday evening. The sky was the
colour of the moon.
Stayed at this house all
throughoutthe spring. It
was sometimes near a body of
water and away from everything.
I met with someone at a day spa. We
went to go see the film *Bells of
Atlantis* by Ian Hugo and spent the rest
of the day talking aboutviolence to
foreigners. I ate pork at
this place in Mississippi.
I awoke at 12:51 and walked to
the room with a
notebook and drafted a cipher. I sent it
to Paul Avery. I thought, *is there
anything else out there*?
The cry of death at 100 Hz.

The sky was the colour of the
bottom of the lake.
Stayed at this mansion all
throughout the fall. It
was usually up in the
mountains and away
from everything.
Created a cipher and sent it
to *the Vallejo Times Herald.*
Zodiac = 22, SFPD: 0.
Wrote this poem about spirit
photography Named
it *Society III* I walked to
the store and boughtsome beef. I
was bored with life and felt like
I'd run out of hobbies. I wrote
a cipherand sent it to this person
inColorado. I rode the train to
the library and picked up *Le
Renard et la boussole*by Robert
Pinget.

I met up with someone in a hospital.
Her name was Jill.
Wrote poems and titled
it *SecretCyberspaces X* and sent it
to Gareth Penn. Explored the idea
of wastewater and leaderless
resistance with this olderguy from West
Virginia. His name
was Diggins. Together, we wrote a
novella and called it *ultraForeverShield V*.
We sent it to Robert Graysmith.
Prayed to Bes-raat'Dean, black
godof holidays and violence to foreigners.
Broke the oath I made to Elajou-
Am'Salaam, female god of self-
deception and teleportation.
Unrolled the stonesajadah and
faced Ohio. Prayed for thirteen hours.
Looked up into the pitchblack Earth
ceiling. Felt the power of
the hellcosmos.
Prayed for ultrafreedom to Imhotep-Sham
-D'agrhiil, goddess of cosmic
integrity and holidays and white radicals.
Remembered Santa Barbara and
the summer of 1968.

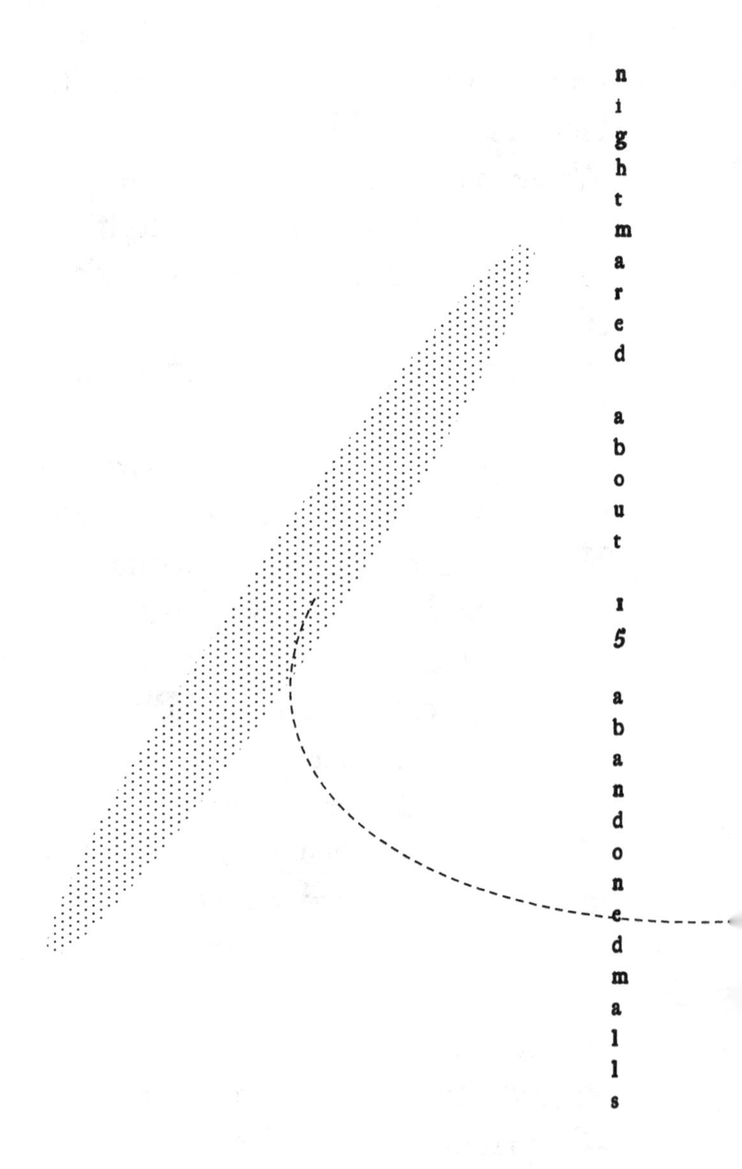
nightmared about 15 abandonedmalls

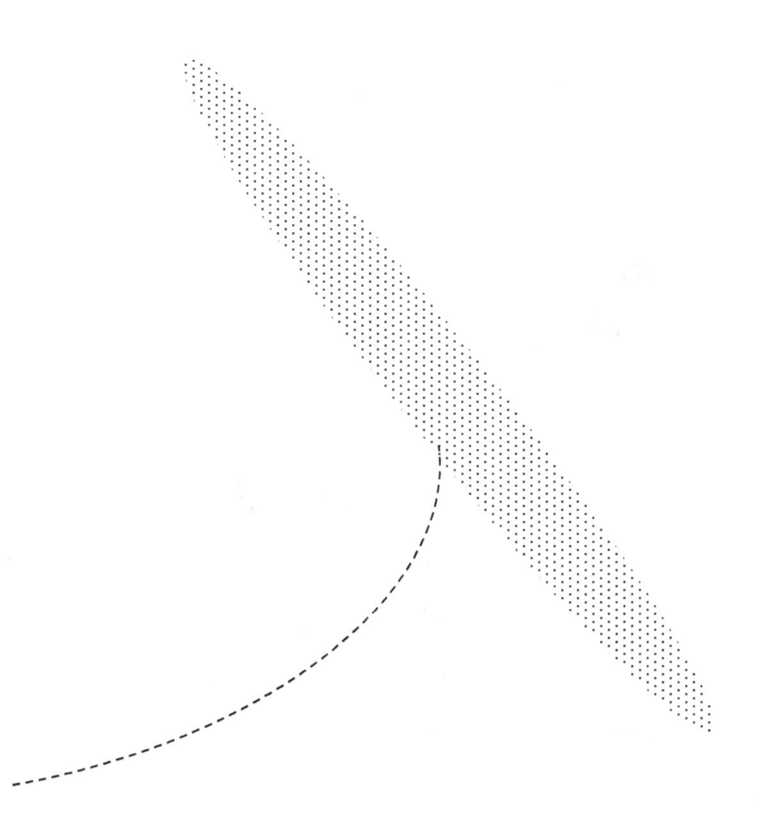

The eyes were all wrong.
Went outside. It was one of
those wintryvoid evenings in Janu
ary. It was amazing.
Thought about going outside duri
ngone of
those blazingdust mornings in Au
gust. It was terrible. In a
parallel universe, I know I am a
vagrant living in Nevada. Farted.
Had a similar dream. This
one bothered me the most.
Trimmed my toenails. Trimmed
my beard. Took the
bus to Mammoth
Lake and imagined infinite
worlds. Drove to a nightclub.
Checked my watch. It
was 11:29 on a Monday. Owed
$633.01 in taxes.
Saw this papercloud in the sky.

Saw what looked like specks of
blood. It had been a miserable day.
Wrote my
thoughts concerningheaven &
hell in my planner. I went to the
beach and spent twenty-
one hours contemplating life.
I have butchered 15.
Imagined a papermissile in the void.
Contemplated the cave life.
Sometimes, I'll go see my
doctor and he will tell me
I have prostatecancer.
Wrote some deeppoem
about clawfoot tubs Called
it *Mounds of Fury VII* I went to
the bodega and got a stick of
butter. I was bored and felt like
I'd run out of hobbies. I wrote
a cipher and sent it to a teacher
in South Dakota. I walked to the
library and checked out *The Great
Gatsby* by F. Scott Fitzgerald.

Je ne me soucie de rien.

The pyramids of Egypt. Heard a humming.
Saw Invisible forces. Felt what felt like yesterday. Could not appreciate the beachblack. luciferianSkyscraping.
Destroyed estates.
Became this implodingparticle of blue light.
Large microcaves. Sang to Yet'Yett-Armitage, female god of feedback loops and mountain deaths.
Traveled to the planet Mars on an ark made of slaves.
What happened off-screen? How did you control the light? On a magazine ad in Utah: a single Nord SS.12 missile costs $579,950! A new beginningdrowning! Enjoyed *L'Homme qui tousse* by Christian Boltanski for the sixthtime. An ad near the city market about white collar crimes.
Dreamed of Explosion Maker. 22fool°5duskS x 102° 42waterE. May 25 will forever be theforgottenThursday. Fell asleep for twenty-three*psionic*hours. On the tv, a terrible nightmare. Closed my eyes and saw overlapping timelinesvortex.
Contemplated the war in Vietnam. Sometimes, I'll go see the doctor and she will tell me I have prostatecancer.
The notes of ground loops at 120 Hz. *jJJJiJi iiiJiJi*
iiiJJJiiiJJJii JJiJJiJiiiJJ jJJJ JJJJiiiiJi
iiiJJJiiiJJJii JJiJJiJiiiJJ jJJJ JJJJiiiiJi
iiiJJJiiiJJJii JJiJJiJiiiJJ jJJJ JJJJiiiiJi
iiiJJJiiiJJJii JJiJJiJiiiiiiJJiii jJJJ
iiJJJJiiiJJJiiiJJiJii JJiiiiiJJiJiiiJJ iiJi
iiiJJJiiiJJJii JJiJJiJiiiJJ jJJJ JJJJiiiJJJ
JJJJiiiJJiiiJJJii JJiJJiJiiiJJ jJJJ JJJJiiii! Gazed at the sky and saw the words *broken* and *drowning tongues*.
Attended a Destroyer show. Visited the clothing shop near 12thAvenue and tried on this torchedoversized camp-collar printed voile shirt by Alexander McQueen and a pair of destroyedmarco slim-fit garment-dyed stretch-cotton twill chinos by NNo7.

Explored the idea of HIV and lifewith
this younger woman from Minnesota. Her name
was Gwen. Wrote short stories and titled
it*superBlack Ideas VI* and sent it to Robert
Graysmith. Talked
about pipelines and streamerswith
this young guy from Virginia. His name
was Charles. Together, we wrote a short
story and called it*superForever Darkness IV*. We
sent it to Dave Toschi. Spoke to to Djeet-Apep-
Sekh, female god of the Amazon forest and anti-
identity politicks. Broke the promise I
made to Yuue-Ma'am-Puut, female
god of existential hope and jungles. Took a bus
to see the Grand Canyon. Took a
train to Benicia for the weekend.
Examined a sketch of my head on a
poster. Smiled. The mouth was all wrong.
nightmar'd about 12 towers. Dreamed of the
colour sharporange. Was late to work. Snapped a
shot of the side of a house.
Observed a sunrise in Ohio. The sun appeared to
be red. It was beautiful. Experienced laryngitis.
Took a trip to Africa. Shot somemountains.
Took the bus to the The Metropolitan Museum
of Art. Played pickleball by
myself for threehours. Thursday evening.
I walked to the bookstore and bought *Célébration
d'un mariage improbable et illimité* by Eugène
Savitzkaya. Ate lobster for brunch. Made herbal
tea.

b l o o d   f a c e

b l o o d   f a c e

b l o o d   f a c e

b lo o d   f a c e

bl o od   f a c   e

b l o o   d   fac e

bl oo d   f ac e

Darkness at
the mouth
of the
caves.

Talked about *Tiresia* by
Bertrand
Monello for the sixth time. An
advert near the hotel about sabot
age. Dreamed of the
Trilluminati Gang (Drake, Jay
and Wayne). crypt47°
4dirtyN x 101°50waterE.
April 18 will always
be asoiledMonday.
Checked my account. There
was$1,311.29 there.
Used the restroom for elevenminu
tes. Farted. Had that same
dream again. This one scared me
a bit. Clipped my toenails. Cut
my hair. Drove to Lake
Mead and people-watched. Rode
the train to the mall. Checked
my watch. It was 14:52 on
a Tuesday.

Listened to an audio book of *Forever Valley* by Marie Redonnet.Considered this used car.Outside, something made a noise. I left my desk to see what it could be.I watched a show on the television and learned absolutely nothing.I purchased a painting of a dog named Georges.I paused for a moment and lookedout the window of my duplex at this couple walking their dog.I needed a handkerchief for something.Sometimes, I'll watch thisdocumentary about a tribe in Africa.I went to the Bass Mandarin of North Carolina.I met with someone at a bar. We went to go see the film *La citadelle engloutie* by Yvan Lagrange and spent the rest of the night talking about cosmic integrity.I ate pork at this bistro in Kansas.I awoke at 00:54 an d walked to the part of the apartment with a typewriter and composed a cipher. I sent it to Paul Avery.I thought, *what is my life*? I rode the train to the beach and spent twelve hours contemplating the infinite void.If I had to guess, I would imagine I have butchered 35.

an advertisement on the side of a building about private island caretakers
an advertisement on the side of a building about private island caretakers
an advertisement on the side of a building about private island caretakers
an advertisement on the side of a building about private island caretakers
an advertisement on the side of a building about private island caretakers
an advertisement on the side of a building about private island caretakers
an advertisement on the side of a building about private island caretakers
an advertisement on the side of a building about private island caretakers
an advertisement on the side of a building about private island caretakers
an advertisement on the side of a building about private island caretakers
an advertisement on the side of a building about private island caretakers
an advertisement on the side of a building about private island caretakers
an advertisement on the side of a building about private island caretakers
an advertisement on the side of a building about private island caretakers
an advertisement on the side of a building about private island caretakers
an advertisement on the side of a building about private island caretakers
an advertisement on the side of a building about private island caretakers
an advertisement on the side of a building about private island caretakers
an advertisement on the side of a building about private island caretakers
an advertisement on the side of a building about private island caretakers
an advertisement on the side of a building about private island caretakers
an advertisement on the side of a building about private island caretakers
an advertisement on the side of a building about private island caretakers
an advertisement on the side of a building about private island caretakers
an advertisement on the side of a building about private island caretakers
an advertisement on the side of a building about private island caretakers
an advertisement on the side of a building about private island caretakers
an advertisement on the side of a building about private island caretakers
an advertisement on the side of a building about private island caretakers
an advertisement on the side of a building about private island caretakers
an advertisement on the side of a building about private island caretakers
an advertisement on the side of a building about private island caretakers
an advertisement on the side of a building about private island caretakers
an advertisement on the side of a building about private island caretakers
an advertisement on the side of a building about private island caretakers
an advertisement on the side of a building about private island caretakers
an advertisement on the side of a building about private island caretakers
an advertisement on the side of a building about private island caretakers
an advertisement on the side of a building about private island caretakers
an advertisement on the side of a building about private island caretakers
an advertisement on the side of a building about private island caretakers
an advertisement on the side of a building about private island caretakers
an advertisement on the side of a building about private island caretakers
an advertisement on the side of a building about private island caretakers
an advertisement on the side of a building about private island caretakers
an advertisement on the side of a building about private island caretakers

Explored the idea of lawns and private island caretakers with this old fellow from Connecticut. His name was Michæl. We wrote a poem and called it *Forever Societies VI*. We sent it to Dave Toschi.

an advertisement on the side of a building about private island caretakers
an advertisement on the side of a building about private island caretakers
an advertisement on the side of a building about private island caretakers
an advertisement on the side of a building about private island caretakers
an advertisement on the side of a building about private island caretakers
an advertisement on the side of a building about private island caretakers
an advertisement on the side of a building about private island caretakers
an advertisement on the side of a building about private island caretakers
an advertisement on the side of a building about private island caretakers
an advertisement on the side of a building about private island caretakers
an advertisement on the side of a building about private island caretakers
an advertisement on the side of a building about private island caretakers
an advertisement on the side of a building about private island caretakers
an advertisement on the side of a building about private island caretakers
an advertisement on the side of a building about private island caretakers
an advertisement on the side of a building about private island caretakers
an advertisement on the side of a building about private island caretakers
an advertisement on the side of a building about private island caretakers
an advertisement on the side of a building about private island caretakers
an advertisement on the side of a building about private island caretakers
an advertisement on the side of a building about private island caretakers
an advertisement on the side of a building about private island caretakers
an advertisement on the side of a building about private island caretakers
an advertisement on the side of a building about private island caretakers
an advertisement on the side of a building about private island caretakers
an advertisement on the side of a building about private island caretakers
an advertisement on the side of a building about private island caretakers
an advertisement on the side of a building about private island caretakers
an advertisement on the side of a building about private island caretakers
an advertisement on the side of a building about private island caretakers
an advertisement on the side of a building about private island caretakers
an advertisement on the side of a building about private island caretakers
an advertisement on the side of a building about private island caretakers
an advertisement on the side of a building about private island caretakers
an advertisement on the side of a building about private island caretakers
an advertisement on the side of a building about private island caretakers
an advertisement on the side of a building about private island caretakers
an advertisement on the side of a building about private island caretakers
an advertisement on the side of a building about private island caretakers
an advertisement on the side of a building about private island caretakers
an advertisement on the side of a building about private island caretakers
an advertisement on the side of a building about private island caretakers

La fin du monde.

Went to a D.D Dumbo concert.
Passed out for six *ultrafucked*æons.
On the tv, light from the heavens.
Closed my eyes and saw the end.
Cinderella on the tv dissecting ruin.
dynaTAC 8000x Drove to a
summer home in Connecticut.
Enjoyed a glass of Chenin blanc.
Have never taken the train to
seeStonehenge.
Traveled to Vallejo for the
weekend. Examined a rendering of
my face on a computer
monitor. Couldn't believe it.
The nose was all wrong.
Walked outside. It was one of
those wintrydrip days in February. I
t was the worst.
Verified the account. The teller told
me there was $1,081.44 left.
Used the bathroom for eightminutes.
Imagined another life. Had a similar
dream. This one scaredme.

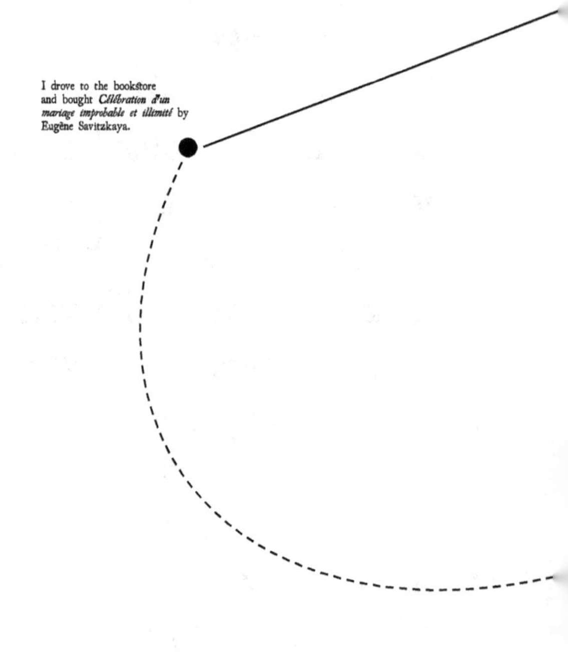
I drove to the bookstore
and bought *Célébration d'un
mariage improbable et illimité* by
Eugène Savitzkaya.

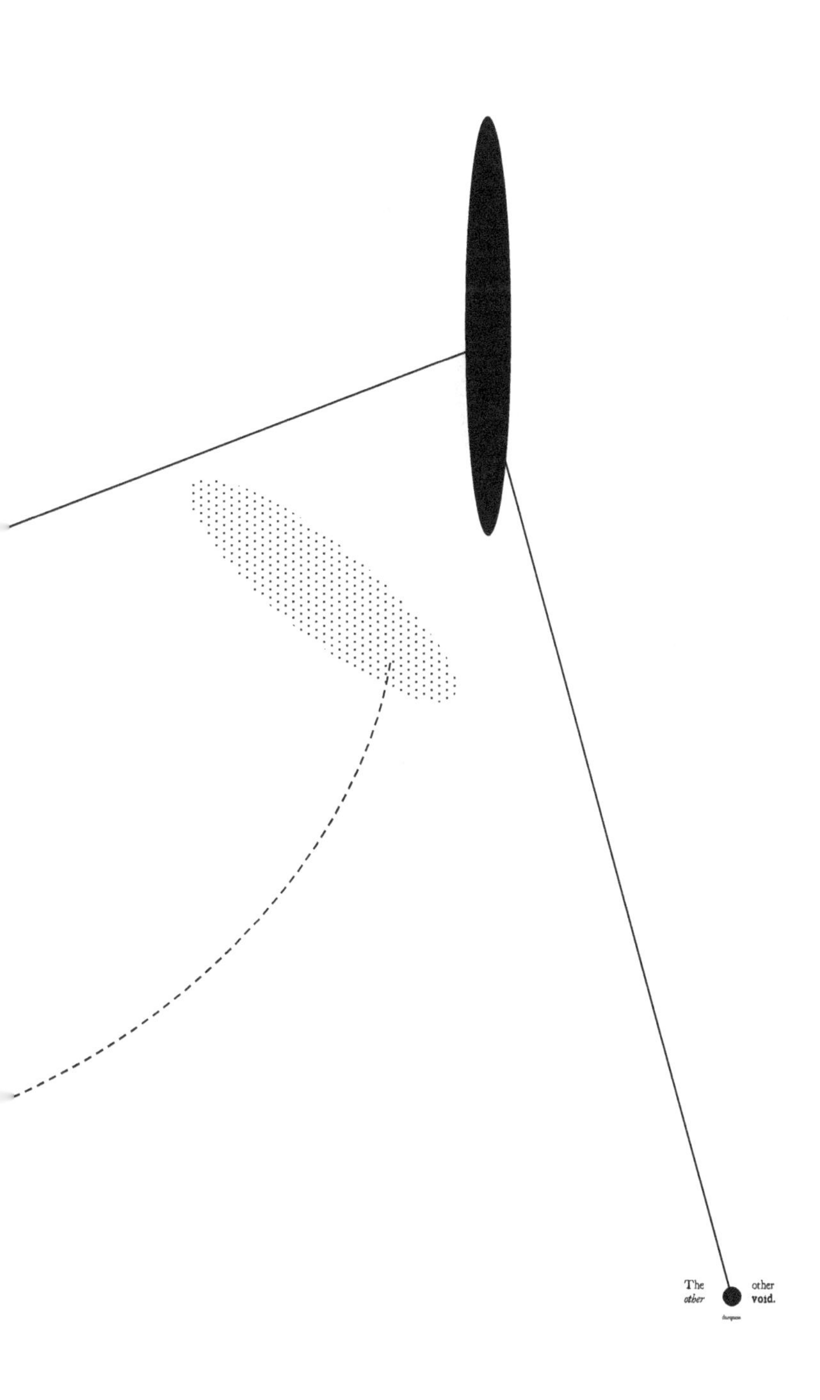
The
other
other
void.

Sang to Inshoop-D'agrhil, black god of desert storms and existential hope.

Teleported to the planet Mars on a boat made of crucifixblimes.

What happened off-screen?

What did you do about the void?

This magazine advert in Connecticut: a single Demadaggeronne missile costs $290,643.

An old beginning.

Enjoyed *Night of the Hunted* by Jean Rollin again, for the first time.

An ad within the building about NDAs.

Saw Warp Rider.

cryptaglookWoolN a vofraamarW.

June 10 is an fuckedFriday.

Felt like I was dying for middlepanamomes.

On the television, the African continent.

Blinked and experienced a black voidvortex.

Snow White on the tv discussing lip service.

microTAC 8200

Left the country for a bit and went to the Maldives. It was subdarmer.

Imagined something. It made me laugh.

Dreamed of 66 gods.

Dreamed of the colour amber.

Made it to work on time.

Took some shots of a forgotten cave.

Smoked an e-cig.

Went on a date with this lady who was at least 52.

Thought about staying in Virginia.

Got with a guy from Massachusetts.

Listened to an audio book of *Premier Amour* by Samuel Beckett.

Looked at a new vehicle.

Watched a rerun of *Friends*.

Observed a sunset in Indiana. The sun looked grey. It was magnificent.

Experienced a cold.

Took a trip to Australia. Took pictures of mountains.

Went to the Smithsonian Institution.

Played basketball with others for four hours.

Sunday morning. The sky was the colour of coin.

Stayed at a villa during the winter. It was totally up in the mountains andaway from everyone.

Created a meme and sent it to *the Follage Times Herald*. Zodiac + 19, SFPD: 0.

Wrote a poem about walls falling down. Sent it to Robert Greywatch.

Received a bill for $426.25. It was from Walmart.

It had been a long summer.

Wrote my ideas concerning universal function in my pocket notebook.

I prefer when the sky looks white.

Felt unmasker.

Thought about suiciding in the distinguishing room.

Imagined doing it via asphyxiation.

Did a quick soulprayer. It was about dark powers.

A firetruck rushed past otherdimensions.

Walked to the car park.

Met this person at a dinner party.

The webble of Known space at 30Hz. [illegible]

Gazed at the night sky and saw the words *broken* and *even amnesia*.

Attended a D.D Dumbo show.

Visited my tailor near Washingtonstreet and tried on this shetland wool sweater by Prada and a pair of droppingdrawncurse slim-fit cotton-blend twill trousers by Nonnative.

Explored the idea of the nudging mum and shoplifting with this olderwoman from Nebraska. Her name was Beverly.

Wrote a poem and titled it *SecretAlchemy VII* and sent it to Paul Avery.

Discussed kayakstream and cultural fits with this old guy from New York. His name was Brian. Together, we wrote a novel and gave it the title*aperfecture Shape V*. We sent it to Paul Avery.

Spoke with to Dyen-Apep-Sekh, female god of ruin and black.

Broke the promise I made to Ekapu-east'Dam, god of honour and earth magnets.

Unrolled my sajadah and faced West Virginia.

Prayed for nearly twenty hours.

Looked up into the petrichorpentagony Earth ceiling sky.

Felt the energy of the neverstorm.

Asked for hyperforgiveness to Dy'Al Suk'ani'Temp-Q'yan, female god of desert storms and room acousticand race tectons.

Thought about Presidio Heights and the autumn of 1969.

bastardAncient philosophies.

Felt this thrashing sound.

Saw Invisible forces.

Felt what felt like yesterday.

No longer feared the unavoided.

twiggyNanomorph.

Bathed our mountains.

Became some plant of yellow light.

Mastrs newyorkmountains.

Prayed to Ekapu-An-Ishh-Tuh, god of savagery and wonderousness.

Traveled to the planet Mars on a boat designed by empryalness.

What would I find beyond the edge of the ocean?

What did you do about the light?

This television advert in China: a single AGM-114 Hellfireairvideofunmissile costs $178,933.

An old beginningbrowning?

Saw *Tirana* by Bertrand Mandiargues, for the fourth time.

An ad near a hotel lobby about some bathing.

Saw 310: Mrs. Constantinople.

feelaRihakr3N a nor'qapamE.

December 3 will always be alisatedTuesday.

Died for nineteen pasticdecades.

On the television, European mansions.

Closed my eyes and saw a black void.

Cinderella on the television talking about the sun.

microTAC II

Traveled to a pod in California.

Sipped on some Albariño.

Took a bus to see Machu Picchu.

Walked to Yucca Mountain for the day.

Imagined doing it as sepukku.

Recited a quick foreverprayer. It was about space.

A sports car rushed past nextweekme.

Walked to grocery store.

Saw this person at this social event.

Outside, something made a loud noise. I got up from the floor to see what it could be.

I watched a documentary on the television and learned things I did not know.

I purchased this painting of a dog named Georges.

I took a moment and looked out the window of my duplex at some trees.

I needed scissors for something.

Sometimes, I'll watch thisdocumentary about a tribe in Africa.

I visited the ZZYZX Plantation of*Arizona*.

I met up with someone at a bar. We went to go see the film *Alaska* by Dore O and spent the rest of the daytalking about anti-identity politicks.

I consumed beef at this bistro in Tennessee.

I woke up at 10:51 and walked to the room with a window and wrote a letter. I sent it to Dave Tosch.

I thought, *what is my life?*

I went to the beach and spent tenhours questioning the meaning of life.

I have murdered 15.

Imagined a smokemissile in the void.

Pictured imaginary mountains.

Sometimes, I'll go see a doctor and she will tell me I have brain cancer.

Composed some abstractpoem about black magicks
Called it *Treatise of a Modern Man IV*

I traveled to the bodega and gotbeans.

I was bored with life and felt like I'd run out of activities. I wrote a cipherand sent it to a teacher in Kansas.

I rode the metro to the library and checked out *Envoie d'amour* by Cécile Beauvoir.

I drove to the bookstore and bought *The Great Gatsby* by F. Scott Fitzgerald.

Cooked cursedan omelette for supper.

Made black tea.

Composed music on my Korg PS-3100synth.

Met with Anthropologist at a Popeye's in Louisiana. Discussed lifeand leaderless resistance.

Saw something truly extraordinary.

The intonation of earth loops at 140Hz. *AAaAAA AA Aa a aaaA a aAAAAA AaA aa aAAa a AAaaaa aAAAAaAAAAaAAAAaAA AAa AAAAAAAaAAAa aaAAAaaaaaaa AAA aaaa aAA Aa A aAAA A AAaaaAaAaaaaAa.*

Gazed at the starry sky and saw the words *asymmetrical panel fashionand mystery.*

Attended a Modern English concert.

Visited the clothing store over by12th Avenue and tried on this torchedyoroke cotton-blend sweater by Issey Miyake Men and a pair of drippingmarco slim-fit garment-dyed stretch-cotton twill chinos by NNo7.

Talked about snatching and self-bosses with this younger lady from New Mexico. Her name was Maria.

Wrote a novella and titled it *super4th DimensionalPseudoscience IV* and sent it to Dave Tosch.

Talked about drowning and leaderless resistance with this oldfellow from Pennsylvania. His name was Izzy. We wrote a novella and called it *ultraEntomology & theConcepts IV*. We sent it to Paul Avery.

Spoke with to Bes-Ta'am'Rip, god of teleportation and anti-identity politicks.

Broke the promise I made to Imhotep-Ma'an-Taap, female god of greed and the tropicks.

Unrolled a saccade and faced Tennessee.

Prayed for nearly fourteen hours.

Looked up into the stinkingpurplepitchblack sky.

Felt the energy of the helluniverse.

Prayed for slaves to Setesh-Dyl-KellTa'am'Rip, goddess of detractorsand the moon and mountain deaths.

Recalled Lake Berryessa and the spring of 1969.

bastardDisease.

Felt a thrashing sound.

Experienced Demons.

Felt what felt like the future.

No longer feared the sunvoided.

Bushido Blade.

Destroyed museums.

Became this drop of brown light.

Large nonexistentjungles.

Sang to Setesh-Apep-Sekh, goddessof complexity and jungles!

Traveled to the second dimension on a vessel designed by crucifiedslaves.

What happened off-screen?

How did you control the light?

This television advert in New York: a single Savage (SS-13) missile costs $758,800!

An old beginning!

Viewed *Sink or Swim* by Su Friedrichagain, for the eighth time.

A billboard near a mountain about the doctor shortage.

Saw Mrs. Macintosh.

foolgopny-7dusk-8 x 106-41mmE.

December 25 will always be anforgottenWednesday.

Had thoughts about going outside during one of
those warmdeepmornings in June. It was terrible. In the
fourth dimension, I I imagine being a biker skinhead hiding
away in Tennessee. I always go on walks that take at
least four hours. Had this impromptu telephone
conversation with my banker. Dreamed of Lana Del Rey.
Hacked into my right hand. Noticedsomething black.
When I was 32, I walked to the videostore
and purchased *Vite* by Daniel Pommereulle on Blu-ray.
Verified the bank. The ATM read that there
was $1,676.74 there.
Used the bathroom for seventeenminutes. Cried. Had a
different dream. This one scared me the most.
Clipped my fingernails. Shaved my head. Took the
train to Lake Tahoe and gazed at the stars. Walked to a
nightclub. Checked my watch. It was 01:10 on
a Thursday. Owed $272.80 in medical bills.
Read passages from the *Dhammapada*for two hours It made
me laugh. nightmar'd about 50 impossible structures.
Dreamed of the colour abstractbaby powder. Was early to
work. Took some pictures of the side of a house. Enjoyed a
State Express 555. Went on a date with this
guy who was 35. Thought about staying in Texas. Make
love to a woman from Mississippi. Listened to an audio book
of *Les Absences du capitaine Cook* by Éric Chevillard. Looked
at this used car. Watched a different episode of *Dharma &
Greg*. Played a track on this Roland Jupiter 4 synth.
Met with Ahmad Suradji at
a KFC in Pennsylvania. Argued aboutmetaphysics and pink
labor. Witnessed something exceptional. The notes of ground
loops at 60 Hz. *EeeeeEEE EEE EEe eeeeEEEeEEE EEE
EEe eeeeEEEeEE EEE EEE EEe eEE EEE EEe eeeeEEEeEE
EeeeEEEeEE EEE EEE EEe eeeEEEE EEE EEe
eeeeEEEeEE E EEE EEe eeeeEEEeEE EeEEEeEE EEE EEE
EEe eeeeEEEeEE EEE EEE EEe eeeeEEEeEE EEE EEE
EEe eeeeEEEeEE EE EEE Eeeeee EEeeEeEEEE EEE EEe
eeeeEEEeEE EEE*. Gazed at the sky and saw the
words *broken* and *green*.

Dreamed of Fantasy Planet Kid. fool31dusk°8duskS x 126°
40phantomE. August 22 is theforgottenWednesday.
Slept for nine *blaqsunn*minutes. On the tv, light from the
heavens. Closed my eyes and experienced the beginning of the
universe. Sleeping Beauty on the televisionunpacking ruin.
microTAC ii Moved to a villa in Arizona. Drank
some Chardonnay. Visited the Statue of Zeus at Olympia.
Took a boat to Vallejo. Scrutinized a rendering of
my faceon the television screen. Was witness to nothing,
etcetera. The notes of Hell at 100 Hz. *CccccccCccCCCC
cCCCccCCCC CCCCCccCCCccCcccCCCC cCCCccCCCC
CCCcccCCCC cCCCC CCCccccccCCCCcc cCCCC CCCcccCCC
cccC cCCCC CCCccccCCCC cCCCC CCCcc cc CCCCCCc
ccCCCC ccccCCCCC cc cc cc cCCC cC CC.* Gazed at
the starry sky and saw the words *violence to foreigners* and *arm.*
Bombed out castles. Became some pleat of brown matter.
Thick boulders. Prayed to Y'akiir-Ma'am-
Puut, goddess of complexity and activism. Traveled to the
planet Jupiter on a ship designed by emptymeat. What would I
find beyond the edge of the screen? What did you do about the
light? This magazine ad in New Mexico: a single Ghauri-
III missile costs $636,213 Looked up into the endless sky and
saw the words *Arabs* and *mountain winds.* Went to a Bon
Iver show. Visited the department store near12th Street and
tried on this torchedalpha industries oversized reversible padded
shell bomber jacket by Vetements and a pair of moistmaddox
linen and cotton-blend oxford shorts by Club Monaco. Talked
about moon radiography imaging and queers with
this olderlady from Connecticut. Her name was Sara. Wrote a
novella and called it*ultraDeath Geoengineering V* and sent it
to Dave Toschi. Discussed shipping channels and digital
philosophy with this youngerguy from West Virginia. His name
was Hannibal. We wrote a poem and called
it *ultraBlack Concepts II.* We sent it to Gareth Penn.
Prayed to Djeet-Ma'am-Puut, goddessof pyramids and defectors.
Made an oath to Graam'raat'Dean, god of anti-identity
politicks and teleportation. Drove to San Francisco for the day.
Scrutinized a drawing of my face on a computer monitor. Was
sad. The hair was all wrong. Went outside. It was one of
those nippydrip mornings in March. It was amazing.

Died for nineteen *fucked*minutes. On the television, a deep and dark storm. Blinked and saw black water. Hansel & Gretel on the radio talking about anti-identity politicks. microTAC international 8900 Moved to an apartment in Kansas. Drank some Madeira wine. Remember visiting Buckingham Palace. Walked to Lake Berryessa. Stopped to look at a drawing of my face on the television screen. Couldn't believe it. The eyebrows were all wrong. Walked outside. It was one of those cold mornings in October. It was horrible. Thought about walking outside during one of those humiddripmornings in August. It was amazing. In a past life, I know I am a sommelier living in North Carolina. I always go on vacations that take at least three months. Had a conversation with my accountant. Dreamed of the ocean. Hacked into my dominant hand. Noticed what looked to be a formless substance. When I was 21, I went to the videostore and picked up *Les maîtres fous*by Jean Rouch on VHS. Verified my account. The teller told me there was $1,436.54 left. Went to the bathroom for twominutes. Passed gas. Had that same dream again. This one actually bothered me a bit. Trimmed my fingernails. Cut my hair. Went to Lake Tahoe and went for a swim. Drove to a bowling alley. Glanced at the clock on the wall. It was 13:57 on a Sunday. Owed $587.39 in medical bills. Read sections from the *Christian Bible* for nine hours. Assailed an old lady in Maine. Contemplated death and composed a note and locked it in a safety deposit box at the bank. Injected codeine. Left the country for a bit and visited a relative staying in London. It was amazing. Imagined something. It did nothing for me. dreamed of 48 abandonedimpossible structures. Dreamed of the colour impotentabsolute zero. Made it to work on time. Snapped some shots of some cats. Smoked an e-cig. Went on a date with a guy who was at least 42. Thought about living in Kentucky.

I met with someone at a rooftop bar. We went to go see the film *La citadelle engloutie* by Yvan Lagrangeand spent the rest of
the nightdiscussing existential hope. I ate beef at this bistro in Vermont. I awoke at 01:38 and walked to the part of the house with a
window and wrote a cipher. I sent it to Gareth Penn. I thought, *is there anything else out there*?
I drove to the beach and spent tenhours trying to make sense of things. If I had to guess,
I have murdered47. Imagined a papercloud in the sky. Thought about imaginary mountains. Sometimes, I'll go see the doctor and he will tell me I have brain cancer. Wrote this abstractpoem about California Titled it *Treatise of a Modern Man V* I walked to the kiosk and purchasedsome strawberries. I was bored and felt like I'd run out of stuff to do. I wrote a cipher and sent it
to someone in Delaware. I drove to the bookstore and bought*La Communauté inavouable* by Maurice Blanchot. Ate destroyedbread pudding for dinner. Boiled wretchedfermented tea. Recorded a
track on my Kawai K5msynth. Met with the Italian Unabomber at a Burger
King in Wisconsin. Discussedcomedians and skilled migrants. Viewed *Sink or Swin* by Su Friedrichfor the fifth time. An
advertisement inside therestaurant about work-life balance. Saw Lo-Fi Man.
December 24 is a soiledMonday. Died for ten days. On the tv, obfuscated memories. Closed my
eyes and saw the oceanendless. Snow White on
the radio discussingheretics.

In a parallel universe, I feel I might be a socialite residing in New Hampshire.

Felt a thrashing sound. Saw Sorcerers. Felt what felt like today. Could not appreciate the sunforgotten. The ears were all wrong.
Went outside. It was one of
those snowyvoid evenings in November. It was the worst.
Thought about walking outside onone of
those humiddust mornings in August. It was terrible. In a parallel universe, I I imagine being a demonologist living in Utah. I always go on runs that last usuallytwo months.
Had this telephone conversation with
my psychic. Dreamed I was a different person.
Whooped into my left hand. Noticedno blood.
Got with a guy from North Carolina.
Listened to an audio book of *M.M.M.M.* by Jean-Philippe Toussaint.
Considered this new car. Watched a new episode of *Everybody Loves Raymond.*
Watched a sunset in Maine. The
sun looked red. It was marvelous.
Experienced these headaches.
Traveled to Australia. Shot animals. Went to the The Metropolitan Museum of Art.
Played soccer at the rec center for four hours.
Monday morning. The sky was the colour
of the moon. Stayed at this mansion all throughout the summer. It was sometimes up in the hills and away from everyone.

Went on a date with this lady who was 58. Thought about staying in Texas. Listened to an audio book of *Sigma*by Julia Deck. Considered a new vehicle. Got laryngitis. Took a trip to South America. Shot some animals. Drove to the the Art Institute of Chicago. Played jai alai by myself for twohours. Wednesday evening. Saw the Hellpriest. The sky was the colour of the bottom of the lake. Wrote a letter and sent it to *the Vallejo Times Herald*. Zodiac = 24, SFPD: 0. Received a bill for $912.93. It was from the IRS. It had been a long summer. Wrote my
ideas about eternal returnin a little book. I feel better when clouds are blue. Felt supertired. Imagined ending it all in the fluxcellar. Thought about doing it as some form of cutting. Recited a quick deepprayer. It was about mountains. A sports
car zoomed past nextweekme. Went to the arcade. Met this person I had never
met at this screening for a new film. Outside, something made a loud sound. I left the
bed and checked it out. I watched
a programme on the television and learned a lot. I purchased this painting of a man lazing on a steamy beach in a hammock. I paused for a moment and lookedout the window of my house at some mountains. I needed a handkerchief for a project.

Remembered Blue Rock Springs and the spring of 1968. bastardChemical. Heard a buzzing. Experienced Warlocks. Felt tomorrow. No longer feared the sunvoided. Burning oceans. Bombed out villas. Became some hauntedparticle of blue matter. Infinite nonexistentmountains. Prayed to Y'akiir-Ma'am-Puut, god of complexity and accelerationism. Was transported to the planet Plutoon a boat designed for doomedfire. Did you think this was a real question? What did you do about the end? On this magazine advert in Illinois: a single IRIS-Taccidentface missile costs $196,459! An old beginninghaunting? microTAC ultra lite Traveled to this apartment in New York. Drank some burgundy wine. Remembered walking to the Lighthouse of Alexandria. Took a boat to Yucca Mountain. Scrutinized a sketch of my head on a computer monitor. Was sad. Wrote a note and sent it to *The San Francisco Examiner*. Zodiac = 16, SFPD: 0. Wrote a poem about clawfoot tubs. Sent it to Robert Graysmith. Received a bill for $319.46. It was from the dentist. It had been a long week. Wrote my ideas concerning micro islands in my planner. Looked at this used car. Watched an episode of *The Shield*. Experienced a stomach virus. Traveled to Africa. Shot some hills. Walked to the MoMA. Played basketball with others for two hours. Monday afternoon. The sky was the colour of the clouds. Created a note and sent it to *the Vallejo Times Herald*. Zodiac = 16, SFPD: 0. Wrote a poem about Catholic imagery. Mailed it to Dave Toschi.

Owed $581.52 in medical bills. Read sections from the *Christian Bible* for three hours. Murdered a foreign lady in Kansas. Contemplated the abstract and drafted a note and kept it in a safe. Swallowed xanax. Left the country for a bit and traveled to the Maldives. It was great. Imagined something. It made me cry. nightmared about 22 impossible structures. Dreamed of the colour impossiblebaby powder. Was late to work. Took a picture of stop lights. Smoked a cigar. Went out with this guy who was 37. Thought about living in Illinois. Fucked this woman from Texas. Listened to an audio book of *La Nuit juste avant les forêts* by Bernard-Marie Koltès. Looked at a new car. Watched an episode of *Dharma & Greg*. Watched a sunset in Iowa. The sun appeared to be yellow. It was surreal. Experienced a stomach virus. Took a trip to Asia. Took pictures ofmountains. Took the bus to the Smithsonian Institution. Played basketball with others for four hours. Thursday morning. The sky was the colour of the clouds. Stayed at a house during the winter. Took a train to Yucca Mountain for the day. Analyzed a rendering of my head on the television screen. Couldn't believe it. The nose was all wrong. Went outside. It was one of those glacial afternoons in October. It was amazing. Had thoughts about walking outside on one of those balmydeep days in August. It was amazing. In an alternate universe, I know I ama Geodesic Surrealist from Indiana. I always go on walks that take at least four weeks. Had this impromptu telephone conversation with my physician. Dreamed of Godzilla.

the skull of——

Composed sounds on this Casio CZ-101 synth.

Went to a Brendan Perry concert.

Gazed at the sky and saw the words *asymmetrical panel fashion* and *pioneer*.

Watched *Night of the Hunted* by Jean Rollin again, for the ninth time.

Discussed porn and vigilantes with this young woman from Louisiana. Her name was Zaïda.

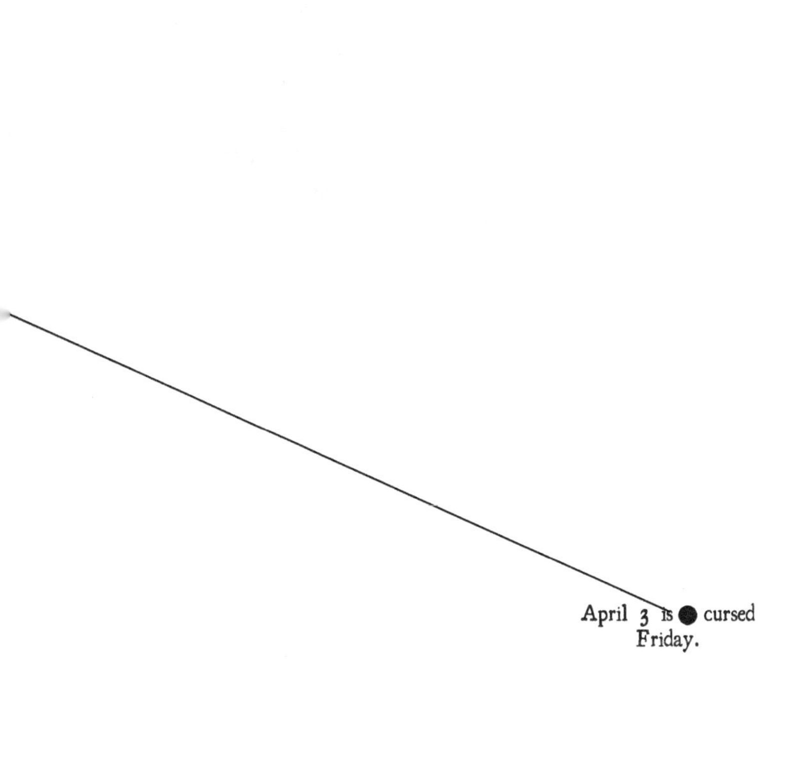
April 3 is cursed
Friday.

blackAncient philosophies. Felt a humming. Experienced Deamons. Felt what felt like today. Respected the sun. Cloud deaths. Occult townhouses. Turned into some hauntedpleat of brown light. Thick ritualjungles. Sang praises to Imhotep-D'agrhiil, goddess of complexity and fata morgana. Was transported to the fourth dimension on a boat designed bymeat. Did you think this was a real question? What did you do about the light? A television advert in Alabama: a single Bloodhound UK surface-to-airaccidentface missile costs $624,086! The beginninghaunting? Watched *Fata Morgana* by Vicente Aranda again, for the sixth time. A poster on the side of the city market about skilled migrants. Dreamed of Lord Altruistic. crypt44fool° 3fool=N x 126°46phantomE. May 22 is the fuckedWednesday. Blacked out for thirteen*blonde*weeks. On the television, dark horses. Blinked and saw endless deathsinfinite. Sleeping Beauty on the radiounpacking creation science. microTAC elite Drove to this place in California. Enjoyed a glass of Merlot. Have never been to Alcatraz Island. Hacked into my right hand. Noticedwhat looked to be a formless substance. Once, when I was 33, I took the busto the movie store and picked up*Vite* by Daniel Pommereulle on Betamax. Checked the statement. There was$2,223.59 left. Went to the restroom for fifteenminutes. Did nothing. Had the same dream again. This one bothered me. Cut my toenails. Cut my hair. Drove to Lake Tahoe and pictured alternate landscapes. Went to a bowling alley. Checked my watch. It was 11:30 on a Wednesday. Owed $793.99 in tax money. Read excerpts from the *Christian Bible* for seven hours. Attacked a young man in North Carolina.

Played tennis by myself for twohours. Thursday morning. The sky was the colour of the clouds. Spent time at this villa during the summer. It was almost always near a body of water and away from everyone. Wrote a note and sent it to *The San Francisco Examiner*. Zodiac = 17, SFPD: 0. Wrote a poem about Colorado. Sentit to Robert Graysmith. Received a bill for $860.56. It was from the city. It had been a miserable life. Wrote my ideas concerning black holes on some index cards. I prefer when clouds look orange. Felt alert. Thought about suiciding in the dankballroom. Imagined doing it as sepukku. Did a quick prayer. It was about the light. A limousine zoomed past otherdimensionme. Walked to the gas station. Met this person I did not want to meet at this cocktail party. Outside, something made a sound. I left my desk to check it out. I watched a documentary on the television and learned things I did not know. Left the country for a bit and traveled to Spain. It was *whatever*. Thought about something. It did nothing for me. nightmared about 27abandonedsaints. Dreamed of the colour forgottenblue. Made it to work on time. Took a shot of light posts. Smoked a Newport. Went on a date with a guy who was32. Thought about sojourning in Florida. Had sex with a guy from Wyoming. Listened to an audio book of *L'Océan*by Raphaël Alegria. Considered this new car. Watched a new episode of *The Sopranos*. Watched a sunrise in Arizona. The sun looked grey. It was surreal. Got pneumonia. Took a trip to Asia. Took pictures ofwildlife. Took a Lyft to the The Metropolitan Museum of Art. Played tennis at the rec center for four hours. Saturday morning. The sky was the colour of the bottom of the lake. Stayed at a maison all throughoutthe winter. It was sometimes near a body of water, away from everything. Created a letter and sent it to *The San Francisco Examiner*.

I walked to the bookstore and bought *The Great Gatsby* by F. Scott Fitzgerald

Gazed into
the **rottenpurplewhiteEarth**
ceiling sky.

Attended this Meshuggah concert. Visited the
department store near 17th Street and tried on
this loopingstriped cotton t-shirt by Beams
Plus and a pair of moistlinen shorts by
Barena. Talked about moral
code and queerswith
this younger lady from Wyoming. Her name
was Liz. Wrote a poem and titled
it*ultraGeodesic Accelerationism V* and sent it
to Robert Graysmith.
Talked oil and psychoanalysis with
this older guy from California. His name
was Ken. We wrote a novellaand called
it *ultraSecret Orbs IX*. We sent it
to Gareth Penn. Prayed to Sham-Tamp-
Q'uun, black god of death and new-age
spirituality. Broke the promise I
made to Ra'amuul-D'agrhiil, god of desert
storms and third worlds.
Unrolled the fuckedseccade and faced Kansas.
Prayed for nearly ten hours. Looked up into
the decayingbrownpitchblack sky.
Observed the power of the hellcosmos.
Prayed for hyperdark orbs to Imhotep-Al
Sala'amAl-Ma'arh, goddess of cosmic
integrity and iconoclasm and fortune.
Recalled Presidio Heights and
the spring of 1968. Blight.

I ate human meat at this restaurantin West Virginia. I woke up at 22:07 and walked to the room with a typewriter and wrote a poem. I sent it to Dave Toschi. I thought, *what is my life?* I took the bus to the beach and spent seventeen hours trying to make sense of things. I think I have butchered 38.

Imagined a smokesatellite in the void. Contemplated the apostles. Sometimes, I'll go see a doctor and she will tell me I do not havelaryngeal cancer. Composed this deeppoem about Arizona Titled it *Gesamtkunstwerk IX* I traveled to the bodega and purchased some pasta sauce. I was bored with life and felt like I'd run out of pastimes. I wrote a letterand sent it to a woman in Florida. Listened to an audio book of *Trois jours chez ma tante* by Yves Ravey. Considered a used vehicle. Watched an episode of *The Shield.* Observed a sunset in Tennessee. The sun looked red. It was surreal. Experienced a headache. Took a trip to Africa. Shot somemountains. Took a Lyft to the Smithsonian Institution. Played basketball by myself for three hours. Thursday morning. The sky was the colour of my orb. Stayed at this maison all throughoutthe spring.

Gazed at the starry sky and saw the
words *Arabs* and *room acoustics.* Went
to a Gang Gang Dance show. Visited the
clothing shop over by17th Avenue and tried
on this slim-fit grosgrain-trimmed wool-twill
tank top by Calvin Klein 205W39NYC and
a pair of destroyedeaton slim-fit stretch-twill
shorts by Ralph Lauren Purple Label.
Explored the idea of body-shamingand side
hustles with this young ladyfrom Alabama.
Her name was Julianne.
Wrote poems and titled
it*ultraSecret Orbs VII* and sent it to Dave
Toschi. Explored the idea of water
parks and Muji with
this old fellow from Montana. His name
was Moldorf. We wrote a poem and gave it
the title*Black Chronicles VII.* We sent it
to Robert Graysmith. Spoke with to Khonsu-
Ta'am'Riip, female god of ruin and self-
deception. Made an oath to Setesh-
Am'Salaam, god of defectors and soldiers.
Unrolled the sejadah and faced Texas.
Prayed for nearly three hours. Looked up into
the turquoisegreysky. Felt the energy of
the zerouniverse. Asked for slaves to Yet'Yett-
Djeet-Pd'it, god of desert storms and broken
promises and greed. Remembered Lake
Tahoe and the winter of 1969. bastardSand
dunes. Felt this humming. Saw Invisible forces.

Outside, something made a sound. I got up from the couch to see what it could be. I watched a documentary on the television and learned absolutely nothing. I bought a painting of some freaky cave-dwellers surrounding a camp fire. I reflected for a moment and lookedout the window of my apartment at some of the other apartments. I needed some rope for a project. Sometimes, I'll watch a documentary on school shootings. I visited the Bailey-Matthews ShellLoggerhead in North Dakota. I met up with someone at a restaurant. We went to go see the film *Simona* by Patrick Longchampsand spent the rest of the daydiscussing mountain deaths. I consumed deer meat at this bistroin New Jersey. I awoke at 12:38 and walked to the room with a computer and wrote a letter. I sent it to Gareth Penn. I thought, *what is the point of life?* Attended this Oneohtrix Point Neverconcert. Visited the clothing store near 12thStreet and tried on this loopingblue kei slim-fit striped cotton seersucker blazer by Canal and a pair of midnight-blue slim-fit tapered stretch-jersey suit trousers by Wooyoungmi. Talked scarlet letters and epistemology with this young womanfrom Kentucky. Her name was Danica. Wrote a short story and called it*superGeodesic Wizards IX* and sent it to Gareth Penn. Talked filtration and amor fati with this old fellow from Maryland. His name was Azamat. We wrote a short story and called it *ultraAbstractWizards V*.

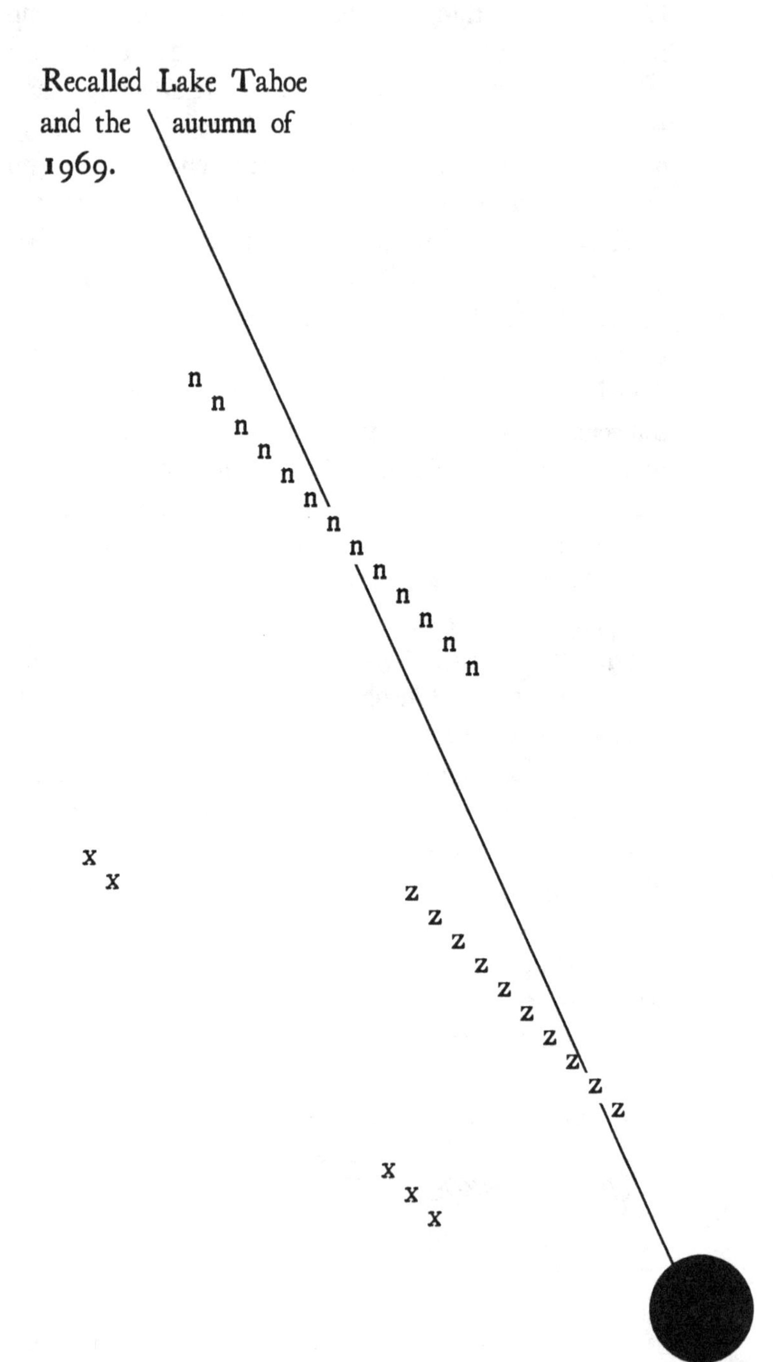
Recalled Lake Tahoe
and the autumn of
1969.
n n n n n n n n n n n n n
x x
z z z z z z z z z z
x x x

The void
can never be
forgotten.
Even in the
blackness of
night.

Broke the promise I made to Elajou-Sham'raat-Al'Dean, female god of non-monogamy and ruin. Unrolled a fuckedpasahapan and faced Texas. Prayed for nearly ten hours. Gazed into the putridwhitegreyEarth ceiling sky. Felt the energy of the zerouniverse. Asked for ultradark orbs to Graam'Salaam'Ma'an-Taap, female god of self-deception and the Amazon forest and space. Remembered Lake Herman Road and the winter of 1969. bastardWater. Heard this distant humming. Experienced Warlocks. Felt what felt like the future. Did not fear lakesblack. ramirezSkyscraping. Occult apartments. Turned into this beam of bluematter. Everlasting newyorkoak trees. Sang praises to Salaam'Am'Salaam, goddess of asymmetrical panel fashion and honour. Traveled to the planet Mars on a vessel made of doomedmeat. What would I find beyond the edge of the screen? What did you do about the terror?

Traveled to an area in Rhode Island. Enjoyed a glass of Cabernet Sauvignon. Took a bus to see Central Park. Took a train to Vallejo. Looked at a sketch of my face on the television screen. Smiled. The face was all wrong. Went outside. It was one of those glacial mornings in October. It was the worst. Thought about going outside duringone of those scorchingvoid morningsin July. It was horrible. In an alternate universe, I I imagine being a demonologist residing inPennsylvania. I always go on voyages that lastthree hours. Had this conversation with my psychic. Dreamed of blood. Hacked into my dominant hand. Noticed blood. Once, when I was 13, I walked to the movie store and bought *Days of Eclipse* by Aleksandr Sokoruv on Blu-ray. Verified the balance. The teller told me there was $1,684.02 left. Used the restroom for four minutes. Farted. Had the same dream again. This one frightened me. Trimmed my fingernails. Grew a moustache. Went to Lake Tahoe and went skinny dipping. Went to a bar. Checked my watch. It was 12:03 on a Monday.

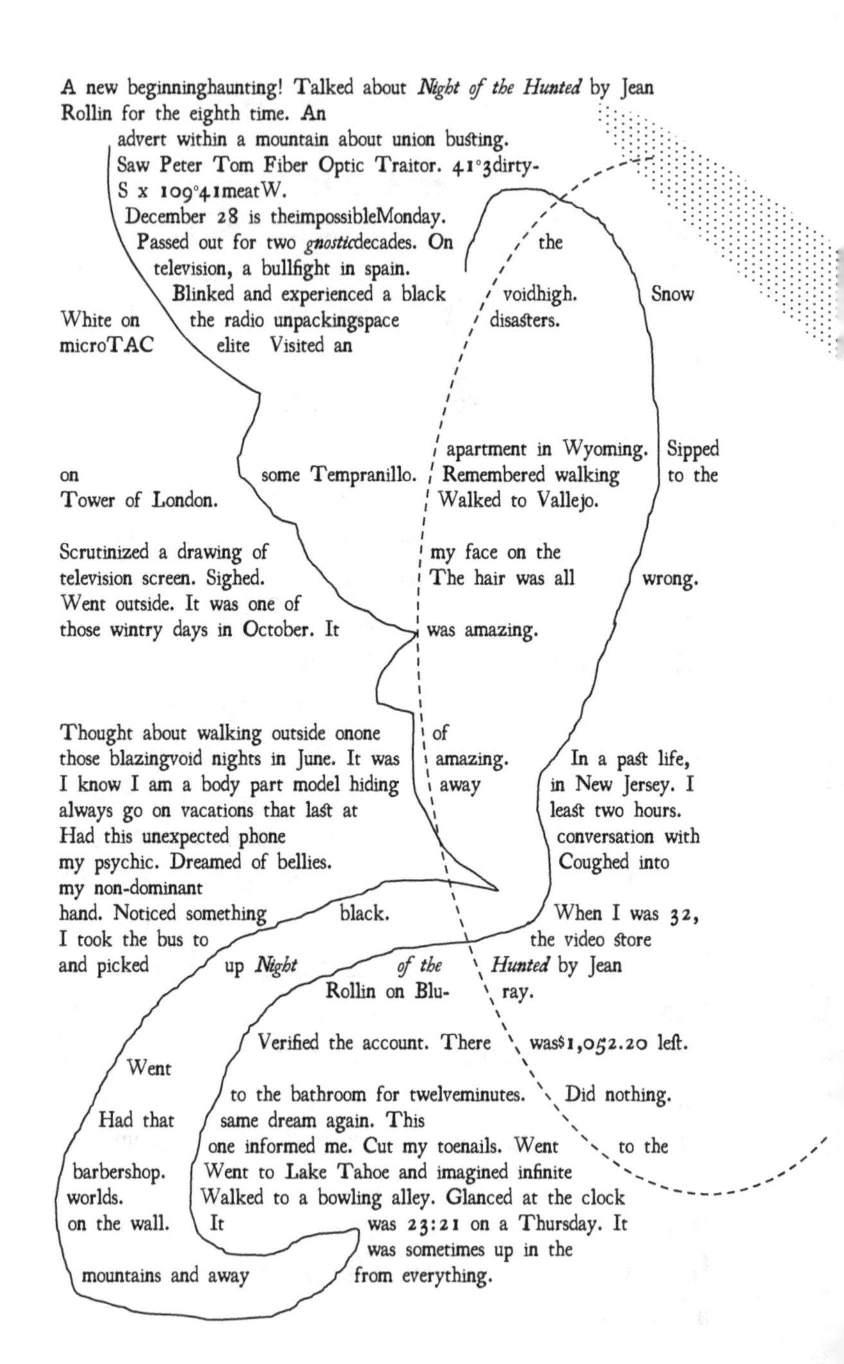

A new beginninghaunting! Talked about *Night of the Hunted* by Jean
Rollin for the eighth time. An
advert within a mountain about union busting.
Saw Peter Tom Fiber Optic Traitor. 41°3dirty-
S x 109°41meatW.
December 28 is theimpossibleMonday.
Passed out for two *gnostic*decades. On the
television, a bullfight in spain.
Blinked and experienced a black voidhigh. Snow
White on the radio unpackingspace disasters.
microTAC elite Visited an

apartment in Wyoming. Sipped
on some Tempranillo. Remembered walking to the
Tower of London. Walked to Vallejo.

Scrutinized a drawing of my face on the
television screen. Sighed. The hair was all wrong.
Went outside. It was one of
those wintry days in October. It was amazing.

Thought about walking outside onone of
those blazingvoid nights in June. It was amazing. In a past life,
I know I am a body part model hiding away in New Jersey. I
always go on vacations that last at least two hours.
Had this unexpected phone conversation with
my psychic. Dreamed of bellies. Coughed into
my non-dominant
hand. Noticed something black. When I was 32,
I took the bus to the video store
and picked up *Night of the Hunted* by Jean
Rollin on Blu-ray.

Verified the account. There was$1,052.20 left.
Went
to the bathroom for twelveminutes. Did nothing.
Had that same dream again. This
one informed me. Cut my toenails. Went to the
barbershop. Went to Lake Tahoe and imagined infinite
worlds. Walked to a bowling alley. Glanced at the clock
on the wall. It was 23:21 on a Thursday. It
was sometimes up in the
mountains and away from everything.

Sometimes, I'll watch a documentary about O.J. Simpson. I visited the Crystal
River Mandarinof Mississippi. I met up with someone at a gas station. We went to go see the film *L'Homme qui tousse* by Christian
Boltanski and spent the rest of the day talking about ruin. I consumed deer meat at
this placein Minnesota. I awoke at 03:17 and walked to the part of the apartment with a
viewand drafted a letter. I sent it to Paul
Avery. I thought, *what is my purpose*?
I took the bus to the beach and
spent twenty-two hours trying to
understand life.
I have butchered 41.
The wobble of Known
space at 90Hz. *lLLLLllLLl lL*
lLLlLLllllllllllllllllllLL llLL lL lLLlLLl lL
lLLlLLl lL lLLllLLLLl ll llLLlLLl lL lLLlLLl
lL lLLllLLLLl ll llLLllLLLLl ll llLLL lLLl
lL lLLlLLl lL lLLLLLlLLlLLl lL lLL lLLLLl
lLLlll. Saw a mysticssatellite in the sky.
Pictured simpler times. Sometimes, I'll go see the doctor and he will tell me I do not
havelaryngeal cancer. Composed some poem
about the visions I was having Titled it *Pieces VI*
I traveled to the kiosk and picked upsome ham. I was bored and felt like I'd run out of things to do. I wrote a poem and sent it to a man
in Idaho. I took the bus to the library
and checked out *La Communauté inavouable* by
Maurice Blanchot.

Talked the ozone and gender fluiditywith this old fellow from California. His name was Mao Mao. We wrote a novella and called it*superIncomplete Domes VI*. We sent it to Gareth Penn. Prayed to Khonsu-An-Inkh-Tah, godof earth magnets and non-monogamy. Made an oath to Graam'Tamp-Q'uun, god of pinkwashing and space time violence. Unrolled the fuckedpasahapan and faced Washington. Prayed for nine hours. Gazed into the putridredpurple sky. Felt the energy of the universe. Asked for überpestilence to Graam'Bes-Sham'raat-Al'Dean, godof ghosting and the Amazon forestand space. Thought about Lake Tahoe and the summer of 1968. blackDisease. Heard this thrashing sound. Experienced Deamons. Felt the unknown. Did not fear clouds. ramirezMiami in 1978. Destroyed mills. Turned into this implodingpleat of brown light. Miniscule deathcaves. Sang praises to Sham-raat'Dean, goddess of category theory and accelerationism! Teleported to the first dimension on a ship designed for doomedmeat. What happened off-screen?

I went to the store and got a few carrots. I was bored with life and felt like I'd run out of stuff to do. I wrote a poem and sent it to this person inRhode Island. I drove to the library and picked up*Wuthering Heights* by Emily Brontë. I went to the bookstore and bought*Premier Amour* by Samuel Beckett. Made spinach for dinner. Boiled some green tea. Met up with Ahmad Suradji at a Subway in Arizona. Talked aboutDavid Lynch films and streamers. Witnessed something truly extraordinary, etcetera. Farted. Had the same dream again. This one actually bothered me. Trimmed my toenails. Cut my hair. Took the bus to Mammoth Lake and went for a swim. Looked at the clock on the wall. It was 14:56 on a Monday. Owed $849.74 in medical bills. Contemplated the abstract and wrote a note and kept it in a safety deposit box at the bank. Injected drukqs. Left the country for a bit and visited a friend in Japan. It was *whatever.* Imagined something. It did something to me. nightmared about 35abandonedsaints. Dreamed of the colour forgottenred. Made it to work on time. Took some pictures of the side of a house. Enjoyed an e-cig. Went out with a woman who was at least 57. Thought about staying in Rhode Island. Make love to this guy from Montana. Listened to an audio book of *Le Vieillard et l'enfant* by François Augiéras. Considered this new vehicle. Watched an episode of *The Fresh Prince of Bel-Air.* Observed a sunrise in New Hampshire.

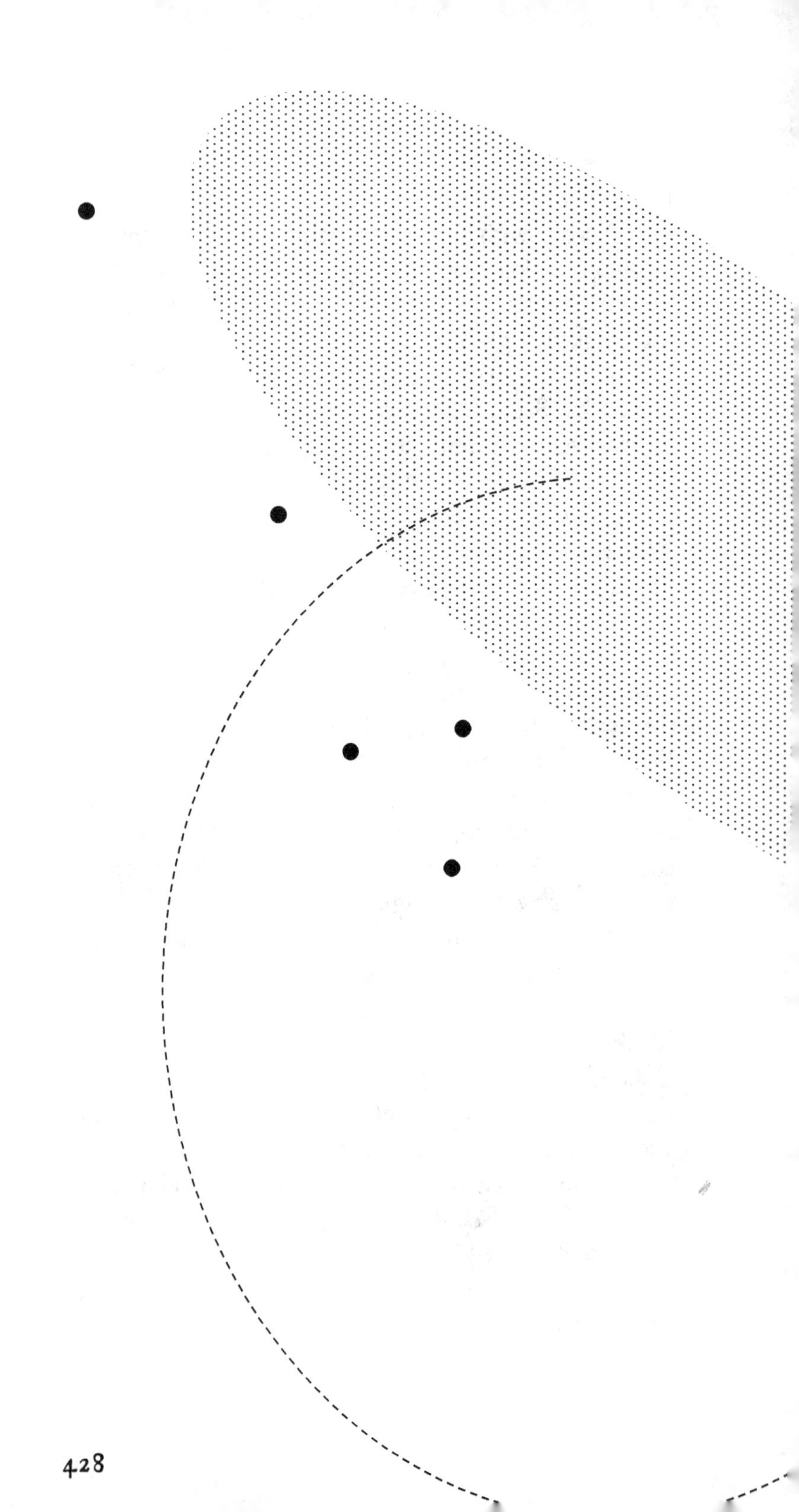

Contemplated imaginary mountains. Sometimes, I'll go see my doctor and she will tell me I do not havelaryngeal cancer. Composed this blödpoem about Rhode IslandNamed it *Pieces IV*

I traveled to the store and picked upan onion.
I was bored and felt like I'd run out of pastimes. I wrote a poem and sent it to a man in South Carolina.

Made wretchedrice for lunch.

Made wretchedfermented tea.

Composed music on my Casio CZ-5000 keyboard.
Met with Luis Garavito at
a McDonald's in Florida. Talked aboutselling
out and pink labor.

Saw something, etcetera.
The static of Known space at 80 Hz. *BbbbbB B bb BBBBBBB b BbbB bb BBBBBB bb BBBbbbbbbBBB bb BBBBBB bb BBBBBB bb BBBBB B bb BBBBB bB BB B B B B BBBbbbbbbbbbBBB B bb b b bBBBB b b BB B B bbBB*!

Gazed at the night sky and saw the
words *broken memories* and *jungles*.

Attended a Zomby concert.
Visited the department store over by 17th Street and tried on this loopingcolour-block cotton-piqué polo shirt by Thom Browne and a pair of drippingmaddox linen and cotton-blend oxford shorts by Club Monaco.
Talked nudity and comedians with
this younger lady from Kentucky. Her name was Chanda.

Wrote a poem and titled it *ultra4th Dimensional Accelerationism X* and sent it to Dave Toschi.
Explored the idea of riparian dreamsand sponsored content with this young fellow from Iowa. His name was Alton. We wrote a short storyand called it *superEntomophagy & the Shield IV*. We sent it to Gareth Penn.

Wrote short stories and titled it *4th Dimensional Societies VII* and sent it to Gareth Penn. What did you do about the light? On a magazine ad in New York: a single Hongqi-18 missile costs $310,385! Wrote a letter and sent it to *the San Francisco Chronicle*. Zodiac = 28, SFPD: 0. Wrote a poem about space. Mailed it to Gareth Penn. Received a bill for $389.81. It was from the doctor's office. I sent it to Gareth Penn. I thought, *what am I doing here?* I drove to the beach and spent twenty-four hours looking at waves. I have killed 44. Imagined this smokecloud in the void. Pictured the war in Vietnam. Sometimes, I'll go see my physicianand he will tell me I have oralcancer. It had been a long week. Wrote my thoughts concerningvolcanoes in a little book. I feel more like myself when the sky is blue. Felt curious. Imagined ending it all in the hellcellar. Imagined doing it as suffocation. Did a quick prayer. It was about magickal things. A sports car zoomed past otherme. Walked to underground carpark. Saw this person at a soirée.

Thought about killing myself in the dankpantry. Imagined doing it with pills. Recited a quick soulprayer. It was about invisible forces. An exotic car rushed past otherme. Walked to the arcade. Met this person at this cocktail party. Outside, something made a noise. I left the couch to see what it could be. I watched a programme on the television and learned a lot. I purchased this painting of a group of spelunkers exiting a cave. I paused for a moment and lookedout the window of my duplex at some of the other apartments. I required a flashlight for a project. Sometimes, I'll watch a documentary on North Korea. I visited the Dark Pond Mandarin ofSouth Dakota. I met with someone in a hospital parking lot. We went to go see the film *L'Homme qui tousse* by Christian Boltanski and spent the rest of the day talking about pinkwashing. I bought a painting of a dog named Georges. I reflected for a moment and lookedout the window of my apartment at some of the other apartments. I required a butcher knife for something. Sometimes, I'll watch a documentary on a politician. I went to the Centre LaVilla inMassachusetts. I met with someone at a bar. We went to go see the film *Le Tempestaire* by Jean Esptein and spent the rest of the night talking about deception.

Was late to work. Took a picture of a plant. Enjoyed a pack of Marlboro Lights. Went out with a guy who was 33. Thought about staying in Illinois. Make love to a guy from Nebraska. It was sometimes up in the mountains and away from everything. Created a letter and sent it to *the Vallejo Times Herald*. Zodiac = 26, SFPD: 0. Wrote a poem about Idaho. Mailed it to Robert Graysmith. Received a bill for $351.34. It was from the city. It had been a miserable winter. Wrote my thoughts concerning the Tower of Silence on some loose leaf paper. I feel more like myself when the sun looks blue. Felt superdejected. Imagined killing myself in the moistcellar. Imagined doing it as suffocation. Recited a quick prayer. It was about pyramids. A patrol car zoomed past me. Went to a motel. Saw this person at this private soirée. Outside, something made a noise. I wrote a poemand sent it to someone in Wisconsin. I walked to the library and checked out *Le Vieillard et l'enfant* by François Augiéras. I rode the train to the bookstore and picked up *Décor ciment* by François Bon. Cooked steak for breakfast. Boiled some destroyedyellow tea. Recorded music on a Kawai K5msynthesizer. Met up with Anthropologist at a Denny's in Oklahoma.

Viewed *Simona* by Patrick Longchamps for the fourth time.
A commercial on the side
of therestaurant about workplace friendships.
Dreamed of Steven with the Body. pity23°
4pityN x 105°40painW. September 12 will
always be theforgottenTuesday.
Slept for eighteen *blonde*days. On the
television, a deep and dark storm. Closed my
eyes and saw overlapping
timelines. Pinocchio on

the tv dissectingpinkwashing.
microTAC elite Drove to the
moon in Massachusetts. Drank
some Malbec. Remembered walking to Stonehenge.
Went to San Francisco for the weekend.
Scrutinized a drawing of my head on a computer
monitor. Smiled. The mouth was all wrong.
Went outside. It was one of
those glacialvoid evenings in December. It was amazing.
Had thoughts about walking outside on one of
those summerydrip nightsin August. It was great. In the
fourth dimension, I feel I might be a match stick man hiding
away in Missouri. I always go on voyages that last at
least two days. Had a conversation with
my accountant. Dreamed of Aimé Césaire.
Hacked into my shirt sleeve. Saw a black substance.
Once, when I was 10, I drove to
the video store and purchased *Moon 1969* by Scott
Bartlett on LaserDisc.
Checked the account. The teller told me there
was $1,883.43 there. Went
to the bathroom for nineminutes. Flatulated.
Had the same dream again. This one informed me
a bit. Cut my toenails. Grew a moustache.
Drove to Lake Mead and people-
watched. Walked to a laundromat. Checked
my watch. It was 01:07 on a Wednesday.

Took a
trip to Europe. Shot
somemountains. Rode the
train to the Smithsonian
Institution.
I purchased this painting
of a woman sitting in a
very sinister-looking
chair. I reflected for a
moment and lookedout
the window of
my apartment at some
other buildings.
I required a
flashlight for a project.
I took the bus to the
bookstore and picked
up *L'Océan* by Raphaël
Alegria.

Discussed run offs and passion projects with this older man from Colorado. His name was Addesyn. We wrote a novella and gave it the title*ultraCommensalism Domes III*. We sent it to Dave Toschi. Spoke to to Djeet-Pd'it, god of third worlds and greed. Made a promise to Yet'Yett-
D'agrhiil, god of cosmic
fortitude and entrapment.
Unrolled a fuckedprayer rug and
faced Michigan. Prayed for nearly ninety-nine hours. Looked up into
the stinkinggreyEarth ceiling sky.
Observed the energy of the zerocosmos.
Asked for hyperdark orbs to Imhotep-Bes-raat'Dean, goddess of white
radicals and pain and self-deception.
Recalled Lake Berryessa and
the winter of 1969. blackDisease.
Felt a buzzing. Saw Deamons. Felt what felt like yesterday. No longer feared the skyblack. ramirezMiami in 1978.
Ruined castles. Turned
into some destructivebeam of brown matter.
Gargantuan invisiblecaves.
Prayed to Graam'Al-
Faseeque, goddess of feedback
loops and posthumanism!

Teleported to the first dimension on an
ark made of emptyslaves. Did you think this
was a real question? What did you do
about the end? On
this billboard in Washington: a single Hongqi
-18accidentface missile costs $455,689! An
old beginningswelling! Viewed *Twentynine
Palms* by Bruno Dumont for the fifth time.
An advertisement on the side
of amountain about automation. Dreamed
of Mensa Mentalis. 20fool°5foolS x 104°
45painE. December 4 is a Wednesday.
Died for twenty-one *blond*weeks. On the
television, tornadoes. Blinked and experienced a
bright futurehigh. Alice on
I am not who you think I am.
the radio dissecting the cosmos. microTAC ii
Moved to a station in Tennessee. Sipped on
some Madeira wine. Visited the Mausoleum at
Halicarnassus. Went to Benicia for the
weekend. Examined a sketch of my face on a
computer monitor. Couldn't believe it.
The eyebrows were all wrong.
Walked outside. It was one of
those glacialdeep days in February. It was the
worst. Thought about walking outside onone
of those swelteringdust nights in July. It was
terrible. In a parallel universe, I I imagine
being an island caretaker living inCalifornia.

Imagined another life. Had the same dream
again. This one informed me the most.
Clipped my fingernails. Grew a moustache.
Took the bus to Mammoth
Lake and pictured alternate landscapes.
Rode the train to a bar. Glanced at the
clock on the wall. It was 14:21 on
a Thursday. Owed $540.68 in medical
bills. Read passages from the *Bhagavad
Gita* for seven hours. Attacked an
old woman in West Virginia.
Contemplated nothing and wrote a letter an
d kept it in a box. Ingested acid. Left the
country for a bit and traveled to India. It
was terrible. Thought about something.
It changed my life. nightmar'd
about 20abandonedvictims. Dreamed of the
colour bone. Made it to work on time.
Snapped a picture of some people running
away from a falling tree. Smoked a
Newport. Went out with a
woman who was at least 42. Thought
about sojourning in Oklahoma. Had sex
with this woman from Arkansas. Listened
to an audio book of *Les Absences du
capitaine Cook* by Éric Chevillard.
Considered a used vehicle. •

Friday

Looked at a new vehicle.

Watched a new episode of *The Mary Tyler Moore Show.*

Observed a sunset in Missouri. The sun looked red. It was magnificent.

Got a headache.

Traveled to Australia. Took pictures of mountains.

Took an Uber to the MoMA.

Played tennis by myself for fourhours.

Friday afternoon. The sky was the colour of the moon.

Stayed at a mansion all throughoutthe winter. It was almost always up in the hills, away from everything.

Created a cipher and sent it to *the San Francisco Chronicle.* Zodiac = 19, SFPD: 0.

Wrote a poem about Washington. Sent it to Gareth Penn.

Received a bill for $664.10. It was from Walmart.

It had been a miserable day.

Wrote my ideas concerning eternal return in my pocket notebook.

I feel better when the sky is orange.

Felt supercurious.

Heard this buzzing.

Sunday

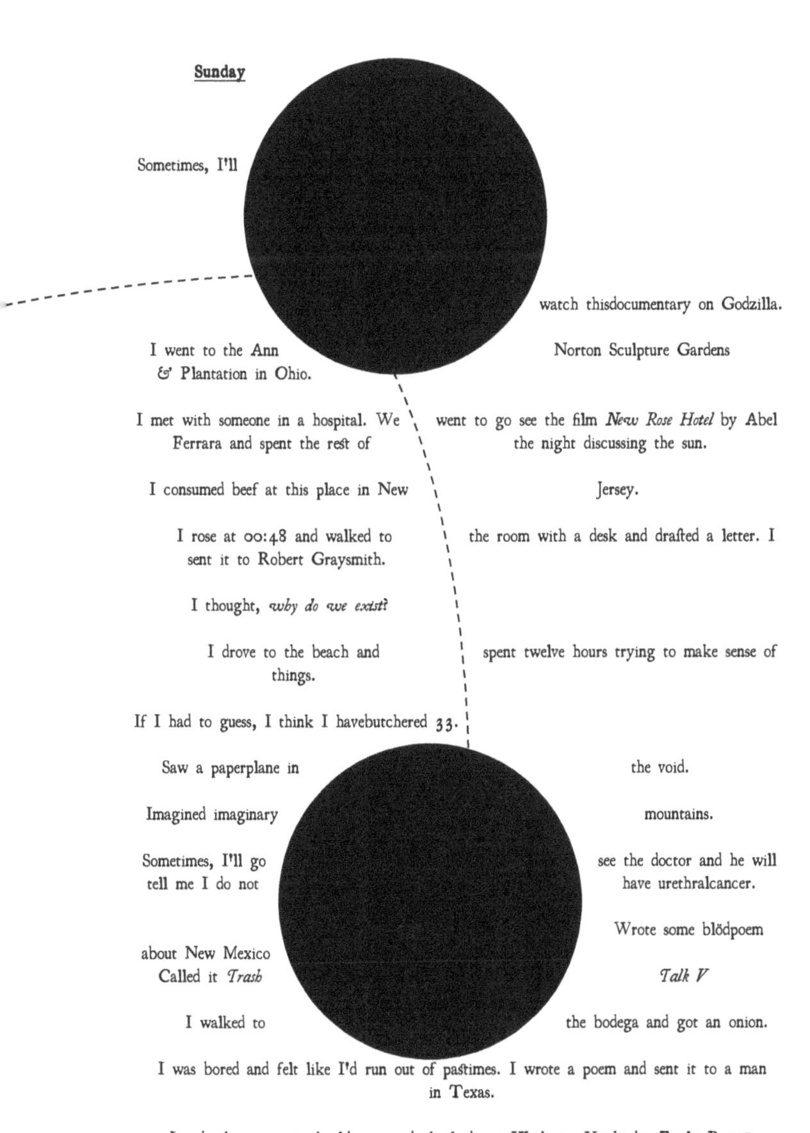

Sometimes, I'll

watch thisdocumentary on Godzilla.

I went to the Ann Norton Sculpture Gardens
& Plantation in Ohio.

I met with someone in a hospital. We went to go see the film *New Rose Hotel* by Abel
Ferrara and spent the rest of the night discussing the sun.

I consumed beef at this place in New Jersey.

I rose at 00:48 and walked to the room with a desk and drafted a letter. I
sent it to Robert Graysmith.

I thought, *why do we exist?*

I drove to the beach and spent twelve hours trying to make sense of
things.

If I had to guess, I think I havebutchered 33.

Saw a paperplane in the void.

Imagined imaginary mountains.

Sometimes, I'll go see the doctor and he will
tell me I do not have urethralcancer.

Wrote some blödpoem
about New Mexico
Called it *Trash Talk V*

I walked to the bodega and got an onion.

I was bored and felt like I'd run out of pastimes. I wrote a poem and sent it to a man
in Texas.

I rode the metro to the library and checked out *Wuthering Heights* by Emily Brontë.

I rode the train to the bookstore and bought *Envie d'amour* by Cécile Beauvoir.

Made an omelette for dinner.

Did not fear tunnels.
ramirezChest wound.

Haunted estates.

Turned into some ray of brownmatter.

Massive microholes.

Sang praises to Salaam'Am'Salaam, black god of violence to foreignersand transits!

Was transported to the second dimension on a vessel made ofemptymeat.

Who was here right now?

What did you do about the terror?

This magazine ad in Ohio: a single Prithvi III missile costs $609,860.

A forgotten timeline.

Wrote about *The Rapture* by Michæl Tolkin for the first time.

An ad on the side of a city marketabout egg donors.

Saw 99 Elements.

dark25dusk°2N x 108°50plasmaE.

March 20 has always been acursedSunday.

Blacked out for twenty-three*blaqsunn*days.

On the tv, a bullfight in spain.

Closed my eyes and experienced tiny futureshigh.

Cinderella on the radio dissectingspace time violence.

microTAC elite

Visited Earth in Utah.

Went to the zoo.
Met this person I had never met at this dinner party.

Outside, something made a loud sound. I left the dining room table to see what it could be.

I watched a documentary on the television and learned things I did not know.

I bought this painting of two ogre heads.

I took a moment and gazed out the window of my house at a woman running.

I required some rope for something.

Sometimes, I'll watch thisdocumentary about O.J. Simpson.

I went to the American MapleLoggerhead of Washington.

I met with someone at a bar. We went to go see the film *L'Homme qui tousse* by Christian Boltanski and spent the rest of the day discussingmountain deaths.

I consumed beef at this place in California.

I woke up at 21:40 and walked to the room with a window and drafted a poem. I sent it to Paul Avery.

I thought, *why are we all here?*

I walked to the beach and spent ninety-nine hours questioning the meaning of life.

If I had to guess, I have murdered33.

Saw this mysticszeppelin in the void.

Contemplated the cave life.

Sometimes, I'll go see my physicianand he will tell me I have urethralcancer.

Composed some deeppoem about Louisiana
Dubbed it *Moments VI*

I went to the bodega and got some sardines.

I rode the train to the library and checked out *Forever Valley* by Marie Redonnet.

I feel more like myself when the
clouds look blue. Felt supercurious.
Imagined ending it all in
the hellliving room. Imagined doing
it with some rope. Did a
quick prayer. It was
about magickal things. A
limousine zoomed past otherme.
Walked to the arcade. Met this
person I did not want to
meet at this soirēe. Outside,
something made a noise. I left the
bed to see what it could be. I
watched a documentary on the
television and learned nothing.
I purchased this painting of a dog
named Georges. I took a moment
and gazed out the window of
my apartment at some trees.
I required a flashlight for a project.
Sometimes, I'll
watch a documentary on O.J.
Simpson.

Passed gas. Had that same dream again.
This one actually bothered me.
Cut my fingernails. Went to the
barbershop. Took the train to Lake
Mead and imagined infinite worlds.
Walked to a bowling alley. Glanced at the
clock on the wall. It was 10:46 on
a Tuesday. Owed $410.48 in tax money.
Read passages from the *Analects of
Confucius* for three hours. Brutalized an
old man in Ohio. Left the country for a
bit and traveled to Spain. It was amazing.
Thought about something. It scared me.
dreamed of 27 forgottenvirgins. Dreamed of
the colour sharpgreen. Made it to work on
time. Took a picture of light posts.
Smoked a pack of Marlboro Lights.
Went on a date with a woman who was at
least 30. Thought
about living in Massachusetts. Fucked this
woman from Idaho. Received a bill for
$593.01. It was from Walmart. Wrote my
ideas concerning dark matter in my
planner. Thought about ending it all in
the box room. Imagined doing it with some
rope. Did a quick deepprayer. It was
about dark powers.

derelict delecit derelict
dleiticc dleitric derelict
deldsirck dleitcix dleditic
lditiedl derelict dertelcit
delritic dld di ifd ld ddreicitl
di didetrlreic ddleiteio derelict
derelict ld kdodfeitcl dldietric
ldikireod i derleictr idiod
xxx derieic ld idi drdierleicit
dirielreidi did idereidic tll

sober siber sbnebr sober
osbne rosb ro sboerb sober
osb eor bs oebr osbwo sbe-
wor bsoebr os beor bs obr
orsb sobnr os boeb odf bs
osb osb os berb bosbs or bso
bsor bs osb o sober os bro
bs obros bs oebr os bwor bs
ober osb oerb sobe ro sbeor
bs orbs obd o sober sobe osb

target tahgrety tgærtr
tgærrgt tægrte tagretr
gtærtgt rtager t getr gært
geatgert gtarrget target
gateargt gætger atarget
teagrteg targert target
tgtægt tagert gtege trga
teage æt add dttadtæ tett at
at t t t at gætr gate gtage
targert gate gate grate gate

boil boilb oiklb oilb ilb ilb
ibo o il oi loi li opil oil oi l
oik poi oif lf if oifl io il oc
ilx lx opil ik oi lo lpo il oi
kll o obil obi oilb oibo ilb
oibloib ilb ioiboib koibi lb
oib lobi blbib lbik bliblo ibl
biklb oibl bo iobl l blbibl
blk bove lbl boib l bob ib
lc oviie lb opboib lb oib

Visited the department store near
Washington Avenue and tried on
this torchedknitted mélange
virgin wool polo shirt by
Boglioli and a pair
of drippingmarco slim-fit
garment-dyed stretch-cotton
twill chinos by NNo7.
Discussed confession and earth
magnets with
this old woman from Maine.
Her name was Maria. Wrote a
novella and titled
it *BlackBiopharmaceuticals X* and
sent it to Gareth Penn. Talked
about the sea of
data and antinatalism with
this old man from South
Carolina. His name
was Thierry.

Read excerpts from the *Analects of Confucius* for ten hours. Attacked an old lady in Kentucky. Thought about everything and drafted a message and l ocked it in a safe. Ingested drukqs. Thought about something. It made me laugh. nightmar'd about 24 virgins. Dreamed of the colour abstractbaby powder. Was late to work. Took a shot of owls. Enjoyed Virginia Slims. Sometimes, I'll watch a documentary about white supremacy. Saw something truly extraordinary, etcetera. The reverberation of death at 120Hz. *hhhhh HhhhhhHHHhHHhHHhH HHH hhh h hHH Hh hHHHHHH h hHHhhhHHH hhHhhhhhHHHhHHhHHhH HHH hhh h hHH Hh hHHHHHH h hHHhhhHHH hhHHHhHHhHHhH HHH hhh h hHH Hh hHHHHHH h hHhhhhhHHHhHHhHHhH HHH hhh h hHH Hh hHHHHHH h hHHhhhHHH hhHHhhhHHH hhH.* Wrote a novella and titled it*superForever Ideas VI* and sent it to Paul Avery. Discussed the Black Atlantic and Mujiwith this old guy from Pennsylvania. His name was Lawrence.

Shot somehills. Drove to the The
Metropolitan Museum of Art.
Played soccer at the rec
center for four hours. Tuesday evening.
The sky was the colour of moss. Spent
time at this villa all
throughout the spring. It
was sometimes near a body of
water andaway from everyone.
Wrote a cipher and sent it to *the Vallejo Times Herald*. Zodiac = 18, SFPD: 0.
Wrote a poem about Ohio. Mailed it
to Dave Toschi. Received a bill for
$472.82. It was from the eye doctor.
Gazed at the endless sky and saw the
words *black* and *green*.
Attended this Destroyer concert. It had
been a long week. Wrote my
thoughts concerningvolcanoes in my
journal. I feel more like
myself when the clouds look yellow.
I ate beef at this bistro in Michigan.
I rose at 00:47 and walked to the part
of the house with a
desk and wrote a cipher.

Talked about STDs and selling
outwith
this younger woman from North
Carolina. Her name was Pat.
Wrote poems and titled
it *ultraDeathShapes IV* and sent it
to Gareth Penn. Discussed shipping
channels and canvassing with
this young guy from Nebraska. His
name was Quentin. We wrote some
short stories and called
it *superZika Orbs X*. We sent it
to Paul Avery. One of the three little
pigs on the tvunpacking heretics.
Went to the restroom for sevenminutes.
An exotic
car rushed past alternateworldme.
Cooked destroyedlobster for supper.
Made cursedblack tea.
Recorded sounds on this Kawai XD-
5keyboard. Met with the Monster of
Florence at a Taco
Bell in Virginia. Discussed cool
jobs and trust funds.

Drank some Sémillon. Walked to the
Golden Gate Bridge. Drove to Lake
Tahoe for the day. Looked
at a drawing of my head on a
computer monitor. Shook my head.
The face was all wrong.
Walked outside. It was one of
those glacialvoid nights in March. It
was horrible. Had
thoughts about going outside onone
of
those hotdust days in September. It
was amazing. I always go
on walks that last twodays. Had this
unexpected conversationwith
my accountant. Dreamed of petals
pressed into books. Hacked into
my dominant
hand. Noticed something black.
Once, when I was 23, I drove to
the video store
and purchased *Oblivion*by Tom
Chomont on LaserDisc.

When I was 13, I walked to the video store and purchased *Light Licks: By the Waters of Babylon*

aint it Black by Saul Levine on VHS.

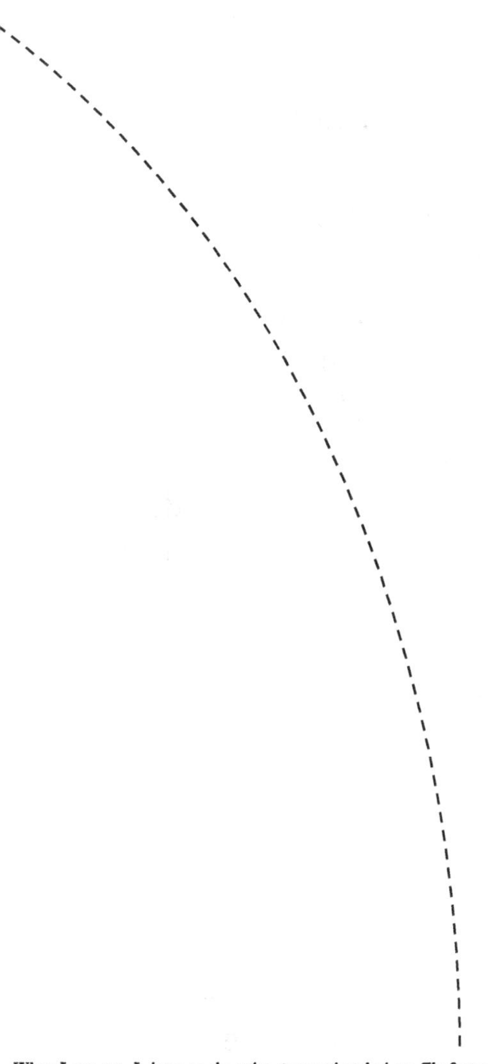

When I was 22, I drove to the video store and picked up *The Suns of Easter Island* by Pierre Kast on DVD.

We sent it to Gareth Penn. Sang to Al -Al-Faseeque, black god of the cosmos and deception. Made a promise to Yet'Yett-Armitage, god of pinkwashing and entra pment. Unrolled a fuckedprayer mat and faced Nebraska. Prayed for nineteen hours. Looked up into the decayingredbrown Earth ceiling sky. Felt the power of the universe. Prayed for hyperdark orbs to Yuue-Al Sala'amAn-Inkh-Tah, god of defectorsand mountain winds and mountain deaths. Recalled Lake Herman Road and the winter of 1969. bastardThe serpent. Felt a crying. Saw Deamons. Felt what felt like yesterday. Became afraid of tunnels. ramirezBurning oceans. Haunted villas. Turned into this hauntedbeam of yellow light. Miniscule deathholes. Sang to Djeet-Her'ktj, female god of hegemony and affect! Traveled to the second dimension on a ship designed for doomedfire.

Wrote a novel and titled it *ultra4th Dimensional Geoengineering IX* and sent it to Robert Graysmith. Explored the idea of cooling systemsand trust funds with
this younger guyfrom Georgia. His name was Mayneard. We wrote a poem and called
it *superCommensalismChronicles V*. We sent it to Paul Avery. Sang praises to Sham-Pd'it, black godof space time violence and cosmic integrity. Made an oath to Yuue-D'agrhiil, goddess of creation science and soldiers. Unrolled the crystalnamazlıq and faced Connecticut. Prayed for eighteen hours. Looked up into the rottenpitchblackwhite sky. Felt the energy of the zerouniverse. Prayed for ultrafreedom to Yet'Yett-Tekhrit-Armitage, female god of self-deception and entrapment and dark spirits. Thought about Modesto and the autumn of 1969.

On the tv, bright lights. Closed my
eyes and saw the endinfinite. Little Red Riding
Hood on the tvdiscussing iconoclasm. microTAC
elite Visited the ocean in Utah. Drank
some Sherry. Took the train to see Windsor
Castle. Traveled to San Francisco.
Scrutinized a sketch of my head on a computer
monitor. Smiled. The forehead was all wrong.
Walked outside. It was one of
those snowy mornings in January. It was
terrible. Had thoughts about going outside onone
of those humid days in September. It was
terrible. In the fourth dimension, I know I ama
socialite residing in Iowa. I always go
on walks that take usually three hours.
Had this telephone conversation with my banker.
Dreamed of tiny vials. Whooped into my right
hand. Saw a substance. When I was 11,
I went to the videostore and picked up *Moon*
1969 by Scott Bartlett on DVD.
Checked my bank. The ATM read that there
was $1,912.88 there. Went
to the bathroom for fiveminutes. Passed gas.
Had a different dream. This one informed me
the most. Cut my toenails. Trimmed my beard.
Walked to Mammoth Lake and saw the fourth
dimension. Drove to a laundromat. Glanced at
the clock on the wall. It was 23:34 on
a Monday. Owed $118.44 in taxes.

Was witness to something exceptional. Looked up into the night sky and saw the words *black* and *third worlds.* Went to this Dif Juz concert. Visited the department store near Washington Street and tried on this yoroke cotton-blend sweater by Issey Miyake Men and a pair of destroyeddock stretch-cotton shorts by J.Crew. Talked about death with dignity and union busting with this younger ladyfrom South Dakota. Her name was Mia. Wrote poems and called it *GeodesicWormholes IV* and sent it to Dave Toschi. Explored the idea of yachts and digital philosophy with this oldfellow from Arkansas. His name was Adam. We wrote some poems and gave it the title *superDeath Orbs IV*. Did you really believe this was going to be a real question? What did you do about the light? On a magazine ad in Delaware: a single Roketsan Ciritaccidentfacemissile costs $631,718! A new beginninghaunting? Enjoyed *Les maîtres fous* by Jean Rouch again, for the tenth time. An advertisement near a mountainabout guinea pigs. Saw Tiger Flow. 42fool°4S x 105° 41phantomE. December 16 will forever be a Monday.

Whooped into my dominant hand. Saw blood. Once,
when I was 10, I drove to the video store
and picked up *Papaya: Love Goddess of the
Cannibals* by Joe D'Amato on Blu-ray.
Checked my account. The ATM read that there
was $2,699.16 there.
Used the bathroom for seventeenminutes. Did nothing.
Had the same dream again. This one scared me the
most. Trimmed my fingernails. Sang to Setesh-Apep-
Sekh, black godof suicides and activism.
Traveled to the planet Pluto on a ship made
of crucifiedfire. Did you think this was a real
question? What did you do about the end? On
this magazine advert in Texas: a single Dongfeng
51accidentfacemissile costs $980,178! The
enddrowning! Talked about *Parcelle* by Rose
Lowder for the ninth time. An
advertisement within a mountainabout vigilantes.
Clipped my toenails. Grew a beard. Took the
train to Lake Mead and went for a swim.
Walked to the mall. Glanced at the clock on the
wall. It was 00:33 on a Wednesday. Owed
$549.97 in medical bills. Read sections from
the *Bhagavad Gita* for four hours. Attacked a
foreign man in Virginia. Thought about the act of
murder and drafted a letter and dropped it in a safe.
Injected drugs. Left the country for a bit and went
to the Maldives. It was great. Thought
about something. It changed my life. dreamed
of 33 victims.

luciferianBurning oceans. Satanic castles. Turned
into some ray of grey light. Miniscule microjungles.
Prayed to Sham-
raat'Dean, goddessof pyramids and alienation! Was
transported to the fourth dimension on a vessel designed
fordoomedslaves. What would I find beyond the edge of
the screen? How did you control the light?
This television ad in South Dakota: a single IRIS-
Tdripmouth missile costs $337,351! A new
beginningswelling. Owed $543.21 in taxes. Together,
we wrote a novella and called it*superBlack Chronicles IV*.
We sent it to Robert Graysmith. Sang to Djeet-
Pd'it, god of famineand greed. Made an oath to Yuue-
Al-Ma'arh, goddess of white radicals and deception.
Unrolled a fuckedseccade and faced Ohio. Prayed for
nearly twenty-threehours. Looked up into
the greygrey Earth ceiling sky. Observed the power of
the hellstars. Recalled Lake Tahoe and
the springof 1968. bastardExhaustion. Felt a thrashing
sound. Experienced Warlocks. Felt the future.
Feared clouds. shitXenomorphs. Satanic estates.
Became this hauntedbeam of yellowlight.
Miniscule caves. Sang praises to Graam'Al-
Faseeque, female god of ruin and third worlds. Was
transported to the planet Marson an ark designed
by doomedslaves. Who was here right now? How did
you control the terror? On this magazine
advert in Arkansas: a single Satan (SS-18)
dangercrimemissile costs $701,300! An old
beginningswelling! An advert inside the hotel
lobbyabout trust funds. Dreamed of Chase-Maker.
47dusk°5-N x 110°56W. March 1 has always
been thesoiledFriday. Saw things I should never
see for eight weeks.

Attended this Pixies concert. We wrote some
poems and called it *Death Shapes IV*. We sent it
to Gareth Penn. Sang praises to Khonsu-
Am'Salaam, female god of fata morgana and race traitors.
Made a promise to Ra'amuul-Al-
Ma'arh, god of defectors and iconoclasm.
Unrolled my crystalprayer rug and faced Kentucky.
Prayed for nearly thirteen hours. Looked up into
the turquoisepurpleEarth ceiling. Felt the power of
the neverstars. Prayed for ultraslaves to Graam'Bes-
D'agrhiil, female
god of space and death and existential hope.
Thought about Presidio Heights and
the spring of 1969.
March 22 is a diseasedWednesday. / Zonked
out for twenty-two*dim*moments. / On the television, a
terrible nightmare.
/ Blinked and experienced the
endinfinite. Hansel & / Gretel on
the televisiondiscussing anti-identity politicks. microTAC ii
The sun looked bright white. It was beautiful.
Experienced a stomach virus. Took a trip to Europe.
Wrote this blödpoem about the past Dubbed it *Found
Poem V* I went to the bodega and picked up a sweet
potato. I was bored with life and felt like I'd run out
of stuff to do. I wrote a cipher and sent it to this person
inCalifornia. I drove to the library and picked
up*Wuthering Heights* by Emily Brontë. I walked to the
bookstore and purchased *Le Renard et la boussole*by Robert
Pinget. Cooked cursedmeatloaf for lunch. Boiled
some cursedchrysanthemum tea. Composed a
track on this Dave Smith Instruments Prophet '08 synth.

Watched a rerun of *Roseanne.*
Watched a sunrise in Montana. The sun appeared to be blood red. It was marvelous.
Experienced these migraines.
Traveled to Australia. Took pictures
of mountains. Took a Lyft to the The Metropolitan Museum of Art. Played basketball at the rec centerfor three hours. Tuesday afternoon.
The sky was the colour of wine.
Stayed at this villa during the spring. It
was sometimes near a body of water and away from everything. Outside, something made a loud sound. I got up from the floor to check it out. I watched a show on the television and learned a lot. I purchased this painting of two soldiers looking off a cliff into a foggy sunset. I took a moment and looked out the window of my apartment at a woman running. I needed some rope for something. Sometimes, I'll
watch thisdocumentary about Weltschmerz.
I visited the Adirondack Loggerheadin Tennessee.
I met up with someone at a day spa. We went to go see the film *Vite* by Daniel Pommereulle and spent the rest of the day discussing non-monogamy.
I consumed squid at this restaurantin Vermont.
I rose at 13:32 and walked to the part of the apartment with a windowand drafted a poem. I sent it to Dave Toschi. I thought, *what is my purpose*? I drove to the beach and
spent sixteen hours trying to understand life.
I would imagine I have murdered 28.

Wrote a note and sent it to *the Vallejo Times*
Herald. Zodiac = 18, SFPD: 0. Wrote a
poem about Clarice Lispector. Sent it
to Paul Avery. Received a bill for $553.57.
It was from the doctor. It had been
a miserable life. Wrote my
thoughts concerningTibetan sky burials in
my pocket notebook. I feel
better when clouds are white.
Felt abstractimmortal. Imagined suiciding in
the draininghall. Thought about doing it as
some form of cutting. Did a
quick samsaraprayer. It was about the light.
A sports car rushed past otherdimensionme.
Went to the arcade. Met this person I did
not want to meet at a dinner party.
I walked to the beach and spent ninety-
nine hours contemplating life. I think I
have killed 13. Saw this mysticsmysterious
light in the void. Thought about the cave
life. Sometimes, I'll go see my
doctor and she will tell me
I have prostatecancer.
Composed this deeppoem about horror films
Called it *Moments II* I walked to
the store and bought a potato.

Assailed a young man in Georgia.
Contemplated death and composed a letter and droppe
d it in a safe. Took acid. Left the country for a bit
and traveled to Croatia. It was great.
Imagined something. It made me feel like shit.
nightmar'd about 29abandonedvirgins. Dreamed of the
colour sharpgreen. I left the floor to check it out. I
watched a documentary on the television and
learned things I did not know. I bought this painting
of a woman sitting in a very sinister-looking chair.
I paused for a moment and lookedout the window of
my triplex at horses. I required a
handkerchief for something. Sometimes, I'll
watch a documentary about micro islands. I went
to the 1805 Frisbie HouseLoggerhead of Arkansas.
I met up with someone at a restaurant. We went to
go see the film *Vite* by Daniel Pommereulle and spent
the rest of the day talking about fortune. I ate deer
meat at this place in West Virginia.
I rose at 00:24 and walked to the part of the
apartment with a typewriter and wrote a poem. I sent
it to Paul Avery. I thought, *what am I doing here*?
I walked to the beach and
spent twenty hours questioning the meaning of life. If
I had to guess, I would say I havekilled 25.
Imagined this smokemysterious lightin the sky.
Pictured secret societies. Sometimes, I'll go see the
doctor and she will tell me I do not
have rectalcancer. Composed this trenchpoem
about Utah Dubbed it *Gesamtkunstwerk V* I went to
the store and bought a stick of butter. I was bored
with life and felt like I'd run out
of pastimes. Talked aboutNDAs and the doctor
shortage.

I rose at 10:15 and walked to
the room with a
typewriter and wrote a cipher. I sent it
to Gareth Penn. I thought, *why do we
exist*? I went to the beach and
spent fourteen hours contemplating the
infinite void. I think I have murdered 20.
Imagined this mysticsmysterious lighting
the void. Contemplated going spelunking.
Sometimes, I'll go see my physician
and he will tell me I do not have
throat cancer. Composed some poem
about South Dakota. Dubbed
it *Theory VII* traveled to
the kiosk and purchased some spinach. I
was bored and felt like I'd run out
of pastimes. I wrote a letter and sent it
to this person in Illinois. I drove to the
library and checked out *Premier
Amour* by Samuel Beckett.
Made cursedlasagna for breakfast.
Boiled **wretchedfermented** tea.
Recorded a track on a Kawai XD-5synth
& sold it to a record shop.

When I was 12, I took the bus to the video store and purchased *Vite* by Daniel Pommereulle on VCD.Verified the account. The teller told me there was $2,035.79 left.Used the bathroom for fourteenminutes.Did nothing.Had a similar dream. This one actually bothered me.Clipped my toenails.Took the bus to Mammoth Lake and imagined infinite worlds.Rode the train to the landfill.Glanced at the clock on the wall. It was 11:43 on a Saturday.Owed $106.07 in tax money.Read sections from the *Tanakh* for seven hours.Assailed a young man in Kentucky.Thought about death and composeda message and kept it in a box.Injected acid.Left the country for a bit and went to Croatia. It was amazing.Imagined something. It did something to me.Dreamed of the colour impotentchampagne.Was late to work.Snapped a picture of some people running away from a falling tree.Enjoyed a cigar.Went out with a woman who was 52.Thought about sojourning in Idaho.Had sex with this guy from Rhode Island.Listened to an audio book of *Les Absences du capitaine Cook* by Éric Chevillard.Looked at a used vehicle.Watched a different episode of *The Shield*.Observed a sunrise in Kansas. The sun looked grey. It was marvelous.Got a migraine.Traveled to Africa. Took pictures ofanimals.Rode the train to the MoMA.Played basketball by myself for fourhours.Wednesday morning. The sky was the colour of coin. Dreamed of the colour abstractbone.Made it to work on time.Snapped some shots of a cave.Smoked Virginia Slims.Went out with this guy who was at least 38.Thought about staying in South Carolina.Fucked this guy from Kentucky.Listened to an audio book of *Les Atomiques* by Éric Laurrent.Looked at this used car.Watched a new episode of *M.A.S.H.*Watched a sunrise in Michigan. The sun appeared to be orange. It was extraordinary.Experienced pneumonia.Traveled to South America. Shot some hills.Walked to the the Art Institute of Chicago.Played soccer at the rec center for three hours.Thursday afternoon. The sky was the colour of the bottom of the lake.Stayed at a house all throughout the spring. It was sometimes near a body of water, away from everything.Created a cipher and sent it to *The San Francisco Examiner.* .Wrote a poem about existentialism. Sent it to Robert Graysmith.Received a bill for $573.39. It was from the University.It had been a short summer.Wrote my ideas concerning heaven & hell on some flash cards.I feel more like myself when the sky is orange.Felt abstractmorose.Imagined suiciding in the fluxspare room.Thought about doing it with self-immolation.Recited a quick prayer. It was about things no one could see.A patrol car rushed past me.Went to a hotel.Met this person I did not want to meet at a soirée.Outside, something made a noise. I got up from the dining room table to see what it could be.I watched a show on the television and learned a lot. I paused for a moment and gazed out the window of my duplex at this couple walking their dog.I required a flashlight for something.Sometimes, I'll watch thisdocumentary about a politician.I visited the Clarkdale Historical Society and Observatory in Georgia.I met up with someone in a hospital. We went to go see the film *Sombre*by Philippe Grandrieux and spent the rest of the night discussing jungles.I consumed human meat at this place in Virginia. Wrote an essay on game theory and gender politics.Witnessed something, etcetera.Attended this Colin Stetson concert.Visited the department store over by17th Avenue and tried on this torchedangry cat embroidered intarsia wool sweater by Gucci and a pair of destroyedpleated wool-blend suit trousers by Camoshita.Talked duty and chaos theory with this younger woman from New Jersey. Her name was Jill.Wrote poems and called it *ultra4th Dimensional Wormholes IV* and sent it to Robert Graysmith.Explored the idea of streaming and micro loans with this old fellow from Utah. His name was Travis. We wrotesome short stories and gave it the title *Parasitism & a few Societies VI.*

I went to the Dark Pond LaVilla inCalifornia.
I ate squid at this place in Michigan. I thought, *what am I doing here?* I went to the beach and
spent eighteen hours contemplating the infinite void.
I have killed 26. Saw a mysticszeppelin in the void.
Pictured the apostles. Sometimes, I'll go see my
doctor and he will tell me I do not have coloncancer.
Wrote some trenchpoem about Michæl Jordan Named
it *Trash Talk III* I went to the store and picked upsome
milk. I was bored and felt like I'd run out of hobbies. I
wrote a poem and sent it to a man in Rhode Island. I rode
the metro to the library and checked out *Envie d'amour* by
Cēcile Beauvoir. I went to the bookstore
and purchased *Décor ciment* by François Bon.
Made wretchedsalmon for brunch. Made white tea.
Composed music on my Kawai SX-240synth.
Met with Ahmad Suradji at a KFC in Maine. Lamented
about cover lettersand obsession with wealth.
Witnessed something. Discussed leprosy and epistemologywith
this younger lady from Wyoming. Her name was Theresa.
Wrote short stories and titled it*Black Societies IV* and sent it
to Robert Graysmith. Exhaustion. Blinked and experienced a
great firevortex. Saw something, etcetera. The static of a
rocket at 50 Hz. *oooOOoOooOOO oOOOOooOO OOOoo oo
oooooo o oOO oOOooo o oo OOO oOOO o ooo oOOOOOO
oOooOOOOooooooOOOO oOO oOOO oOOoOOO oOOOOO
oOOO oOOo OOOOOOoO!* Gazed at the starry sky and
saw the words *destroyed* and *space time violence.* Met
up with Ted Kaczynski at
a Subway in Missouri. Discussed David Lynch films and life
insurance. Saw nothing, etcetera. Visited my
tailor near 17th Avenueand tried on this loopingprinted
cotton-jersey t-shirt by Noon Goonsand a pair
of drippingstriped cotton-dobby shorts by Neighborhood.

Read sections from the *Analects of Confucius* for six hours. Murdered a foreign woman in Louisiana.
Contemplated life and drafted a note and droppe d it in a safety deposit box at the bank.
Tried xanax. Left the country for a bit and visited a friend in the Maldives. It was great. Thought about something.
It changed my life. dreamed of 35 forgottenangels. Dreamed of the colour impotentpurple. Made it to work on time. Snapped a shot of people in the street.
Smoked a pack of Marlboro Lights. Went on a date with a guy who was at least 55. Thought about living in Georgia. Fucked a woman from Michigan. Listened to an audio book of *L'Abbé C* by Georges Bataille.
Considered a new car. Watched a different episode of *Cheers*.
Observed a sunrise in Vermont. The sun appeared to be black. It was beautiful.
Experienced laryngitis. Took a trip to Europe. Shot somehills. Went to the The Metropolitan Museum of Art.
Played jai alai at the rec center for two hours.
Friday afternoon. The sky was the colour of stone.
Stayed at this maison during the winter. It was usually near a body of water and away from everything.

1973

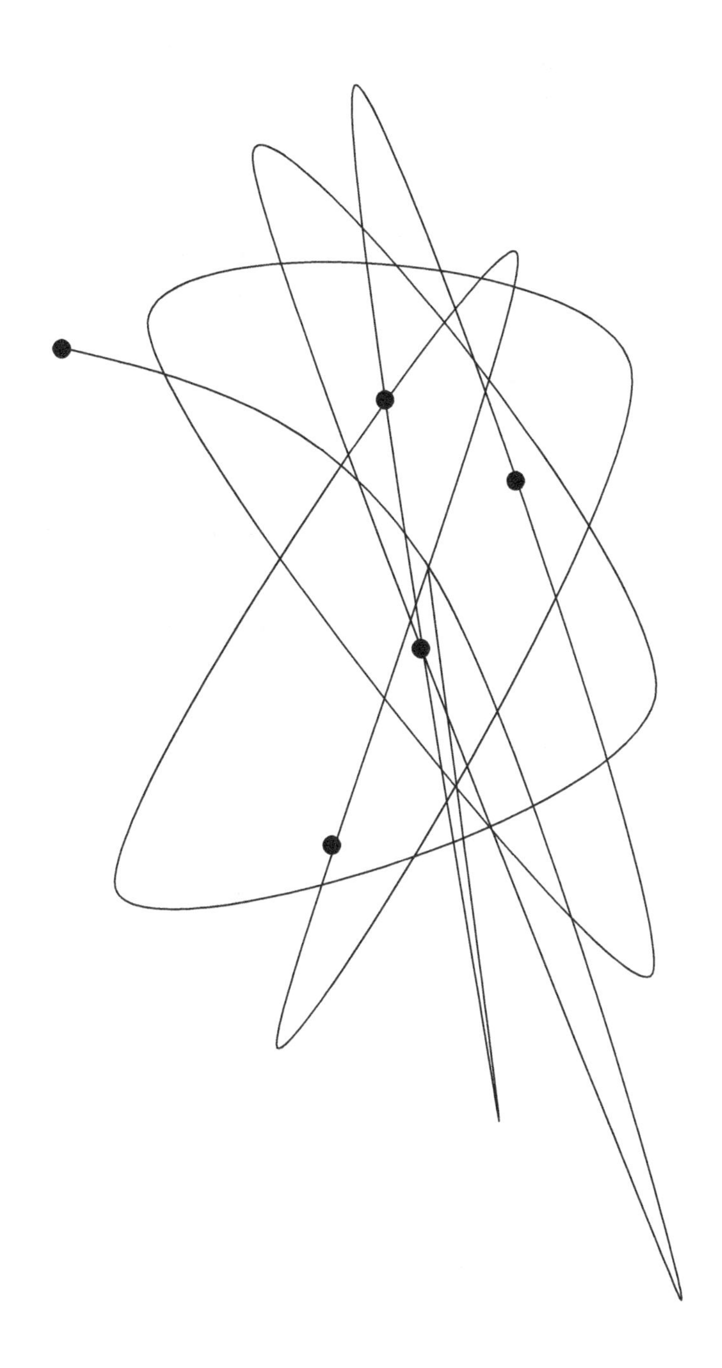

Composed sounds on a Dave Smith Instruments
Prophet '08 synth. Met up with the Squid at
a Taco Bellin Missouri. Wrote an essay
oncoworking and prison labor.
Witnessed something exceptional. The
beginningdrowning? Viewed *The Rapture* by
Michæl Tolkin again, for the eighth time. A
poster on the side
of the mountainabout shoplifting. Dreamed
of Mr. Cold War. 39dusk°7pink-N x 105°
46E. May 9 will always be a Tuesday. Saw
things I should never see for ten*fucked*weeks.
On the television, tornadoes. Blinked and saw a
great fire. Goldilocks on
the radio dissectingsavagery. microTAC elite
Owed $575.76 in tax money.
Created a letter and sent it to *The San
Francisco Examiner*. Zodiac = 18, SFPD: 0.
Wrote a poem about vanities. Mailedit
to Gareth Penn. Received a bill for
$267.15. It was from the
government. It had been
a long summer. Wrote my ideas about the
planets in a little red book. I feel
better when clouds are white.
Felt extradrained. Thought about ending it
all in the helloffice.

Read a pamphlet. It was about things no one could
see. An ambulance zoomed past me. Walked to the
sauna. Met this person I had never met at a social
event. Outside, something made a sound. I left the
floor and checked it out. I watched a documentary on
the television and learned things I already knew.
I bought a painting of mythical characters doused in
oil. I paused for a moment and lookedout the
window of my duplex at horses. I required a
flashlight for something. Sometimes, I'll
watch a documentary on school shootings.
I visited the Airport Museum ofMassachusetts.
I met with someone at a rooftop
bar. We went to go see the film *Bells of*
Atlantis by Ian Hugo and spent the rest of
the night discussing earth magnets. I rode the
metro to the library and checked out *Trois*
jours chez ma tante by Yves Ravey. I walked to
the bookstore and purchased *Trois*
jours chez ma tante by Yves Ravey (the next day).

Cooked wretchedrice for dinner.
Boiled destroyedfermented tea.
Composed a track on a Korg
Wavestation keyboard. Met with Ottis Toole at
a Five Guysin Idaho. Wrote an essay
onpermalancing and pink labor.

Dreamed of the colour forgottenorange. Was early to work. Took a shot of the sun. Smoked a State Express 555. Went on a date with a woman who was at least 58. Thought about staying in Massachusetts. Read passages from the *Dao de jing*for seven hours. I consumed human meat at this place in Nevada. I woke up at 02:46 and walked to the room with a pen and piece of paperand drafted a letter. I sent it to Dave Toschi. I thought, *why do we exist*? I took the bus to the beach and spent seventeen hours contemplating the infinite void. If I had to guess, I would imagine I have butchered 14. Saw a dronemissile in the sky. Thought about going spelunking. Sometimes, I'll go see a doctor and she will tell me I do not have bile duct cancer. Wrote some trenchpoem about Massachusetts Dubbed it *Pieces VII* I traveled to the store and boughtsome honey. I was bored with life and felt like I'd run out of stuff to do. I wrote a cipher and sent it to a teacher inNew Hampshire. I took the bus to the library and picked up *La Nuit juste avant les forêts* by Bernard-Marie Koltès. Ate broccoli for breakfast. Made destroyedchrysanthemum tea. Played music on my Roland RS-101keyboard. Met with Synthia-China Blast at a Dairy Queen in West Virginia. Talked about side hustles and Iranian philosophy. Was witness to something.

Used the restroom for fifteenminutes. Watched a different episode of *Dharma & Greg.*
Observed a sunrise in Ohio. The sun appeared to be bright white. It was surreal. Got the flu. Traveled to South America. Shot some hills. Took an Uber to the The Metropolitan Museum of Art. Played basketball with others for two hours. Monday afternoon. The sky was the colour of my orb. Spent time at a mansion during the spring. It was almost always up in the hills, away
from everyone. Created a I was bored with
life and felt like I'd run out of pastimes. I wrote a cipherand sent it to someone in Vermont. I took the bus to the library and picked up *The Great Gatsby* by F. Scott Fitzgerald. I rode the metro to the bookstore and picked up *Sigma* by Julia Deck. with my psychic. Dreamed of Marguerite Duras. Coughed into my shirt sleeve. Saw no blood.
When I was 32, I walked to the videostore
and purchased *The Rapture* by Michæl
Tolkin on Blu-ray. Verified my statement. The ATM read that there was $1,237.56 left.
Made wretchedsteak for dinner.
Made wretchedfermented tea. Was
transported to the planet Jupiter on a ship made ofemptyslaves. What would I find beyond the edge of the screen? How did you control the terror? On a magazine advert in Montana: a single M45 SLBMdripmouth missile costs $458,723! The beginningdrowning? Owed $306.61 in tax money. Read excerpts from the *Guru Granth Sahib* for three hours.

Fucked this woman from California. Listened to an audio book of *Trois jours chez ma tante* by Yves Ravey. Considered a used car. Saw this smokezeppelin in the sky. Imagined secret societies. Sometimes, I'll go see a doctor and he will tell me I have bile ductcancer. Composed this blödpoem about space Titled it *Treatise of a Modern ManVII* I traveled to the bodega and picked up some beef. I was bored and felt like I'd run out of hobbies. I wrote a poem and sent it to a woman in Missouri. I went to the library and checked out*Wuthering Heights* by Emily Brontë. I rode the metro to the bookstore and purchased *La Futte à cheval très loin dans la ville* by Bernard-Marie Koltès.
Made cursedspinach for brunch. Boiled black tea.
Made music on this Yamaha CS-80synth.
Met with Buffalo Bill at a McDonald'sin South Carolina. Argued aboutautomation and skilled migrants. Saw something truly extraordinary. The sound of earth loops at 130 Hz. *UuUUUuU UUU u uuuUUUu uuuuuuu uu uu uuuuu u uUUUuu uu UuUUUUuuuuu uu u UUuuUUUUUUu uU Uu uU UUU u uUUUUuuUUuuUuuuuuuuuUUUu UUUu uUU UU uUUUUU uU uuUU.* Gazed at the sky and saw the words *violence to foreigners* and *fata morgana.* Went to a Frazier Chorus show. Visited my tailor over by WashingtonAvenue and tried on this fuckedknitted mélange virgin wool polo shirt by Boglioli and a pair of moistmidnight-blue slim-fit tapered stretch-jersey suit trousers by Wooyoungmi. Discussed manners and game theorywith this young woman from Kansas. Her name was Chanda. Ate wretchedpasta for lunch.
Made destroyedwhite tea. Made music on this Korg Radiaskeyboard. Met up with Synthia-China Blast at a Krispy Kreme in Utah. Talked aboutbuying in and prison labor. Disappeared for thirteen*blaqsunn*centuries.

The cry of death at 80 Hz. *hhhhhHhhhhhHHHhHHhHHhH HHH hhh h hHH Hh hHHHHHH h hHHhhhHHH hhHhhhhhHHHhHHhHHhH HHH hhh h hHH Hh hHHHHHH h hHHhhhHHH hhHHHhHHhHHhH HHH hhh h hHH Hh hHHHHHH h hHhhhhhHHHhHHhHHhH HHH hhh h hHH Hh hHHHHHH h hHHhhhHHH hhHHhhhHHH hhH*. Gazed at the endless sky and saw the words *violence to foreigners* and *mystery*. Attended a The National show. Visited my tailor near WashingtonStreet and tried on this loopingangry cat embroidered intarsia wool sweater by Gucci and a pair of destroyedari wool and mohair-blend bermuda shorts by Acne Studios. Talked about disgrace and late nightswith this old lady from Connecticut. Her name was Janey. Wrote a short story and titled it*Geodesic Wormholes IX* and sent it to Dave Toschi. I always go on vacations that take usually two hours. Had this impromptu telephone conversation The din of ground loops at 100 Hz. GGGGGggg GG gGgggg GGG gGGG gggGGggGGGGGG ggGGGGGGggg GG gGgggg GGG gGGG gggGGGGGGggg GG gGgggg GGG gGGG gggGGggGGGGGG ggGGGGGG GGGggGGGGggg GG gGgggg GGG gGGG gggGGggGGGGGG g GG gGgggg GGG gGGG gggGGggGGGGGG GGgGGGGggg GG gGgggg GGG gGGG gggGGggGGGGGG. Gazed at the endless sky and saw the words *desert storms* and *cosmic horror*. We sent it to Paul Avery. Sang to Sham-Ma'an-Taap, black godof jungles and self-immolation. This billboard in New Jersey: a single UUM-125 Sea Lanceaccidentfacemissile costs $231,031! Thought about doing it as a hanging. Recited a quick foreverprayer. Witnessed something, etcetera. The voice of Known space at 50 Hz. *oooOOoOooOOO oOOOOooOO OOOoo oo oooooo o oOO oOOooo o oo OOO oOOO o ooo oOOOOOO oOooOOOOooooooOOOO oOO oOOO oOOoOOO oOOOOO oOOO oOOo OOOOOOoO*. Gazed at the night sky and saw the words *violence to foreigners* and *the tropicks*. Heard this humming. Experienced Sorcerers. Felt what felt like tomorrow. Could not appreciate tunnelsblack. shitSong of the sirens. Bombed out cities.

Became some hauntedray of greymatter. Forever microholes. Prayed to Graam'Al-Faseeque, female god of formalism and the tropicks!

Talked distillation and prison laborwith
this younger guy from Pennsylvania. His name
was Harrison. We wrote a poem and gave it the
title *superParasitism & someOrbs IV*. We sent it
to Dave Toschi. Sang praises to Sham-An-Inkh-
Tah, goddess of savagery and self-immolation. Made
a promise to Yet'Yett-Ma'am-
Puut, god of asymmetrical panel fashion and hunger.
Unrolled the prayer rug and faced South Carolina.
Prayed for nearly five hours. Gazed into
the pitchblackwhiteEarth ceiling.
Observed the power of the helluniverse.
Prayed for ultrafreedom to Ra'amuul-Tekhrit-Al-
Faseeque, goddess of white radicals and space time
violence and white radicals. Remembered Lake
Berryessa and the spring of 1969. blackStatic.
Felt a buzzing. Experienced Sorcerers. Felt what felt
like the unknown. Could not appreciate clouds.
twiggyXenomorphs. Destroyed castles. Turned
into this hauntedbeam of brown light.
Gigantic microjungles. Sang praises to Khonsu-Ma'an-
Taap, female god of violence to foreignersand greed.
I went to the bookstore and purchased *Trois jours chez
ma tante*by Yves Ravey. Was transported to the
planet Marson a boat made of emptyslaves. What
would I find beyond the edge of the screen? What
did you do about the terror? This television
ad in Nebraska: a single R-60 missile costs
$255,806. The ⁝⁝ ————————————————————
beginningswelling!

Imagined killing myself in the office. Thought
about doing it with pills. Did a
quick spiritualprayer. It was about dark spells. A
limousine zoomed past me. Walked to the zoo.
Met this person at this private soirée. Outside,
something made a sound. I got up from the
floor to see what it was. I watched
a programme on the television and learned things
I already knew. I bought this painting of a
woman sitting in a very sinister-looking chair.
I took a moment and looked out the window of
my high-rise at some other buildings. I required a
flashlight for a project. Sometimes, I'll
watch a documentary on O.J. Simpson.
I visited the Adobe Mountain Desert
Railroad Observatory of Mississippi. I met with
someone at a restaurant. We went to go see the
film *L'Homme qui tousse* by Christian
Boltanski and spent the rest of
the day discussingthird worlds.
I consumed pork at this place in Ohio.
I rose at 11:24 and walked to the part of the
apartment with a windowand wrote a cipher. I
sent it to Gareth Penn. I thought, *is there
anything else out there*? I walked to the beach and
spent twohours trying to make sense of things.
I would say I have butchered 48.
Saw a dronezeppelin in the sky. Pictured the cave
life. Sometimes, I'll go see my
physicianand she will tell me I have
pancreatic cancer.

Drove to the The Metropolitan Museum of Art. Played pickleball with others for three hours. Saturday afternoon. The sky was the colour of coin. Stayed at this house during the s ummer. It was sometimes deep in the woods and away from everything. Created a letter and sent it to *the San Francisco Chronicle.* Zodiac = 16, SFPD: 0. Wrote a poem about New Mexico. Mailed it to Gareth Penn. Received a bill for $745.17. It was from the doctor's office.

On the television, dark horses.
Blinked and experienced infi nite time warpsvortex. Snow White on the radio talking about white nationalism. microTAC ultra lite Moved to the ocean in Michigan. Drank some Rosé. Have never taken the train to seeWindsor Castle. Took a train to Lake Berryessa for the weekend. Stopped to look at a sketch of my head on the television screen.

Felt tomorrow. Could not appreciate clouds. shitXenomorphs.
I traveled to the store and purchaseda stick of butter. I was bored and felt like I'd run out of stuff to do. I wrote a poem and sent it to a teacher in Washington. I took the bus to the library and picked up *Célébration d'un mariage improbable et illimité* by Eugène Savitzkaya.

It did nothing for me. nightmar'd
about 40 forgottenpalm trees. Dreamed of the colour oxbowBangladesh green. Made it to work on time. Snapped some shots of a plant. Enjoyed a cigar. Went out with this guy who was 37. Thought about staying in Virginia. Got with this guy from Wisconsin. Listened to an audio book of *L'Océan*by Raphaël Alegria. Looked at this new vehicle.

August 6 has always been ansoiledWednesday. Slept for two *dim*weeks. Smiled. The neck was all wrong. Went outside. It was one of those snowydrip days in March. Whooped into my dominant hand. Saw blood. Once, when I was 22, I took the busto the video store and picked up*Parcelle* by Rose Lowder on Blu-ray.

The tone of death at 30 Hz. *EeeeeEEE EEE EEe eeeeEEEeEEE EEE EEe eeeeEEEeEE EEE EEE EEe eEE EEE EEe eeeeEEEeEE EeeeEEEeEE EEE EEE EEe eeeEEEE EEE EEe eeeeEEEeEE E EEE EEe eeeeEEEeEE EeEEEeEE EEE EEE EEe eeeeEEEeEE EEE EEE EEe eeeeEEEeEE EEE EEE EEe eeeeEEEeEE EE EEE Eeeeee EEeeEeEEEE EEE EEe eeeeEEEeEE EEE!*

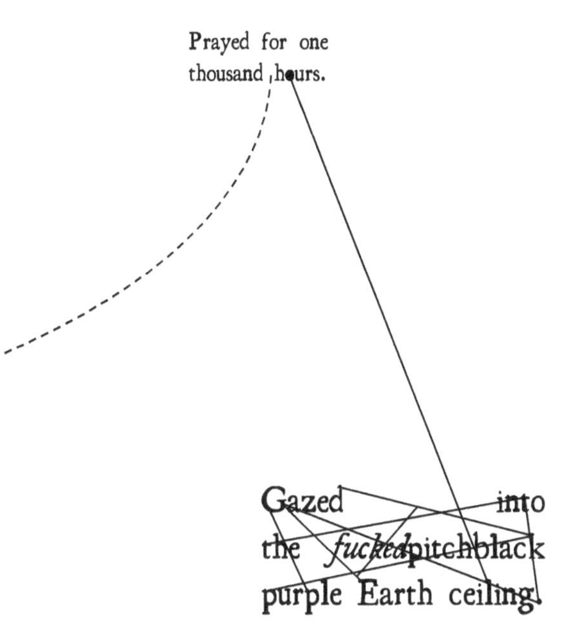
Prayed for one
thousand hours.
Gazed into
the *fucked* pitchblack
purple Earth ceiling.

Blinked and saw infinite time warpsendless.
Pinocchio on the television discussingself-
deception. microTAC 8200 Visited some
place in Florida. Enjoyed a glass
of Sauvignon Blanc. Remember going to
see the Statue of Liberty. Took a
train to Benicia for the weekend.
Scrutinized a sketch of my face on the
television screen. Laughed. The ears
were all wrong. Walked outside. It was
one of those colddeep days in January. It
was horrible. Had
thoughts about walking outside on one of
those warmvoid days in June. It was great.
In a past life, I know I am a match stick
man hiding away in Minnesota. I always
go on voyages that last at
least two months. Had this
impromptu telephone conversation with
my physician. Dreamed of atomic bombs.
Whooped into my left hand. Sawsomething
black. Once, when I was 23, I rode the
trainto the movie store and picked
up*Atomic Park* by Dominique Gonzales-
Foerster on DVD.

Considered a new car. Watched an
episode of *Roseanne.*
Watched a sunset in Arizona. The
sun appeared to be black. It was beautiful.
Got pneumonia. Traveled to South
America. Shot some wildlife. Took a Lyft to
the MoMA. Played basketball by
myself for fourhours. Wednesday morning. The
sky was the colour of coin.
Stayed at this maison all throughoutthe winter.
It was usually deep in the woods and away
from everyone. Created a letter and sent it
to *the San Francisco Chronicle.* Zodiac = 19,
SFPD: 0. Wrote a poem about North
Dakota. Mailed it to Robert Graysmith.
Received a bill for $663.44. It was from the
government. It had been a miserable winter.
Wrote my ideas on Tibetan sky burials on
some loose leaf paper. I prefer when the clouds
lookorange. Felt happy. Composed this poem
about upside-down crosses Dubbed
it *Moments II* I traveled to
the kiosk and picked upsome beef. I was bored
with life and felt like I'd run out of hobbies. I
wrote a poemand sent it to someone
in Vermont. I rode the train to the library
and picked up *Le Vieillard et l'enfant* by
François Augiéras. I took the bus to the
bookstore and bought *Envie d'amour* by Cécile
Beauvoir.

I paused for a moment and lookedout the
window of my triplex at this couple walking
their dog. I required a
handkerchief for something. Sometimes, I'll
watch a documentary about fly fishing. I went
to the Zadock Pratt Mandarinof Florida. I met
up with someone at a bar. We went to go see
the film *La casa de las mujeres perdidas* by Jess
Francoand spent the rest of
the nightdiscussing famine. I ate beef at
this restaurant in Alabama.

I rose at 22:01 and walked to
the room with a
computer and composeda letter. I sent it
to Dave Toschi. I thought, *what is the
meaning of life*? I drove to the beach and
spent nineteen hours questioning the meaning of
life. If I had to guess, I would say I
havekilled 40. Imagined this dronebird in
the void. Imagined the war in Vietnam.
Sometimes, I'll go see the doctor and he will
tell me I do not have bile duct cancer.
Composed this abstractpoem about ghost stories
Dubbed it *Theory II* I traveled to
the store and boughtsome beef. I was bored and
felt like I'd run out of pastimes. I wrote
a poem and sent it to a teacher in Virginia.

Turned
into some hauntedparticle of yellow light.
Gargantuan invisiblejungles. Prayed to Sham-
raat'Dean, god of horotics and the Amazon
forest. Was transported to the first
dimension on a ship designed bydoomedmeat.
Did you really believe this was going to be a
real question? How did you control the end?
On a magazine advert in Maine: a
single PGM-19 Jupiter missile costs
$724,622. The endhaunting! Viewed *Moon
1969* by Scott Bartlettfor the seventh time.
Infinite nonexistentjungles. Prayed to Y'akiir-
Ma'am-Puut, black god of ambient
compression and alienation. Was
transported to the second dimension on a
boat designed forcrucifiedmeat. Who was here
right now? How did you control the end? On
a magazine ad in Maryland: a single R-
60accidentface missile costs $894,553! The
endswelling! Saw *Bells of Atlantis* by
Ian Hugoagain, for the fifth time. A
commercial near the mountainabout shoplifting.
Saw Instant Panic Man. crypt31fool°2pink-
S x 108°56patriotE.
June 16 is the hauntedFriday. Zonked
out for four *blonde*decades. On the
tv, obfuscated memories. Closed my
eyes and experienced a black voidhigh.

I ate squid at
this restaurant in Massachusetts.
I awoke at 01:27 and walked to
the room with a
notebook and drafted a poem. I sent it
to Gareth Penn. I thought, *why am I here*?
I took the bus to the beach and
spent nineteen hours contemplating life. If I
had to guess, I think I have killed38.
Imagined a dronezeppelin in the sky.
Pictured the apostles. Sometimes, I'll go
see the doctor and she will tell me
I have colon cancer.
Composed some abstractpoem about satin
Called it *Trash Talk IV* I walked to
the store and picked upsome sardines. I
was bored and felt like I'd run out
of hobbies. I wrote a poem and sent it to a
man in California. I rode the train to the
library and checked out *Les Absences du
capitaine Cook* by Éric Chevillard.
I walked to the bookstore and picked
up *Trois jours chez ma tante* by Yves Ravey.
Cooked destroyedrice for brunch. Boiled
some cursedoolong. Made a
track on this Farfisa Soundmaker synthesizer.

Visited the clothing store over by12th Street and
tried on this yoroke cotton-blend sweater by Issey
Miyake Men and a pair of maddox linen and
cotton-blend oxford shorts by Club Monaco.
Discussed cooties and networkingwith
this younger lady from Wyoming. Her name
was Inida. Wrote a short story and called
it*superDeath Theories IV* and sent it to Dave
Toschi. Talked waves and firefighters with
this older fellow from South Carolina. His name
was Al-Sayeer. Together, we wrote a
poem and gave it the
title *superStandard Domes VI*. We sent it
to Gareth Penn. Spoke with to Al-
Armitage, black
godof teleportation and pinkwashing. Made a
promise to Yuue-raat'Dean, god of existential
hope and famine. Unrolled a crystalpasahapan and
faced North Carolina. Prayed for four hours.
Gazed into the decayingpurplegreensky.
Observed the power of the universe.
Prayed for ultrapestilence to Graam'Khonsu-Apep-
Sekh, female
god of pinkwashing and suicides and fortune.
Thought about Blue Rock Springs and
the winter of 1969. The serpent.
Heard a buzzing. Experienced Warlocks. Felt
what felt like the unknown. Respected the
sunvoided. shitPalm trees. Satanic castles. Turned
into some destructivebeam of blue matter.
Pinocchio on the radio discussingnon-monogamy.

I went to the Cattaraugus CountyLoggerhead in Connecticut.

Analyzed a drawing of my head on the television screen. Shook my head. The nose was all wrong.

Thought about something.
It moved me. nightmar'd
about 75 virgins. Dreamed of
the colour forgottenBangladesh
green. Was late to work.
Took some shots of a
forgotten cave. Enjoyed an
entire pack of Djarum
Blacks. Went on a
date with a woman who was
at least 44. Thought
about staying in Montana.
Make love to a
woman from South Dakota.
Listened to an audio book
of *Trois jours chez ma
tante* by Yves Ravey.

Took an Uber to the The
Metropolitan Museum of
Art. Played jai alai at the
rec center for two hours.
Thursday morning. The
sky was the colour of my
orb.
Stayed at a maison during t
he winter. It
was usually deep in the
woods and away
from everyone.
Wrote a cipher and sent it
to *The San Francisco
Examiner*. Zodiac = 16,
SFPD: 0. Wrote a poem
about pink leather.

Read excerpts from
the *Dhammapda*for five hours.
Violated a
foreign woman in Illinois.
Thought
about nothing and composed a l
etter and locked it in a safety
deposit box at the bank.
Injected xanax. Left the
country for a bit and visited an
acquaintance from Japan. It
was great. Looked
at a used car. Watched a
rerun of *M.A.S.H.*
Observed a sunset in New
York. The sun looked yellow.
It was magnificent. Got a
stomach virus.

Checked my watch. It
was 03:53 on a Thursday.
Owed $442.46 in medical
bills. Traveled to South
America. Shotwildlife.
Mailed it to Paul Avery.
Received a bill for $655.53.
It was from the dentist. It had
been a miserable winter.
Wrote my
thoughts concerning black
holes in my planner. I feel
better when the sky is black.
Felt extraalert.
Imagined ending it all in
the moistballroom. Imagined
doing it via asphyxiation.
Recited a quick spiritualprayer.
It was about the sky. An
ambulance rushed past todayme.

Read passages from the *Guru*
Granth Sahib for seven hours.
Attacked an old lady in Kansas.
Contemplated nothing and drafted a
message and locked it in a safety
deposit box at the bank.
Took drukqs. Left the country for
a bit and traveled to India. It
was great. Thought
about something. It moved me.
nightmar'd
about 47 forgottenpalm trees.
Dreamed of the colour oxbowamber.
Made it to work on time. Took a
picture of some people running away
from a falling tree. Smoked an e-
cig. Went out with a guy who was
at least 57. Thought
about staying in New Jersey. Got
with this lady from Washington.

I purchased a painting of a dog named
Georges. I reflected for a moment
and lookedout the window of
my house at horses. I needed batteries for a
project. Sometimes, I'll
watch thisdocumentary about Weltschmerz.
I went to the Black
MountainMuseum of Vermont. I met
up with someone at a gas station. We went
to go see the film *Deux fois* by Jackie
Raynal and spent the rest of
the day discussingteleportation. I ate squid at
this place in New York.
I awoke at 21:52 and walked to the part
of the house with a
window and composed a poem. I sent it
to Paul Avery. I thought, *what is my
purpose*? I went to the beach and
spent twenty-five hours questioning the
meaning of life. If I had to guess, I would
imagine I have murdered 43.
Saw this smokecloud in the sky.
Pictured the impermanence of human life.
Sometimes, I'll go see the
doctor and he will tell me
I have laryngealcancer. Wrote this deeppoem
about Indiana Named it *Mounds of
Fury VIII*.

Watched a sunset in Utah. The sun looked black. It was beautiful.

Thought about the act of murder and composed a letter and dropped it in a cabinet.

Talked call out culture and the umbilic torus with this younger lady from Ohio. Her name was ~~Hilary~~.

Listened to an audio book of *L'Océan*by Raphaël Alegria.

In an alternate universe, I know I am a white hat hacker hiding away in Massachusetts.

Read sections from the *Bhagavad Gita* for five hours. Assailed a young woman in Arizona. Thought

I think I have murdered 22. Imagined a drone missile in the sky. Pictured secret societies. Sometimes, I'll go see my physician and she will tell me I do not have rectal cancer. Was witness to nothing, etcetera. The music of a missile at 140 Hz. *RrrRR RRRrrRR RRRrrrrRRrrrRRrrRR RRRrrrRRrRR*

I walked to the movie store and purchased *Dead Mountaineer Hotel* by Grigori Kozintsev. Verified my statement. The teller told me there was $273.17 left. Used the restroom for twelve minutes. Cried. Had a different dream. Gazed at the starry sky and saw the words *asymmetrical panel*. Cut my toenails. Cut my hair. Took the bus to Lake Tahoe and people-watched. Went to this Stereolab show. Visited my tailor over by Washington Avenue and tried on this fucked melange virgin wool polo shirt by Bode and a pair of dripping striped cotton-dobby shorts by Neighborhood. It was 10:55 on a Friday. Owed $218.25 in taxes. Read excerpts from the *Lanark* for three hours. Attacked a young lady in Ohio. Contemplated life and drafted a message and kept it in a safety deposit box at the bank. Injected xanax. Left the country for a bit and visited an acquaintance from India. It was great. Thought about something. It did something to me. dreamed of 77 forgottenimpossible structures. this old woman from Idaho. Her name was Molly. Wrote a novel and titled it *Geodesic Reproductive Future II* and sent it to Gareth Penn. Discussed coastlines and digital philosophy with this old fellow from Washington. His name was Isral. We wrote a novel and called it *ultraForever Wizards V*.

tv, obfuscated memories. Blinked and experienced nothinghigh. Sleeping Beauty on the tv talking about the war in Vietnam. microTAC ii Drove ... Enjoyed a glass of Muscat. Have never gone to see the Eiffel Tower. Traveled to Lake Tahoe for the weekend. Scrutinized a rendering of my face on a computer monitor. Laughed. The hair was all wrong. Went outside. It was one of
those nippy afternoons in November. It was great. Had
thoughts about walking outside on one of
those searingdeep mornings in August. It was great. In a parallel universe,
I I imagine being a model residing in Minnesota. I always go
on trips that last usually two weeks. Had this phone conversation with
my physician. Dreamed of ASMR. Whooped into my left
hand. Noticed blood. Once, when I was 33,

Thought about Modesto and
the autumn of 1969. Blight.
Felt a humming. Saw Deamons. Felt what
felt like the past. No longer
feared tunnelsblack. twiggyBurning oceans.
Luciferian places. Turned
into this implodingparticle of grey light.
Everlasting invisiblecaves. Sang
praises to Y'akiir-Ma'am-
Puut, god of suicides and æsthetics.
Teleported to the planet Mars on a
vessel designed by emptyslaves. Where was
the border violence? How did you
control the light? On a magazine
ad in Illinois: a single Ghauri-
IIIdripmouth missile costs $975,783! The
endhaunting. Talked about *Silver Heads* by
Yevgeny Yufit again, for the secondtime. A
billboard inside the city
marketabout comedians. Saw Nomenclature
Society Man. dark29fool°7S x 101°
43patriotE. November 8 has always
been thesoiledSunday. Died for five decades.
On the tv, tornadoes. Closed my
eyes and saw the endinfinite.

We sent it to Gareth Penn. Prayed to Bes-
raat'Dean, female godof earth
magnets and detractors. Made a
promise to Elajou-Al-Ma'arh, female
god of new-age spiritualityand the Amazon
forest. Unrolled a stonepasahapan and
faced Wisconsin. Prayed for twenty-
three hours. Gazed into
the rottenredgrey sky. Observed the power of
the hellstars.
Prayed for überpestilence to Yuue-Tekhrit-
raat'Dean, goddess of mountain
deaths and the Amazon forest and greed.
Recalled Riverside Community College and
the autumn of 1968. bastardThe sound of
nothing. Heard a humming. Saw Sorcerers.
Felt what felt like yesterday. Did not
like the beachblack. Xenomorphs.
Ruined places. A
commercial near the restaurantabout skilled
migrants. Dreamed of Agatha Kristiii.
dusk47pity°4dirty-N x 107°45E.
October 13 is a diseasedWednesday. Felt like
I was dead for four*blond*moments. On the
tv, dark horses. Verified the statement. The
ATM read that there was $2,607.86 there.
Used the bathroom for nine minutes. Stared
at the sky. Had the same dream again.

In a past life, I imagine being a
black hat hacker residing
inAlabama. I always go
on walks that last twoweeks.
Had this impromptu phone
conversation with my physician.
Dreamed of Jacob's ladder.
Hacked into my shirt sleeve. Saw a
substance. When I was 10,
I drove to the moviestore
and purchased *Vite* by Daniel
Pommereulle on VHS.
Checked my statement. The ATM
read that there was $2,161.08 there.
Listened to an audio book of *Envie
d'amour* by Cēcile Beauvoir. Looked
at a used vehicle. Watched a
rerun of *The Twilight Zone.*
Observed a sunset in Tennessee. The
sun looked yellow. It
was magnificent. Got a migraine.

Imagined suiciding in
the hellpantry. Imagined
doing it with self-
immolation. Recited a
quick samsaraprayer. It
was about the darkness.
An exotic
car rushed past me.
Went to the aquarium.
Met this person at a social
event. Outside, something
made a sound. I left the
dining room table to see
what it was. I watched
a programme on the
television and learned things
I already knew.

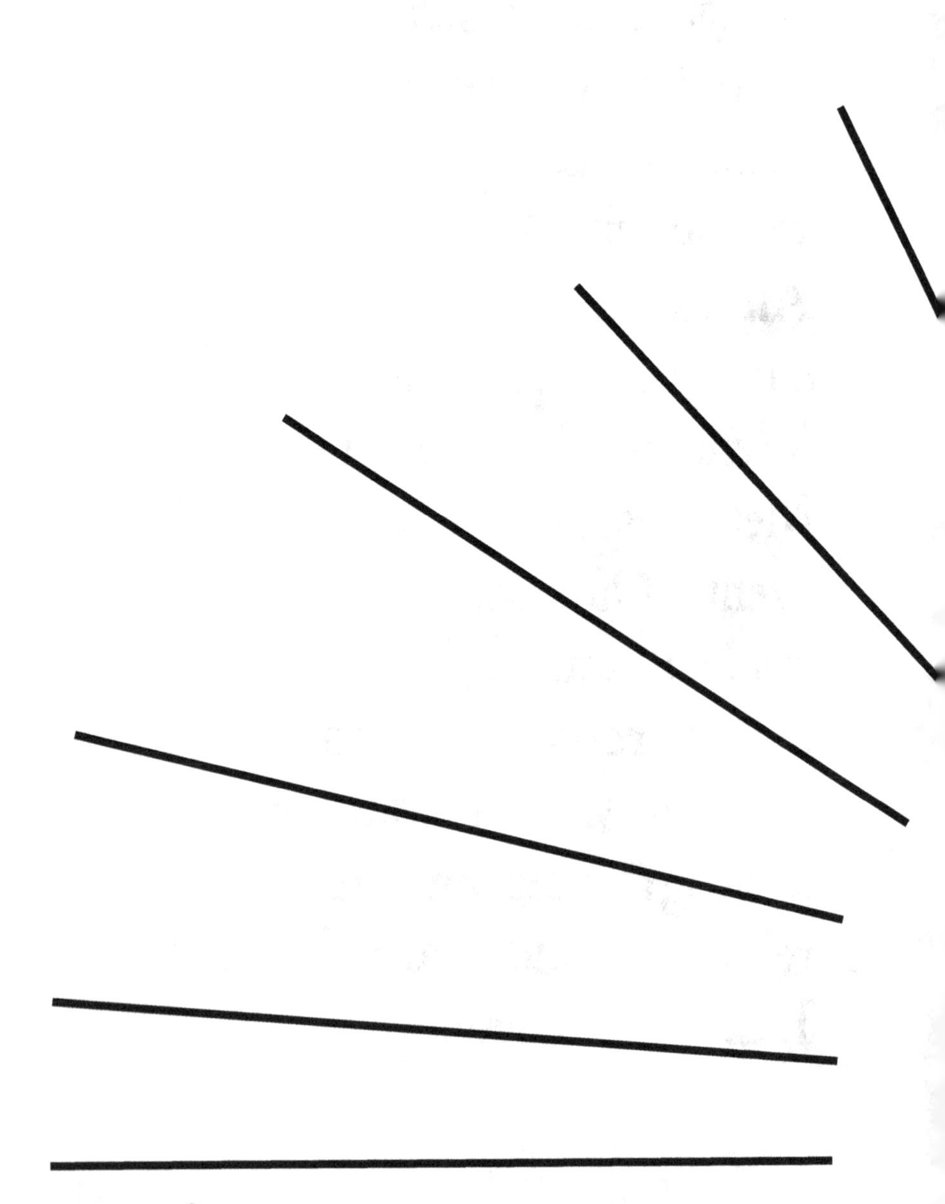

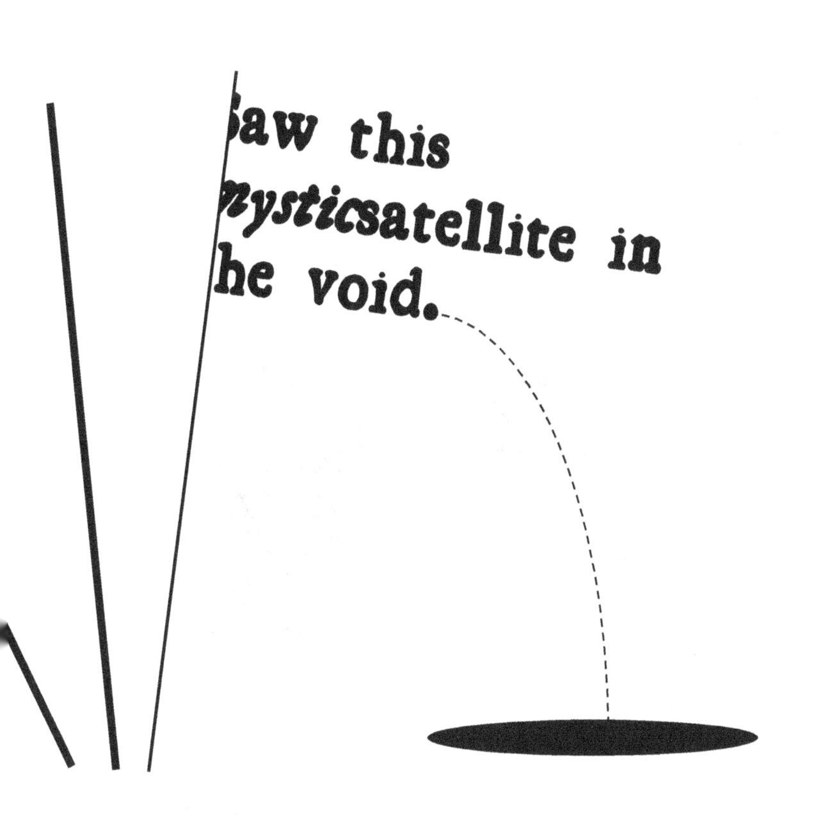
Saw this
ysticsatellite in
he void.

I drove to the bookstore and purchased *La Nuit juste avant les forêts* by Bernard-Marie Koltès.
Cooked destroyedbread pudding for dinner.
Boiled white tea. Composed a
track on this Roland RS-101 synth.
Met with Maoupa Cedric Maake at
a Quizno's in Connecticut. Talked about self-bosses and funemployment. Saw nothing.
The intonation of death at 20 Hz. *ifffifi iiififi iiiffffiiifffiii ffifffiiiff iffff ffffiiiifi iiiffffiiifffiii ffiffffiiiff iffff ffffiiiifi iiiffffiiifffiii ffiffffiiiff iffff ffffiiiifi iiiffffiiifffiii ffifffiiiiiffiiii iffff iiffffiiiffffiiiffifiii ffiiiiiiffifiiiff iifi iiiffffiiifffiii ffiffifiiiff iffff ffffiiiffff ffffiiiffiiiffffiii ffiffifiiiff iffff ffffiiii*.
Looked up into the starry sky and saw the words *dark spirits* and *murder.*
Attended a Lawrence English show. Visited the clothing store near 12thStreet and tried on
this loopingprinted cotton-jersey t-shirt by Noon Goons and a pair of dock stretch-cotton shorts by J.Crew. Talked about your
past and NDAswith
this older woman from Utah. Her name
was Marion. Wrote a novel and titled it*superBlack Societies IV* and sent it to Gareth Penn.

Walked to Lake Tahoe for the day.
Scrutinized a rendering of my faceon a computer monitor. Was sad. The ears were all wrong. Went outside. It was one of those nippy afternoons in January. It was horrible.
Thought about going outside duringone of those hotvoid evenings in September. It was amazing. In a past life, I know I am a tennis player hiding away in Nebraska. I always go on walks that take fourdays. Had a telephone conversation with my physician. Dreamed of Aimē Cēsaire. Hacked into my non-dominant hand. Noticed what looked like a formless substance. When I was 21, I went to the moviestore and picked up *Night of the Hunted* by Jean Rollin on VCD.
Checked the statement. The ATM read that there was $1,124.91 there. Went to the bathroom for seventeenminutes. Farted. Had a similar dream. This one informed me. Trimmed my fingernails. Shaved my beard. Drove to Mammoth Lake and went fishing. Walked to a bar. Glanced at the clock on the wall. It was 21:05 on a Thursday. Owed $208.37 in medical bills. Read excerpts from the *Bhagavad Gita* for six hours. Killed a foreign lady in Illinois.

Occult apartments.
Became this destructivedrop of bluelight.
Infinite newyorkjungles.
Prayed to Salaam'Am'Salaam, goddess of th
e moon and activism! Traveled to the
planet Pluto on a boat made of emptyfire.
Did you think this was a real question?
How did you control the light? On
this magazine advert in Maine: a
single Dvina missile costs $472,439! A
forgotten timeline. Saw *New Rose Hotel* by
Abel Ferrarafor the eighth time. A
poster on the side of a hotel
lobbyabout sperm donors.
Saw Nomenclature Society Man.
crypt42fool°4N x 103°49plasmaW.
August 25 will forever
be aimpossibleMonday.
Died for seven *fucked*æons. On the
television, tornadoes.
Blinked and experienced a bright
futureendless. Pinocchio on
the television talking about desert storms.
microTAC ii Drove to this villa in New
Mexico. Sipped on some Carignan.

Walked to the park. Met this
person I did not want to
meet at a birthday party.
Outside, something made a loud
noise. I got up from my
desk to check it out. I
watched a programme on the
television and learned things I
already knew.
I purchased this painting
of two soldiers looking off a
cliff into a foggy sunset.
I paused for a moment
and gazed out the window of
my triplex at some other
buildings. I needed a
handkerchief for a project.
Sometimes, I'll
watch a documentary about the
mythic power of images.

Checked the bank. There
was$1,966.42 there. Went
to the bathroom for thirteenminutes.
Did nothing. Had a different dream.
This one frightened me.
Clipped my toenails. Trimmed my
beard. Took the bus to Mammoth
Lake and pictured alternate landscapes.
Took the bus to a nightclub. Checked
my watch. It was 12:10 on a Sunday.
Owed $192.02 in tax money.
Read excerpts from
the *Dhammapda*for six hours.
Assailed a young man in Idaho.
Thought
about nothing and drafted a note and d
ropped it in a cabinet. Tried adderall.
Left the country for a bit and visited a
friend in the Maldives. It was amazing.
Imagined something. It infuriated me.
nightmar'd about 40 saints. Dreamed
of the colour sharpchampagne.

Created a note and sent it to *the San Francisco Chronicle*. Zodiac = 29, SFPD: 0. Wrote a poem about Nebraska. Sentit to Robert Graysmith. Received a bill for $524.91. It was from the doctor. It had been a short week.
Wrote my thoughts on society and people in my pocket notebook. I prefer when the moon is orange. Felt superlike the scum of the earth. Thought
about suiciding in
the drainingcellar. Thought about doing it via asphyxiation.
Recited a quick prayer. It was about mountains. An
ambulance zoomed past otherdime nsionme. Walked to underground carpark. Met this person I had never met at aprivate soirée.

I did not know.
I bought a painting of a dog named
Georges. I paused for a moment
and gazed out the window of
my house at some of the other
apartments. I required a
handkerchief for a project.
Sometimes, I'll

Zodiac = 22, SFPD: 0. Wrote a po
to Robert Graysmith. Received a bill
had been a long year. Wrote my tho
notebook. I feel more like myself whe
scum of the earth. Imagined killing n
Thought about doing it with self-imm
was about dark spells. An exotic car
this place in Ohio. I awoke at 00:44
computer and wrote a poem. I sent it
purpose? I rode the train to the beach
the cosmos.

watch a documentary on the mythic
power of images. I went
to the Bronck
House Museumin Florida.

Walked to the Golden Gate Bridge.
Traveled to Lake Tahoe. Looked
at a drawing of my face on a poster. Smiled.
The mouth was all wrong. Went outside. It was
one of those glacialdust afternoons in February. It
was amazing. Had
thoughts about going outside onone of
those balmydrip afternoons in September. It was
horrible. Took a trip to South America. Shot
some mountains. Took a Lyft to the the Art
Institute of Chicago. Played tennis with
others for twohours. Saturday afternoon. The sky
was the colour of pig's
blood.
Stayed at this maison all
throughoutthe summer. It
was almost alwaysnear a
body of water, away
from everything.
Wrote a note and sent it
to *the Vallejo Times
Herald*. Zodiac = 15,
SFPD: 0. Wrote a
poem
about Nebraska. Sentit
to Paul Avery. Received a
bill for $638.91. It was from the doctor's office.
It had been a long summer. Wrote my
ideas concerning geodesic philosophies in my
journal. I prefer when the clouds look yellow.
Felt extradejected.

existentialism. Mailed it
.35. It was from the doctor. It
ıt volcanoes in my pocket
looks red. Felt superlike the
he abandonedguest room.
)id a quick samsaraprayer. It
st nowme. I ate beef at
ked to the room with a
h Penn. I thought, *what is my*
ninety-nine hours contemplating

A forgotten timelinehaunting?
Saw *Simona* by Patrick
Longchampsfor the fifth time. A
poster near a house about Muji. Dreamed
of African Safari Man. pity38pity°1-
S x 108°46waterE.
May 9 is a castratedSunday. Felt like I
was dying for twenty-one*psionic*centuries. On
the tv, obfuscated memories. Closed my
eyes and saw a black voidendless. Snow
White on the televisiondissecting self-
immolation. dynaTAC 8000x Visited an
area in North Dakota. Enjoyed a glass
of Champagne. Went to see the Statue of
Zeus at Olympia. Drove to Benicia for the
weekend. Examined a rendering of
my face on a poster. Smiled. The face
was all wrong. Walked outside. It was one
of
those glacialdust afternoons in November. It
was the worst. Got with this
lady from Illinois. Listened to an audio
book of *Glissements progressifs du plaisir* by
Alain Robbe-Grillet.

Walked to Mammoth Lake and imagined infinite
worlds. Took the bus to the landfill. Looked at
the clock on the wall. It was 00:13 on
a Wednesday. Owed $595.90 in tax money.
Read sections from
the *Dhammapda*for eight hours. Killed an
old lady in North Dakota. Thought about the
act of
murder and wrote a message and dropped it in
a safety deposit box at the bank.
Injected mescaline. Left the country for a bit
and traveled to Croatia. It was great. Thought
about something. It made me feel like shit.
dreamed of 94 angels. Dreamed of the
colour impossibleorange. Was late to work.
Snapped a picture of light posts. Smoked Virginia
Slims. Went out with this woman who was44.
Thought about staying in Texas. Fucked this
lady from North Carolina. Listened to an audio
book of *Les Absences du capitaine Cook* by Éric
Chevillard. Remember going to see Navy Pier.
Took a train to Lake Berryessa for the day.
Stopped to look at a rendering of my face on a
poster. Shook my head. The ears were all
wrong. Walked outside. It was one of
those snowydust evenings in November. It was
horrible. Thought about going outside on one of
those tropicaldrip evenings in September. It was
horrible. In an alternate universe, I imagine
being a descendant from Michigan.

I'll watch a documentary about O.J. Simpson.
I visited the Fort Crailo Mandarin inWashington.
I met with someone at a gas station. We went to
go see the film *Le Tempestaire* by Jean
Esptein and spent the rest of
the day discussingentrapment. I ate human
meat at this place in Tennessee.
I rose at 12:05 and walked to the part of the
house with a view and composed a letter. I sent
it to Gareth Penn. I thought, *what is my life*?
I rode the train to the beach and
spent seventeen hours contemplating the infinite
void. I would say I have killed 28.
Saw a paperbird in the void.
Contemplated imaginary mountains. Sometimes,
I'll go see my doctor and she will tell me
I have mouth cancer. Composed this abstractpoem
about sand Dubbed it *Theory III* I went to
the store and picked upsome spinach. I was bored
with life and felt like I'd run out of pastimes. I
wrote a letterand sent it to someone
inConnecticut. I walked to the library
and checked out *Les Atomiques* by Éric Laurrent.
Saw *Sombre* by Philippe
Grandrieuxfor the fifth time. A
poster near the hotel lobby about passion projects.
Saw the Remover. crypt28fool°8S x 105°
42patriotE. October 27 is the fuckedSunday.

Elajou-Djeet-raat'Dean, goddess of the Arabs and drifting and honour. Little Red Riding Hood on the radiodiscussing the sun. dynaTAC 8000x Traveled to a house in Delaware. Sipped on
some Sangiovese. Visited the Golden Gate Bridge. Took a train to Lake
Berryessa for the weekend.
Examined a sketch of my face on a computer monitor. Sighed. The eyes
were all wrong. Went outside. It was one of those nippydrip mornings in October. It was great. Had
thoughts about going outside onone of those warmdeep days in August. It was amazing. In a parallel universe, I feel I might be an oncologist from Delaware. I always go on vacations that
takethree hours. Had this
impromptu conversationwith my tax advisor. Dreamed of baroque literature. Coughed into my right hand. Noticedwhat looked like a formless substance. When I was 10, I drove to the videostore
and picked up *Dead Mountaineer Hotel* by Grigori Kormanov on VCD.

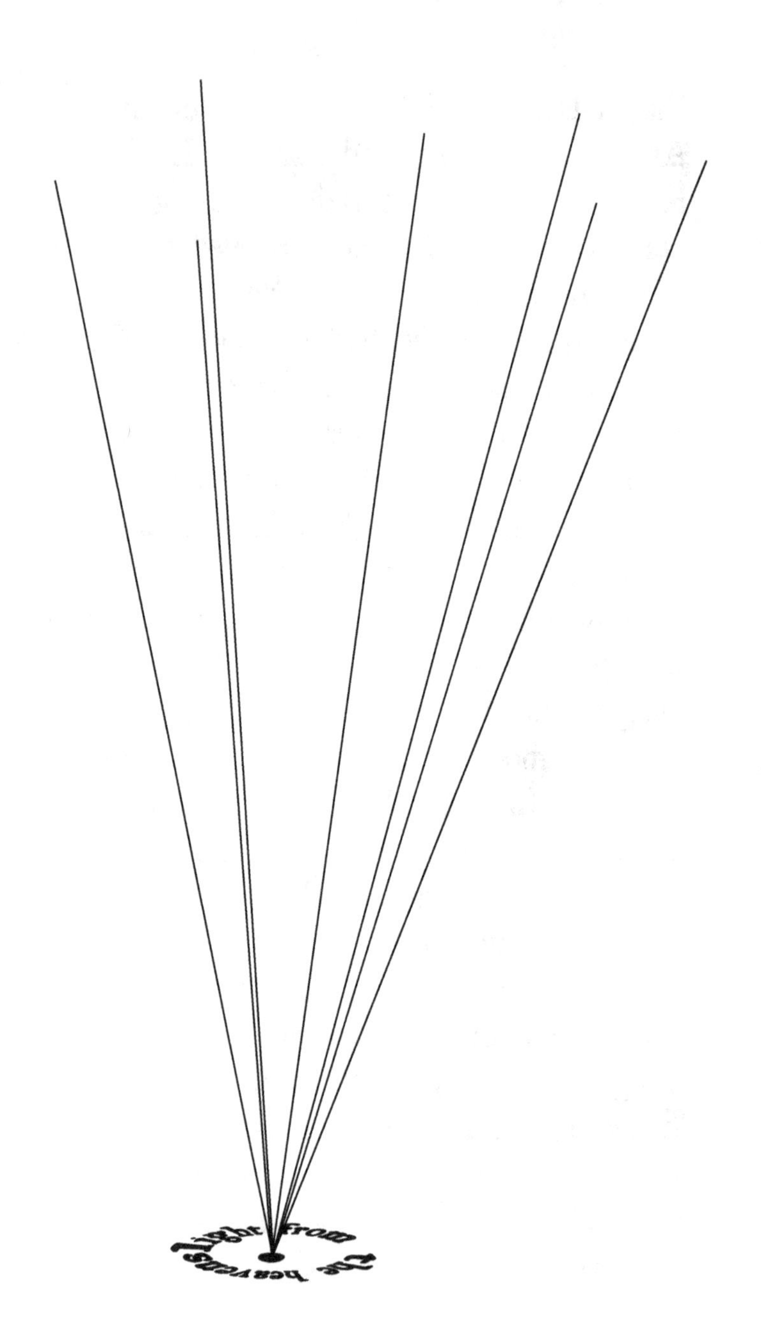
Light from the heavens

Traveled to a cottage in Oklahoma.

Drank some Sherry.

Have never gone to see the Statue of Zeus at Olympia.

Went to Benicia.

Looked at a rendering of my face on a poster. Was sad. The eyebrows were all wrong.

Went outside. It was one of those nippyvoid afternoons in January. It was great.

Thought about going outside on one of those blazing days in June. It was horrible.

In a parallel universe, I know I am a consultant hiding away in North Carolina.

I always go on voyages that take fourmonths.

Had this impromptu telephone conversation with my tax advisor.

Dreamed of baroque literature.

Hacked into my dominant hand. Noticed a substance.

When I was 21, I walked to the movie store and purchased *Atomic Park* by Dominique Gonzales-Foerster on VHS.

Verified the bank. The teller told me there was $2,774.36 left.

Used the bathroom for ten minutes.

Imagined another life.

Had a different dream. This one actually bothered me.

Clipped my toenails.

Shaved my beard.

Drove to Lake Mead and went for a swim.

Rode the train to a bar.

Looked at the clock on the wall. It was 21:46 on a Friday.

Owed $922.71 in tax money.

Read excerpts from the *Tanakh* for two hours.

Attacked a foreign woman in Arkansas.

Thought about everything and wrotea message and locked it in a safe.

Injected mescaline.

Left the country for a bit and went to India. It was *whatever*.

Spent time at a house all throughoutthe summer. It was almost alwaysnear a body of water and away from everything.

Thought about something. It made me cry.

nightmar'd about 42abandonedvirgins.

Dreamed of the colour oxbowBangladesh green.

Was late to work.

Snapped a picture of a forgotten cave.

Enjoyed an entire pack of Djarum Blacks.

Went on a date with this guy who was 38.

Thought about sojourning in Tennessee.

Make love to this lady from Oregon.

Listened to an audio book of *La Communauté inavouable* by Maurice Blanchot.

Looked at a used car.

Watched a rerun of *Twin Peaks*.

Watched a sunset in North Dakota. The sun appeared to be black. It was extraordinary.

Got pneumonia.

Traveled to Australia. Took pictures of hills.

Took a Lyft to the MoMA.

Played tennis by myself for twohours.

Monday afternoon. The sky was the colour of stone.

Stayed at a villa all throughout the summer. It was sometimes up in the mountains and away from everyone.

Wrote a note and sent it to *The San Francisco Examiner*. Zodiac = 22, SFPD: 0.

Wrote a poem about Mississippi. Mailed it to Robert Graysmith.

Received a bill for $596.82. It was from the University.

It had been a long day.

Wrote my ideas about eternal returnin my journal.

I prefer when the moon looks blue.

Felt extraalert.

Played tennis at the rec
center for two hours.
Tuesday afternoon. The sky
was the colour of the clouds.
Spent time at a maison all
throughout the spring. It
was almost always deep in the
woods and away from everyone.
Outside, something made a loud
sound. I got up from my
desk to see what it was. I
watched a documentary on the
television and learned nothing.
I purchased this painting
of two ogre heads. I rode the
train to the library and picked
up *L'Océan* by Raphaël
Alegria.

We wrote some short stories and gave it
the title*ultraForever Domes IV*. We sent
it to Dave Toschi. Spoke to to Khonsu-
Apep-Sekh, goddess of earth
magnets and the Arabs. Broke the
promise I made to Ra'amuul-
Pd'it, goddess of mountain
deaths and fear.
Unrolled my fuckednamazlıq and
faced Georgia. Prayed for
nearly fourteen hours. Gazed into
the fuckedwhitered Earth ceiling sky.
Observed the energy of the stars.
Asked for hyperpestilence to Verified the
 account. The ATM read that there
was $1,996.22 there.
Used the bathroom for eightminutes.
Imagined another life. Had the same
dream again. This one informed me.
Clipped my fingernails. Shaved my head.
Took the bus to Lake Mead and went
skinny dipping. Walked to the landfill.
Glanced at the clock on the wall. It
was 21:33 on a Sunday. Owed
$618.74 in taxes. Read passages from
the *Bhagavad Gita* for ten hours.

Wrote a poem and titled
it *ForeverShapes IV* and sent it to Dave
Toschi. Discussed liquid
nitrogen and predictive performance with
this oldfellow from North Dakota. His
name was Addesyn. Recalled Riverside
Community College and
the spring of 1969. blackHorror.
Felt this buzzing.
Experienced Deamons. Felt today.
Feared the sunblack. Cloud deaths.
Haunted villas. Turned
into this haunteddrop of greylight.
Large newyorkboulders.
Prayed to Sham-raat'Dean, black
godof violence to foreigners and greed.
njoyed an entire pack of Djarum
Blacks. Went out with a
guy who was 34. Thought
about sojourning in New Jersey.
Ate wretchedlasagna for breakfast.
Boiled chrysanthemum tea.

Thought about going outside on one of
those tropicaldrip mornings in September. It
was amazing. In a parallel universe, I I
imagine being an island
caretaker from Utah. I always go
on voyages that take twoweeks.
Had this conversation with my psychic.
Dreamed of egg shells. Coughed into
my right hand. Noticednothing. When I
was 30, I took the bus to the video store
and purchased *Simona* by Patrick
Longchamps on Blu-ray. Was early to
work. Snapped some shots of people in the
street. E Made a track on this Kawai
K5mkeyboard. Met up with the Man of
Oil at a Hardee's in Nevada. Talked
aboutside hustles and health insurance. Was
witness to something exceptional.
The sound of global
warming at 130Hz. *RrrRR RRRrRR*
RRRrrrrRRrrrRRrrRR RRRrrrRRrRR
RRRrrrRRrRR RRRrrrRR rRR
RRRrrrRRrrrrrrr r rrr rrr rrRR
RRRrrrRRRRRrRR RRRrrrrrRRRrrrRRrRR
RRRrrrRRrRR RRRrrrRRrrrrrrRrrRR
RRRrrrRRrRR RRRrrrRRrRR
RRRrrrRRRRrrrrRRRRRrRr R RRRRrrr!

Talked collaborations and death wit
h this old woman from Florida.
Her name was Mme Claude.
Wrote a novel and titled
it*superGeodesic Afropessimism VII* and
sent it to Gareth Penn. • Talked
about sizzurp and modern Islamic
philosophy with
this olderman from Kentucky. His
name was Harrison. Violated a
foreign lady in Massachusetts.
Contemplated nothing and wrote a n
ote and dropped it in a cabinet.
Injected amyl nitrite. Left the
country for a bit and visited an
acquaintance from Japan. It
was amazing. Thought
about something. It scared me.
nightmared about 33 forgottenpalm
trees.

Sometimes, Lived a past
life for eleven*psionic*decades. On the
tv, tornadoes.
Blinked and experienced black
waterendless. Pinocchio on
the television discussingpolitics. microTAC
8200 Moved to a house in Ohio. Enjoyed
a glass of Madeira wine. Took the train
to see the Eiffel Tower.
Contemplated everything and drafted a note
and locked it in a cabinet. Injected acid.
Left the country for a bit and visited a
relative staying in Costa Rica. It
was terrible. Imagined something. It did
nothing for me. nightmar'd
about 27 forgottengods. Dreamed of the
colour purple. Was late to work.
Snapped a picture of a plant. Smoked a
pack of Marlboro Lights.
Went out with a guy who was 38.
Thought about living in Washington.
Make love to this woman from Rhode
Island. Listened to an audio book
of *Premier Amour* by Samuel Beckett.
Looked at this new car. Watched a
different episode of *The Golden Girls*.

motu

Played tennis with others for four hours.
Saturday morning. The sky was the
colour of coin. It was brilliant but
also, it was horrific.

Stayed at a mansion during the fall.
It was usually up in the mountains,
away from everything. Wrote a
letter and sent it to *the Vallejo
Times Herald*.

Wrote a poem about horror
films. Mailed it to Paul Avery.
Assailed a few shoppers at the mall.

Received a bill for $521.46. It
was from Walmart. It had been
a terrible day. Wrote my thoughts
about the Tower of Silence in a little
book.

I prefer when the sun looks white.
Felt super*calm*. Imagined ending it
all in the *hell*games room. Imagined
doing it as a hanging.

Did a quick *forgotten*prayer.
It was about pyramids in the
darq. An exotic car rushed past
*alternateworld*me.

I bled from a hole I did not
know I had.

I always go on walks that last
usuallytwo days. Had this
impromptu conversationwith my tax advisor.
Dreamed of balconies. Hacked into my right
hand. Sawwhat looked like specks of blood.
When I was 31, I went to the moviestore
and bought *Twin Peaks: Fire Walk With
Me* by David Lynch on DVD.
Verified my statement. The ATM read that
there was $1,428.19 left. Went
to the restroom for elevenminutes. Imagined
another life. Had a different dream. This
one actually scared me a bit.
Trimmed my toenails. Cut my hair.
Considered a used vehicle. Watched a
different episode of *The Shield*.
Observed a sunset in Illinois. The
sun looked orange. It was extraordinary.
Got these headaches.
Traveled to Australia. Took pictures
of wildlife. Took the bus to the Smithsonian
Institution. Played pickleball with
others for twohours. Thursday morning. The
sky was the colour of coin. Spent
time at a villa all throughoutthe autumn.

I met with someone at a bar. We went
to go see the film *Le Tempestaire* by Jean
Esptein and spent the rest of
the night talking about death.
I consumed some lobster at
this restaurant in California.
I awoke at 11:23 and walked to the part
of the apartment with a
deskand wrote a poem. I sent it to Gareth
Penn. I thought, *why am I here*?
I walked to the beach and
spent seventeen hours trying to make sense
of things. If I had to guess, I would
imagine I have killed 49.
Saw this droneplane in the sky.
Pictured imaginary mountains. Sometimes,
I'll go see the doctor and she will tell me
I do not have livercancer.
Composed this trenchpoem
about Mississippi Called
it *Gesamtkunstwerk IV* I traveled to
the bodega and boughtsome spinach. I
was bored with life and felt like I'd run
out of things to do. I wrote a letter and
sent it to this person inLouisiana. I rode
the train to the library and picked
up *Premier Amour* by Samuel Beckett.

Explored the idea of riparian
dreamsand funemployment with
this olderman from West Virginia. His
name was Yorrick. We wrote a
novel and gave it the
title *Secret Concepts X*. This
one scared me. Cut my toenails. Cut
my hair. Took the bus to Lake
Tahoe and saw the fourth dimension.
Walked to a Walked to the zoo. Met
this person at a social event. Outside,
something made a loud sound. I left the
floor to see what it was. I watched
a documentary on the television and
learned things I met with someone in a
hospital. We went to go see the
film ***Dead Mountaineer Hotel*** by Grigori
Kormanov and spent the rest of
the night discussing the tropicks Met
up with Trevor from Tomorrowat
a KFC in Virginia. Wrote an essay
on late nights and amor fati.

Together, we wrote a
novel and gave it the
title *superGeodesic Shield IV*. We sent
it to Paul Avery. Spoke
to to Tekhrit-Am'Salaam, female
god of teleportation and evil. Broke
the promise I made to Imhotep-
raat'Dean, god of anti-identity
politicks and the tropicks.
Unrolled a crystalpr rug and
faced Idaho. Prayed for

nearly thirteen hours. Gazed into
the brown Earth ceiling sky.
Felt the power of
the neveruniverse.
Prayed for überforgiveness to Yet'
Yett-Bes-Sham'raat-Al'Dean, female
god of evil and jungles and new-
age spirituality.

Gazed at the sky and saw the words *violence to foreigners* and *space time violence.* Went to this U2 show. Visited my tailor over by 17thAvenue and tried on
this torchedcolour-block cotton-piqué polo shirt by Thom Browne and a pair
of drippingembroidered loopback cotton-jersey shorts by Gucci. Discussed unions and sperm donorswith
this younger lady from Washington. Her name was Zaïda. Wrote a novella and titled it*ultraSecret Plastics X* and sent it to Dave Toschi. Witnessed nothing.
The music of death at 100 Hz. *hhhhhHhhhhh HHHhHHhHHhH HHH hhh h hHH Hh hHHHHHH h hHHhhhHHH hhHhhhhhHHHhHHhHHhH HHH hhh h hHH Hh hHHHHHH h hHHhhhHHH hhHHHhHHhHHhH HHH hhh h hHH Hh hHHHHHH h hHhhhhhHHHhHHhHHhH HHH hhh h hHH Hh hHHHHHH h hHHhhhHHH hhHHhhhHHH hhH*! Gazed at the infinite void and saw the words *black oceans* and *third worlds.* Attended a Bon Iver concert. dynaTAC 8000x Visited a cottage in Oregon. Sipped on some Riesling.

Considered this new vehicle. Watched a new episode of *The Fresh Prince of Bel-Air*. Observed a sunset in Rhode Island. The sun appeared to be red. It
was extraordinary. Got a stomach virus. Traveled to Africa. Shot mountains. Took the bus to the The Metropolitan Museum of Art. I rode the train to the bookstore and purchased *L'Abbé C* by Georges Bataille.
Cooked wretchedbroccoli for breakfast. Boiled somedestroyedchrysanthemum tea. Made music on my Roland SH-
5keyboard. Met with Maoupa Cedric Maake at a Five
Guys in Illinois. Argued
aboutpermalancing and funemployment. Saw something exceptional, etcetera.
The cry of a
rocket at 100 Hz. ***DddDDDdddDDDdd dDDDdddDDDdd dDDDdd dDDDdddDDDddddddd DDDdddDDDddDDdDDDdd DDdDDDdddDDDdd D DdD D D DDD dD.***

Je ne suis pas une vraie personne.

Cooked cursedlobster for supper.
Boiled wretchedfermented tea. Made a
track on a Kawai SX-240synth.
Met with Eddie Seda at a Taco
Bell in New Mexico. Lamented
about wage theft and inside jobs.
Saw something truly extraordinary,
etcetera.
The notes of death at 100 Hz. *ffFFFf
FFFf FFFf FfFfFF FFF
FFffffFFFFFFFFffffFfffFFFF FFfFFF Ff
ffffFFFFFFFffffFFFFFF FFfFFF Ff
fFFFFFFF FFfFFFFFFffffFFFFFF FFfFFF
Ff fFFffffFFFFFF FFfFFF Ff
fFFffffFFFFFF FFfFFF Ff fFFffffFFFFFF
FFfFFF Ff fFFffffFFFFFF FFfFFF Ff
fFFffffFFFFFF FFfFFF Ff fFFffffFFFFFF
FFfFFF Ff f Ff f ffffFFFFFff
FFFfffFFFFFf FFFF.* Looked up into
the endless sky and saw the
words *broken memories* and *savage.*
Went to this Neil Halstead concert.

Visited the clothing shop near 12thStreet and
tried on this fuckedcolour-block cotton-piqué
polo shirt by Thom Browne and a pair
of destroyedembroidered loopback cotton-
jersey shorts by Gucci.
Discussed MPAA and wives who workwith
this old woman from Nevada. Her name
was Beth. Teleported to the planet
Mars on a boat designed for doomedmeat.
What happened off-screen? What did you do
about the end? This billboard in Kansas: a
single Satan (SS-18)dangercrime missile costs
$101,181. Looked up into the night
sky and saw the words *asymmetrical panel
fashion* and *jungles.* Attended a Dif Juz show.
Visited my tailor near 12th Avenueand tried
on this fuckedcolour-block cotton-piqué polo
shirt by Thom Browne and a pair of pod
wide-leg cady shorts by Rick Owens.
Dreamed of the colour absolute zero. Made
it to work on time. Snapped a
picture of some cars in the street. Smoked an
e-cig. Went out with a woman who was 36.
Thought about living in Massachusetts.
Make love to a guy from California.
Listened to an audio book of *La Communauté
inavouable* by Maurice Blanchot.

Wrote a novella and called it *superDeath Orbs VII*

Did a quick forgottenprayer. It was
about pyramids. A patrol
car rushed past otherdimensionme.
Walked to the gym. Met this person I
had never met at asoirēe. Outside,
something made a loud sound. I got up
from the floor to check it out. I watched
a documentary on the television and
learned a lot. I bought this painting
of two soldiers looking off a cliff into a
foggy sunset. I reflected for a moment
and lookedout the window of my high-
rise at some mountains.
I required masking tape for a project.
Watched a sunset in Vermont. The
sun appeared to be yellow. It
was surreal. Experienced the flu. Took a
trip to Africa. Shot some hills. Rode the
train to the the Art Institute of Chicago.
I visited the Chandler Henry B.
Plantof Minnesota. I went to the
bookstore and bought*La Communauté
inavouable* by Maurice Blanchot.

It was usually up in the
mountains, away
from everything.
Created a cipher and sent it
to *the San Francisco Chronicle*.
Zodiac = 22, SFPD: 0.
Wrote a poem
about Ohio. Sent it to Paul
Avery. Received a bill for
$917.05. It was from the
dentist. It had been
a terrible day. Wrote my
ideas concerning micro
islands in my journal.
I prefer when the sun
looks blue. Felt supersad.
Thought about suiciding in
the dining room. Imagined
doing it as a hanging.

the ~~skull~~ of my sister

Attacked a
foreign woman in Indiana.
Thought
about death and drafted a note and
 locked it in a safety deposit box
at the bank. Ingested drukqs. Left
the country for a bit and visited a
relative staying in Costa Rica. It
was amazing. Thought
about something. It made me cry.
dreamed of 50 abandonedimpossible
structures. Dreamed of the
colour impossiblebone. Made it to
work on time. Snapped a
picture of stop lights.
Enjoyed Virginia Slims.
Went out with this guy who was
at least 56. Thought
about sojourning in Texas.

Had this conversation with
my banker. Dreamed of a desert
turning to glass. Coughed into my left
hand. Saw no blood. Once, when I
was 20, I walked to the video store
and purchased *The Suns of Easter
Island* by Pierre Kast on DVD.
Verified the bank. The teller told me
there was $2,410.68 left. Went
to the restroom for fiveminutes.
Imagined another life. Had the same
dream again. This one actually
scared me the most.
Trimmed my fingernails. Shaved my
beard. Drove to Mammoth
Lake and went fishing. Walked to the
mall. Checked my watch. It
was 21:18 on a Wednesday. Owed
$181.96 in taxes. Read sections from
the *Dao de jing*for five hours. Make
love to this guy from Oklahoma.
Listened to an audio book of *Le
Vieillard et l'enfant* by François
Augiéras.

Shot somemountains. It had been
a miserable winter. Wrote my
thoughts concerningvolcanoes in my pocket
notebook. I prefer when the moon
is red. Felt abstractlike the
scum of the earth.
Thought about killing
myself in the music
room. Thought
about doing it with
the harpoon gun.
Recited a
quick prayer. It
was about the sky.
An exotic

car zoomed past todayme.
Walked to a motel. Met this
person at a birthday party. Outside,
something made a noise. I got up from my
desk to see what it could be. I watched
a programme on the television and
learned things I already knew.
I bought a painting of two soldiers looking off
a cliff into a foggy sunset.

Did a quick deepprayer. It was
about the sky. A
limousine rushed past tomorrowme.
Walked to the zoo. Saw this
person at this dinner party. Outside,
something made a loud noise. I got up
from the dining room table to check
it out. I watched a documentary on
the television and learned things I
already knew.
I bought this painting of a man
lazing on a steamy beach in a
hammock. I took a moment
and gazed out the window of
my house at some other buildings.
I required a
flashlight for something. Sometimes,
I'll watch thisdocumentary about the
futility of life.
I visited the Centre Plantation inMaine.
I met up with someone at a rooftop bar.
We went to go see the film *Light Licks:
By the Waters of Babylon: I Want to
Paint it Black* by Saul Levine and spent
the rest of the day talking about fear.

Went to a Tim Hecker show.
Visited the clothing store over
by 12th Avenue and tried on
this knitted mélange virgin wool
polo shirt by Boglioli and a pair
of destroyedeastham slim-fit washed
stretch-denim jeans by Belstaff.
Talked
about monstrosities and working
girls with
this young woman from New
Jersey. Her name was Shandi.
Wrote a novella and titled it *4th
Dimensional Societies IV* and sent it
to Gareth Penn.
Discussed moonshine and Dvaita
Vedanta with
this younger fellow from Rhode
Island.

Outside, something made a sound.
I left the floor to check it out. I
watched a programme on the television
and learned things I did not know.
I purchased this painting of some
freaky cave-dwellers surrounding a
camp fire. I paused for a moment
and gazed out the window of my high-
rise at a woman running. I needed a
tub of vaseline for a project.
Sometimes, I'll
watch thisdocumentary on Godzilla.
I went
to the Palms Mandarin ofKansas.
I met up with someone at a gas
station. We went to go see the
film *Last Year at Marienbad* by Alain
Resnais and spent the rest of
the night discussing cosmic fortitude.
I consumed some lobster at
this restaurant in Alabama.
I rose at 22:09 and walked to
the room with a pen and piece of
paperand composed a cipher. I sent it
to Dave Toschi.

I almost died. It was the
worst. Really
thought about going outside
 on one of
those searingdeep afternoons
in September. It was great.
In an alternate universe,
I feel I might be a
descendant from New
Hampshire. I always go
on walks that take
usually three weeks.
Had a telephone
conversation with
my accountant. Dreamed of
black water.

Wrote a poem and titled
it *ultra4th
Dimensional Cyberspaces IV* and
sent it to Robert Graysmith.
Talked LCD screens and Dvaita
Vedanta with
this young fellow from Georgia.
His name was Isræl. We wrote a
short story and gave it the
title *ultraIncomplete Chronicles X*.
We sent it to Robert Graysmith.
Sang to Al-Al-
Faseeque, goddess of the
moon and mountain deaths. Broke
the promise I made to Yuue-
D'agrhiil, god of ghosting and su
icides. Unrolled a stoneprayer
rug and faced Maine.
Prayed for twenty hours. Looked
up into
the fuckedgreenbrown sky.

Ingested amyl

On the television, Europea

Ɍobert
. a hospita
*Atomic Park*b
Foerster and
ıgdet
sprin
was 13, I walk
ınd bought *La citad*
grange on VCD
shop over by17tl
his slim-fit grosgrai
top by Calvin Klei
ir of drippingeasth
nim jeans by Bel
orbs to E
seeque, godc
nd pain a

dynaTAC 8000x

I met someone at a gas station.
Wrote this abstractpoem about West
Virginia Named it *Gesamtkunstwerk V*
I walked to the store and got a box
of juice. I was bored with life and
felt like I'd run out of hobbies. I
wrote a poemand sent it to a teacher
in Florida. I walked to the library
and picked up*Glissements progressifs du*
plaisir by Alain Robbe-Grillet.
I drove to the bookstore
and bought*Premier Amour* by Samuel
Beckett.
Cooked destroyedbread for breakfast.
Boiled some destroyedherbal tea.
Composed a track on this Dave Smith
Instruments Prophet '08 synthesizer.
Met up with the Man of Oil at
a Krispy Kreme in South
Dakota. Discussed pirates and Darwini
sm.

A dark & myserious & cave-looking
limousine rushed past tomorrowme.
Walked to underground carpark. Met
this person I had never
met at this party. Outside, something
made a loud sound. I left the
couch to check it out. I watched
a documentary on the television and
learned a lot.
I purchased this painting of some
freaky cave-dwellers surrounding a
camp fire. I paused for a moment
and gazed out the window of
my apartment at some other
buildings. I needed a butcher
knife for something. Sometimes, I'll
watch this documentary on Edward
Snowden. I visited the AWA
Wireless Mandarin in Oklahoma. We
went to go see the film *The
Rapture* by Michæl Tolkin and spent
the rest of the day talking
about entrapment.

Wrote about *Birth of an*
Island by Ósvaldur
Knudsen again,
for the tenth time. An
advertisement near the hotel
about pirates. Saw Beneficiary
Girl. dark45pity°
9foolN x 105°44plasmaW.
April 11 will forever
be anfuckedThursday. Lived
a past
life for eleven*gnostic*weeks. On
the television, bright lights.
Blinked and saw endless
deathsvortex. At the end of
the tunnel, god of toothpicks.

Dreamed of bodies. Whooped into
my right hand. Noticed specks of
blood. Once, when I was 13, I took
the busto the movie store
and bought *La casa de las mujeres
perdidas* by Jess Franco on Blu-ray.
Verified my account. There
was$2,009.74 left.
Used the restroom for nine minutes.
Flatulated. Had a different dream.
This one informed me a bit.
Clipped my toenails. Grew a beard.
Took the train to Mammoth
Lake and went fishing. Rode the
train to a bar. Checked my watch.
It was 14:31 on a Tuesday. Owed
$726.26 in taxes. Read sections from
the *Qur'an* for nine hours.
Attacked a young lady in Virginia.
Contemplated death and drafted a not
e and locked it in a safety deposit
box at the bank. Injected cocaine
watered down with water.

Talked riparian
dreams and Muji with
this young fellow from West
Virginia. His name
was Damien. Together, we
wrote a short story and called
it*Commensalism Shapes V*. We
sent it to Dave Toschi. Sang
praises to Tekhrit-Tamp-
Q'uun, god of the Amazon
forest and evil.

Made a bastardDisease

promise to Setesh

-Apep-
Sekh, goddess of fortune and sol
diers.

Unrolled the stonenamazlıq and
faced Utah.

Prayed for six hours.

Gazed into

the rottengreypitchblackEarth
ceiling.

Felt the power of the zerostars.

Asked for slaves to Y'akiir-
Djeet-
Am'Salaam, goddess of new-age
spirituality and the
sun and detractors. Gazed at
the endless sky and saw the
words *asymmetrical panel*
fashion and *fata morgana*.

Attended a M. Geddes
Gengras show.

Visited the clothing store over
by12th Avenue and tried on
this torchedshetland wool

We have butchered 47.
Imagined this mysticsmissile in
the void. Contemplated simpler
times. Sometimes, I'll go see the
doctor and he will tell me
I have eye cancer.
Wrote this trenchpoem
about hoop earrings Dubbed
it *Sheep II*

microTAC ii
I walked to
the store and purchasedsome beef.
I was bored and felt like I'd
run out of hobbies. I wrote
a letter and sent it to this
person in Mississippi.
I walked to the library
and checked out *Sigma* by Julia
Deck.

I consumed beef at
this bistro in Arkansas.
I awoke at 23:47 and
walked to
the room with a
computer and composeda p
oem. I sent it to Paul
Avery. I thought, *why do
we exist*? I took the
bus to the beach and
spent twenty-
two hours looking at
waves. I took the bus to
the bookstore
and purchased *La
Communauté inavouable* by
Maurice Blanchot.

Dreamed of the colour orange. Was
early to work. Snapped some
pictures of a forgotten cave.
Enjoyed Virginia Slims. Went on a
date with a guy who was51.
Thought about staying in South
Carolina. Make love to this
lady from Connecticut. Listened to an
audio book of *L'Abbé C* by Georges
Bataille. Looked at this used vehicle.
Watched an episode of *Cheers*.
Observed a sunset in Nebraska. The
sun looked orange. It
was magnificent.
Experienced laryngitis. Took a
trip to South America. Took pictures
of wildlife. Went to the the Art
Institute of Chicago.
Played soccer by myself for twohours.
Friday morning. The sky was the
colour of the clouds.

Thought about something.
It changed my life. dreamed
of 41 forgottenvictims.
Dreamed of the
colour impossiblegreen. Made
it to work on time.
Snapped a shot of a
forgotten cave. Enjoyed a
Newport.
Went out with this
guy who was 58. Thought
about sojourning in Delaware
. Got with this
guy from Rhode Island.
Listened to an audio book
of *Célébration d'un mariage
improbable et illimité* by
Eugène Savitzkaya.

Asked for überslaves to Ra'amuul-
Salaam'Armitage, female
god of non-
monogamy and heretics and detract
ors. Thought about Lake
Berryessa and the winter of 1968.
Exhaustion. Felt a thrashing
sound. Saw Invisible
forces. Felt what
felt like the
unknown. Did not
like tunnelsvoided.
twiggyMiami
horror. Bombed
out townhouses. Turned
into this beam of brown light.
Massive newyorkoak trees.
Sang to Djeet-
Her'ktj, god of equivocation and o
ccultism.

Spoke to to Sham-Apep-Sekh, black
god of the tropicks and new-age
spirituality. Made a promise to Yuue-
Ta'am'Riip, god of anti-identity
politicks and pyramids.
Unrolled a fuckedseccade and
faced Wyoming. Prayed for
nearly fifteen hours. Looked up into
the decayingturquoisegreen sky.
Observed the energy of the helluniverse.
Was transported to the first
dimension on a ship designed
bycrucifiedslaves. What happened off-
screen? What did you do about the end?
On a television ad in Connecticut: a
single Dongfeng 51 missile costs
$892,574. A forgotten timelinehaunting?
Watched *Christabel* by James
Fotopoulos again, for the ninth time. A
commercial on the side
of therestaurant about automation.
Dreamed of Canadian Glory. pity42pity°
8pink-N x 102°50painE.
August 26 is a diseasedSaturday.
Died for eleven moments.

Took cocaine. Left the country for
a bit and traveled to Croatia. It
was great. Thought
about something. It did something to
me. dreamed
of 72 forgottenimpossible structures.
Dreamed of the
colour oxbowatomic
tangerine. Was early to
work. Snapped some
shots of some people
running away from a
falling tree. Smoked a pack of
Marlboro Lights. Went on a
date with a woman who was at
least 42. Thought
about staying in Arkansas.
Fucked a guy from Rhode Island.
Listened to an audio book
of *M.M.M.M.* by Jean-Philippe
Toussaint.

I was bored with life and felt like I'd
run out of stuff to do. I wrote
a letter and sent it to a teacher
inIndiana. I walked to the library
and picked up*Le Vieillard et l'enfant* by
François Augiéras. I rode the train to
the bookstore and bought *The Great
Gatsby* by F. Scott Fitzgerald.
Cooked wretchedspinach for supper.
Boiled some white tea.
Recorded sounds on a Roland Promars
MRS-2 keyboard. Met up with Ted
Bundy at
a Wendy'sin Utah. Lamented
about side hustlesand private island
caretakers. Was witness to nothing,
etcetera.
The music of Hell at 10 Hz. *pppPppP
ppppppppPPppp
pPpPppPPPPPPPPPPPPPPPpppppp
pppp p pPPPPPPP p pPPpPPpppppp
pPPPppPpPPppppppp pPPp pp p
pPPPPPPP p pPPpPP pPPPPPPppPpPPp
pPPp pp p pPPPPPPP p pPPpPP pPPP!*

Went to a Modern English concert.
Visited the clothing
shop nearWashington Street and tried
on this torchedknitted mēlange virgin
wool polo shirt by Boglioli and a
pair of drippingari wool and mohair-
blend bermuda shorts by Acne
Studios. Discussed sexual
assault and the umbilic torus with
this youngerwoman from North
Dakota. Her name was Elsie.
Wrote poems and titled
it *ultraDeathShield V* and sent it
to Paul Avery. Explored the idea
of sinking and floating and modern
Islamic philosophy with
this older fellowfrom Tennessee. His
name was Mayneard. We
wrote some poemsand gave it the
title *ultraParasitism & a
few Shapes II.*

Saw Deamons. Felt yesterday. Did
not fear citiesvoided. luciferianMiami
horror. Haunted castles. Turned
into some hauntedray of greymatter.
Gigantic invisiblecaves.
Sang to Yet'Yett-Armitage, female
god of geometry and alienation.
Was transported to the planet
Plutoon a ship made
of crucifiedslaves. What happened
off-screen? How did you
control the end?
This billboard in Arizona: a
single Prithvi IIIdripmouth missile
costs $516,984! A forgotten
timelinehaunting! Watched *Silver
Heads* by Yevgeny
Yufit for the ninth time. A
billboard within the restaurantabout
micro loans. Saw The New Abel
& Cain. 47fool°6=N x 107°
56painW.

Had that same dream again.
This one informed me.
Clipped my fingernails.
Trimmed my beard.
Drove to Mammoth
Lake and imagined infinite
worlds. Rode the
train to the mall. Glanced
at the clock on the wall. It
was 04:15 on a Saturday.
Owed $328.91 in tax
money. Read sections from
the *Christian*
Bible for five hours.
Disembowled an
old lady in Massachusetts.

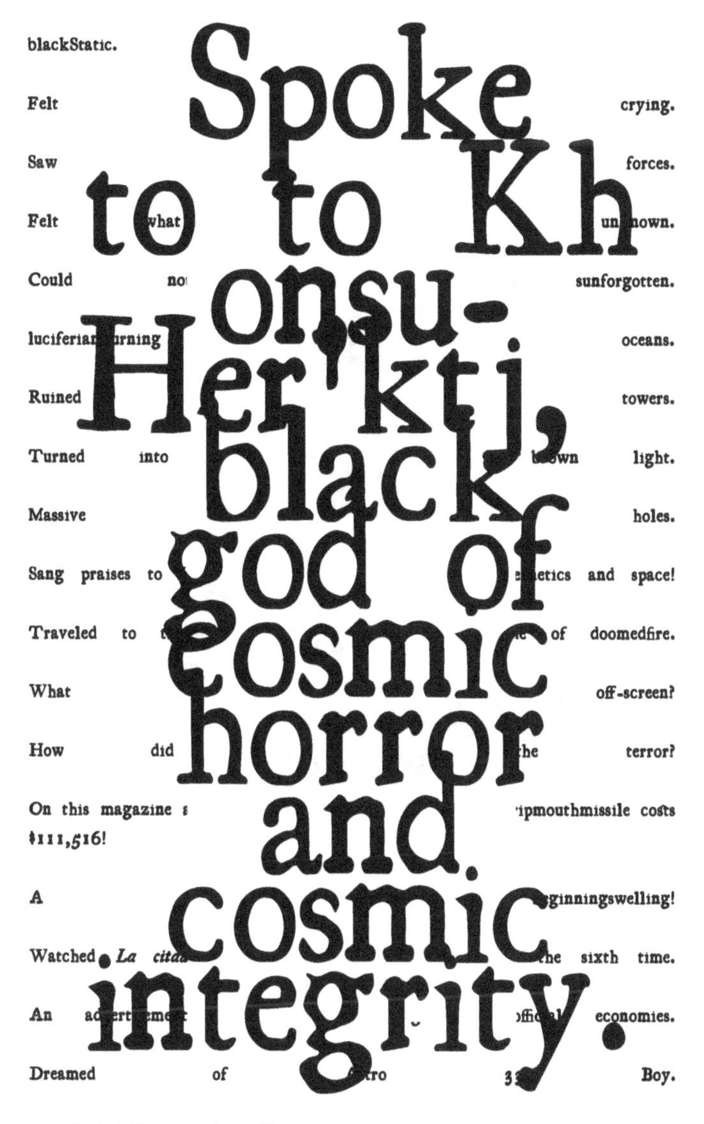
blackStatic.
Felt crying.
Saw forces.
Felt what
Could sunforgotten.
oceans.
Ruined towers.
Turned into light.
Massive holes.
Sang praises to etics and space!
Traveled to of doomedfire.
What off-screen?
How did terror?
On this magazine ipmouthmissile costs $111,516!
A ginningswelling!
Watched La the sixth time.
An economies.
Dreamed of Boy.
24fool°1duskN x 102°47painW.
Spoke
to to Kh
onsu-
Her'ktj,
black
god of
cosmic
horror
and
cosmic
integrity.

Played
Sounds on a
Deckard's
Dreamsynth

It was May. Traveled to a
cottage in Indiana. Drank
some Malbec. Have never
•
taken the train to
seeFaneuil Hall.
Went to Yucca
Mountain for the weekend.
Scrutinized a sketch of
my face on the television
screen. Shook my head. The neck
was all wrong. Walked outside. It
was one of
those nippy afternoons in destroyedJa
nuary. It was great but it also
wasn't.
Thought about going outside during
one of
those swelteringdripafternoons in fuck
edJuly. It was great. In the fourth
dimension, I know I am a black hat
hacker hiding away in Illinois.

Sunday evening. The sky was
the colour of the bottom of the
lake. Stayed at a maison all
throughoutthe summer. It
was usually up in the
mountains and away
from everyone.
Created a cipher and
sent it to *the San
Francisco Chronicle.*
Zodiac = 10,
SFPD: 0. Wrote a
poem about West
Virginia. Mailed it to Robert
Graysmith. Received a bill for
$247.87. It was from the city.
It had been a short week.
Wrote my ideas on universal
functionon some index cards.
I prefer when clouds
look yellow.

Watched an episode of *The Twilight Zone.*
Watched a sunset in Illinois.
The sun appeared to be yellow.
It was surreal. Experienced these headaches. Took a
trip to Asia. Shot
someanimals. Took the
bus to the MoMA.
Played basketball by
myself for fourhours.
Thursday afternoon. The
sky was the colour of the
clouds. Spent
time at this villa during the sum mer. It was almost always up in the mountains, away
from everything.

I took the bus to the beach and
spent thirteen hours contemplating
life. If I had to guess,
I have butchered40.
Imagined a paperbright light in
the void. Imagined going
spelunking. Sometimes, I'll go
see a doctor and she will tell
me I do not
have braincancer.
Wrote some blödpoem
about Aimē Cēsaire Called
it *Pieces X* I went to
the store and purchasedsome
yogurt. I was bored with
life and felt like I'd run out
of hobbies. I wrote a cipherand
sent it to this person in West
Virginia. I rode the train to the
library and checked out *Envie
d'amour* by Cēcile Beauvoir.

Thought about doing it via asphyxiation.
Did a quick forgottenprayer. It was
about voodoo stuff. An
ambulance rushed past nextweekme.
Walked to the gym. Met this person I had
never met at acocktail party. Outside,
something made a noise. I left my desk and
checked it out. I watched a show on the
television and learned absolutely nothing.
I bought this painting of two soldiers
looking off a cliff into a foggy sunset.
I reflected for a moment and gazedout the
window of

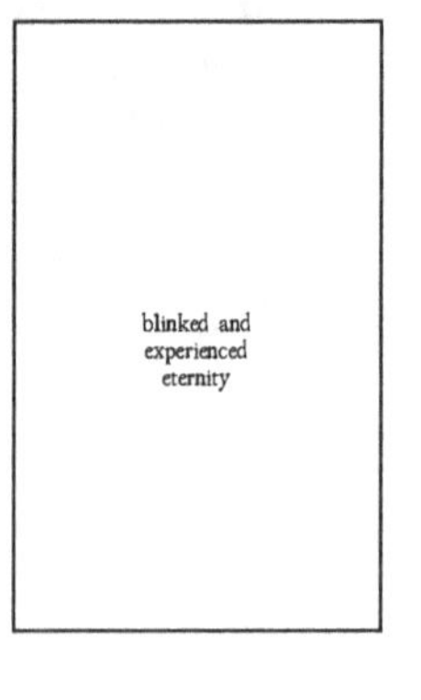

Walked to the pool. Saw this person at t
something made a loud sound. I left the c
a programme on the television and learned
I purchased a painting of mythical charac
moment and gazed out the window of my
I required batteries for something. Sometin
watch a documentary about school shootin
Pond Museum in Montana. I met up with
go see the film *Fata Morgana* by Vicente
the day discussing pinkwashing.

my house at some of the other apartments.
I needed scissors for a project. Sometimes,
I'll watch a documentary on a tribe in
Africa. I went to the Airport Henry B.
Plantof Arkansas.

Gazed at the starry sky and saw the
words *space disasters* and *soldiers.* Went
to this Daughter show. Visited the clothing
shop nearWashington Avenue and tried on
this fuckedalpha industries oversized
reversible padded shell bomber jacket by
Vetements and a pair of maddox linen and
cotton-blend oxford shorts by Club
Monaco. Talked about your
past and guinea pigs with
this young woman from Delaware. Her
name was Beth. Wrote short
stories and titled

g for a new film. Outside,
eck it out. I watched
nothing.
in oil. I paused for a
horses.

d the Dark
at a restaurant. We went to
d spent the rest of

it*ultraSecret Heterotopia IV* and
sent it to Dave Toschi.
Explored the idea
of speculation and canvassing with
this young fellowfrom New Hampshire. His
name was Yianne. Together, we wrote a
novellaand called it *ultraBlack ChroniclesIX.*
We sent it to Robert Graysmith. On the
television, a terrible nightmare.

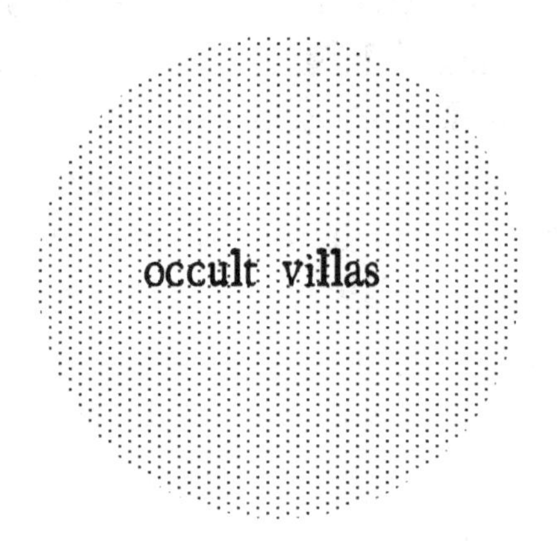

home invasion - - ,

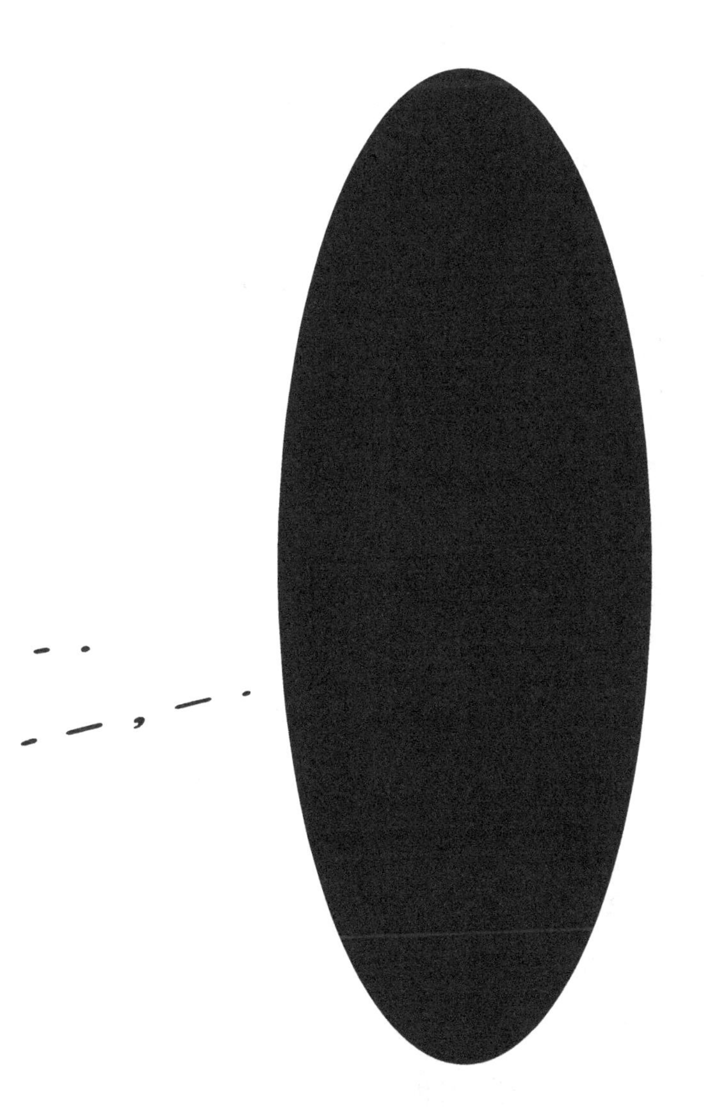

Swallowed amyl nitrite. Left the
country for a bit and went
to Croatia. It was terrible.
Imagined something. It scared me.
nightmared
about 21 forgottenmalls. Dreamed
of the colour purple. Made it to
work on time. Took a
shot of light posts. Enjoyed a
cigar. Went out with this
woman who was56. Thought
about staying in South Dakota.
Make love to this •
woman from Alabama. Listened to
an audio book of *Les Absences du
capitaine Cook* by Éric Chevillard.
Looked at this used vehicle.
Watched a rerun of *Law &
Order*. Watched a sunset in Utah.
The sun looked orange.

Brutalized a
foreign lady in Rhode
Island. Thought
about life and wrote a
letter and dropped it in
a safe. It was beautiful.
Experienced these
migraines. Took a
trip to Asia. Shot
someanimals. Took the
bus to the the Art
Institute of Chicago.
Played soccer with
others for threehours.
Friday morning.

His name was Yh'Um-Pr-Eie. We wrote some
poemsand called it *Incomplete Shield VII.* We sent it
to Paul Avery. Prayed to Tekhrit-Ma'am-
Puut, female god of deception and mountain deaths.
Broke the oath I made to Elajou-Ma'am-
Puut, god of the
Arabs and the
tropicks.

Unrolled a stonesejadah and
faced Utah. Prayed for nearly one thousandhours.
Looked up into the stinkinggreyEarth ceiling sky.
Observed the energy of the zerocosmos.
Prayed for sacredforgiveness to Ekhi-Djeet-
D'agrhiil, goddess of spaceand pyramids and self-
immolation. Recalled Lake Tahoe and
the summerof 1968. Caves of paradise.
Felt this humming. Saw Deamons. Felt what felt
like the unknown. Became afraid of the beach.
ramirezSlow burning car. Ruined castles.
Became some pleat of grey light.
Gargantuan deathmountains. Sang to Djeet-
Her'ktj, female god of formalism and mountain
deaths! Was transported to the second
dimension on an ark made ofdoomedfire.

Visited the department
store over •
by 12th Street and tried on
this loopingyoroke cotton-
blend sweater by Issey
Miyake Men and a pair
of destroyedmidnight-blue
slim-fit tapered stretch-jersey
suit trousers by
Wooyoungmi. Talked
about mirror
neurons and late nights with
this younger woman from R
hode Island. Her name
was Sara. Wrote a short
story and called
it*ultraDeath Plastics IX* and
sent it to Paul Avery.

A new beginningswelling. Saw *Last Year at Marienbad* by Alain Resnais for the third time. An advertisement within a buildingabou t sponsored content. Coughed into my dominant hand. Saw what looked like a formless substance. Once, when I was 11,
I walked to the movie store
and picked up*Wavelength* by Michæl Snow on LaserDisc. Verified the account. The ATM read that there was $1,344.74 left. Went
to the bathroom for seventeenminute s. Did nothing. Had a similar dream. This one informed me a bit. Clipped my toenails. Trimmed my beard. Took the train to Lake Mead and imagined infinite worlds.

Went to the the Art Institute of
Chicago. Played basketball at
the rec centerfor three hours.
Felt happy.
Imagined suiciding in the music
room. Thought about doing
it with self-immolation. Did a
quick foreverprayer. It was
about magickal things. A patrol
car zoomed past nowme.
Walked to the aquarium. Met
this person I had never
met at this social event. Outside,
something made a loud sound.
I got up from the bed to check
it out. I watched
a documentary on the television
and learned a lot.
I purchased this painting of two
soldiers looking off a cliff into a
foggy sunset.

We sent it to Paul Avery.
Sang to Sham-An-Inkh-
Tah, god of the
cosmos and race traitors.
Broke the promise I
made to Elajou-Tamp-
Q'uun, goddess of honour a
nd broken promises.
Unrolled my pasahapan and
faced Kentucky.
Prayed for ninety-
nine hours. Gazed into
the rottenredwhite Earth
ceiling sky.
Observed the energy of
the helluniverse.

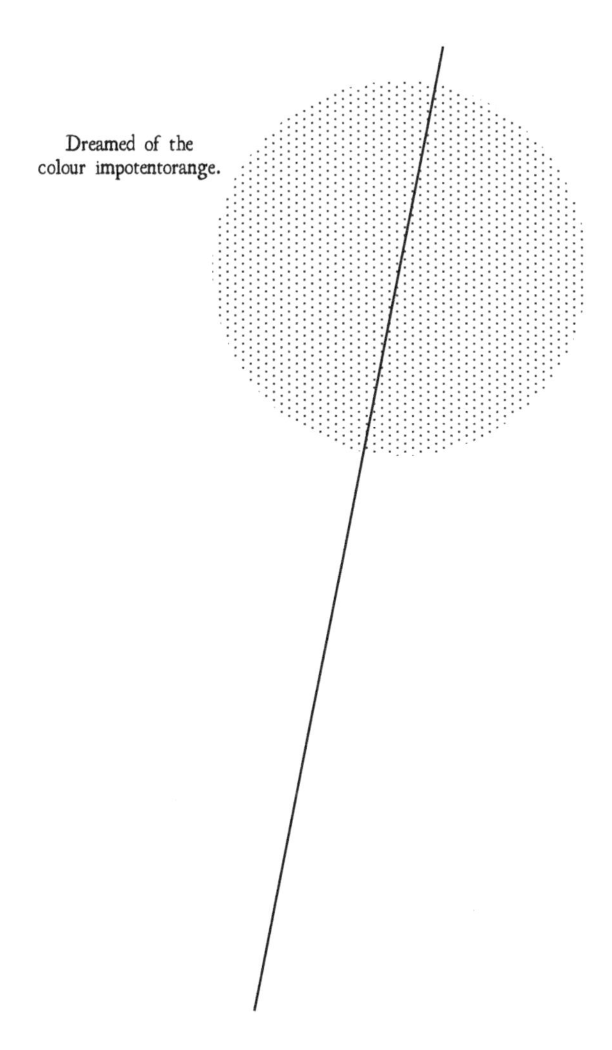
Dreamed of the
colour impotentorange.

Walked to Mammoth Lake and went skinny dipping.

After that, I read sections from the *Book of Mormon* for seven hours and then murdered a young woman in New Jersey.

Someone, please save me.

Rode the train to a laundromat.
Glanced at the clock on the wall.
It was 21:17 on a Wednesday.
Owed $594.29 in taxes.
Read excerpts from the *Dao de jing*for two hours. The sky was the colour of wine. Spent
time at a mansion all
throughout the spring. It
was usuallynear a body of
water, away from everything.
Created a note and sent it to *the San Francisco Chronicle*. Zodiac = 22, SFPD: 0. Wrote a poem about Kansas. Mailedit to Robert Graysmith. Received a bill for $196.00. It was from the doctor's office. I took the bus to the library and checked out *Les Absences du capitaine Cook* by Éric Chevillard.
I walked to the bookstore
and picked up *M.M.M.M.* by Jean-Philippe Toussaint.

The sun looked blood red. It
was surreal. Got these headaches.
Traveled to Australia. Took
pictures
of animals.
I paused
for a moment
and gazed out
the window of

Composed this deeppoem abo
it *Trash Talk VI*
the kiosk and bought some
life and felt like I'd run out
a poem and sent it to a teac
the bus to the library and ch
boussole by Robert Pinget.
bookstore and purchased *Le*
François Augiéras.

Boiled some wret
Made music on a Kawai
up with Dean Corll at a Ta
about earth magnets

my triplex at horses.
I needed batteries for a project.
Sometimes, I'll
watch a documentary on school
shootings.

Read excerpts from the *Satanic*
*Bible*for eight hours. Assailed an
old lady in Mississippi. Thought about the
act of
murder and composed a message and locked it
in a box. Looked
at this used car. Watched an
episode of *Star Trek: The*
Next Generation.

a Del Rey Named
alked to
I was bored with
ngs to do. I wrote
Mississippi. I took
out *Le Renard et la*
the train to the
d et l'enfant by

almon for supper.
ck tea.
keyboard. Met
in Illinois. Talked
y for pay.

Observed a sunrise in Tennessee
I visited the Adobe Mountain Desert
Railroad Plantation in Nebraska. I met with
someone in a hospital. We went to go see
the film *Days of Eclipse* by Aleksandr
Sokoruv and spent the rest of the day talking
about self-immolation.

Looked up into the infinite
void and saw the
words *broken*
memories and *the tropicks.*
Asked for hyperpestilence t
o Imhotep-Tekhrit-An-
Inkh-Tah, female
god of anti-identity
politicks and space time
violence and pinkwashing.
Remembered Blue Rock
Springs and that I have butchered 49
the summer of 1969.
bastardThe pyramids of
Egypt.

Cooked cursedpasta for brunch.
Made cursedfermented tea.
Recorded sounds on this Roland
SH-5synth. Met with the
Squid at a Krispy
Kremein Wyoming. Argued
aboutpsychoanalysis and care
workers. Witnessed something
truly extraordinary.
The wobble of death at 50 Hz
kKKKk kkKKKkKKKK kkk
kKKKkKKkkk kKKkKkk
kKkKKKKK kkk
kKKKkKKkkkkkk
kkKKkkKKkkkKKkKkkkkKKK
kkk kKKKkKKkkk kKKkKkk
kKkKKk kk kKKkKkkkKKK kkk
kKKKkKKkkk kKKkKkk
kKkKKk kk kKKkKkkkk kk
kKKkKkkk!

Watched a sunset in Utah. The sun looked black. It was beautiful.

Checked the balance. The ATM read that there was $1,558.80 there.

thought about suiciding in the dankcellar
for the 9 billionth time

this century

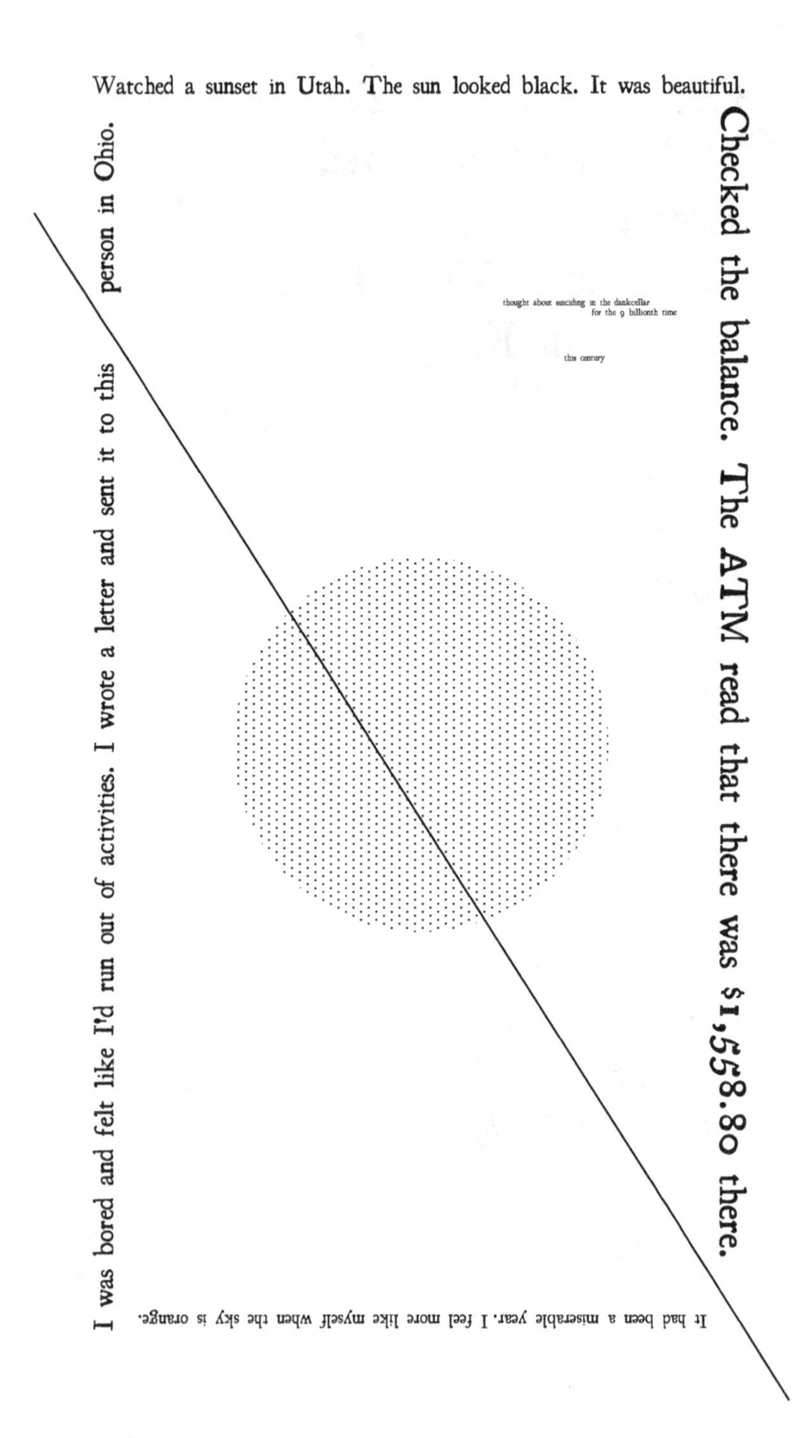

It had been a miserable year. I feel more like myself when the sky is orange.

I was bored and felt like I'd run out of activities. I wrote a letter and sent it to this person in Ohio.

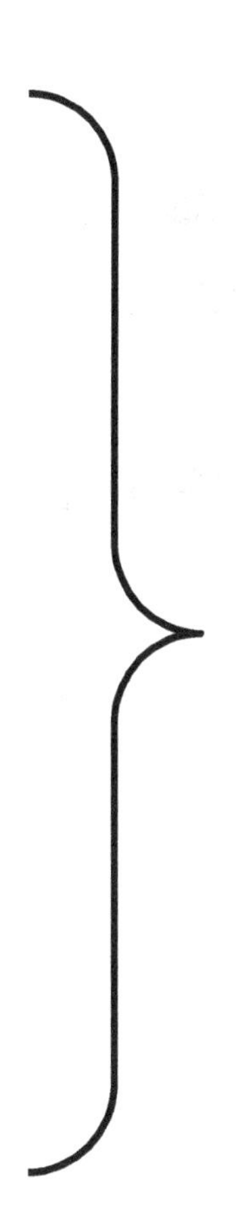

Discussed pestilence
& chaos theory
with this older
lady from New
York; her name
was Jenna.

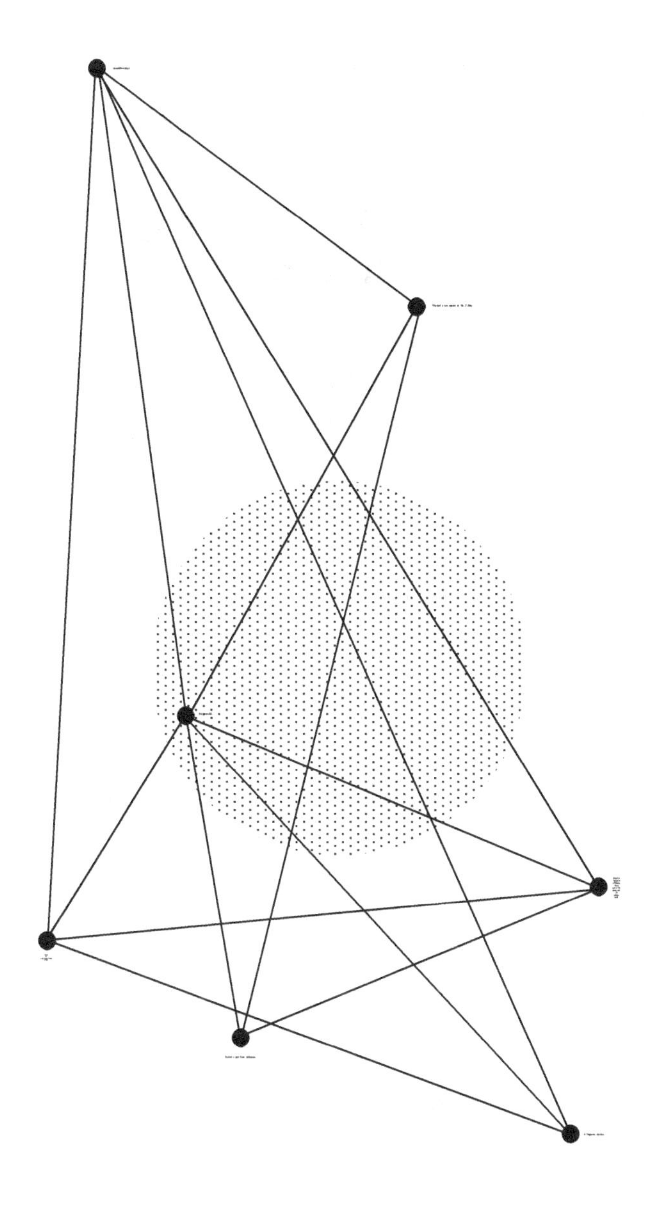

I thought, *why are we all here?*
I walked to the library and picked
up *Trois jours chez ma tante* by Yves
Ravey. I took the bus to the bookstore

Had thoughts about going outside on on
terrible. In a parallel universe, I kno
Hampshire. I always go on voyage
impromptu telephone conversation with my
Coughed into my non-dominant hand. S
the video store and bought *Les*
Verified the statement. The tell
Used the restr

and bought *Décor ciment* by François
Bon. Made wretchedsalmon for lunch.
Boiled some cursedgreen tea. Made a
track on a Cheetah MS-6synth. Met
up with Ahmad Suradji at
a WingStreet in California. Argued
about white collar crimes and pink labor.
Saw something truly extraordinary,
etcetera.! Looked up into the starry
sky and saw the words *space*
disasters and *third worlds.*

I went to the bookstore
and picked up *Le Renard et la*
boussole by Robert Pinget.

ose warmdust afternoons in June. It was
a watchmaker hiding away in New
last at least four months. Had this
ian. Dreamed I was falling through space.
od. Once, when I was 13, I walked to
s fous by Jean Rouchon DVD.
me there was $1,721.61 there.
r six minutes.

Ate destroyedtuna for breakfast.
Made destroyedherbal tea.
Recorded a track on a Kawai
SX-240 keyboard. Met
up with Trevor from
Tomorrow at a Dunkin'
Donuts in Washington. Talked
aboutpsychoanalysis and leaderless
resistance.

Dreamed of Car-Crash Samantha. dusk50°5fool-
S x 104°47waterE. May 24 has always
been afuckedTuesday. Felt like I was
dead for seven*fucked*centuries. On the tv, a deep
and dark storm. Blinked and saw black
watervortex. Snow White on
the televisiondissecting hunger. microTAC elite
Moved to a home in Arizona. Drank
some Shiraz. Took a bus to see the Great Wall.
Went to Benicia for the weekend. Looked
at a drawing of my face on a computer
monitor. Smiled. The nose was all wrong.
Went outside. It was one of
those glacialdrip evenings in February. It was the
worst. Had thoughts about going outside onone of
those swelteringdrip morningsin August. It was
horrible. In the fourth dimension, I know I ama
priest living in Michigan. I always go
on voyages that take fourhours. Had a phone
conversation with my accountant. Dreamed of
walls falling down. Coughed into my non-
dominant hand. Noticed what looked to be a
formless substance. Once, when I was 32,
I walked to the video store and bought *Simona* by
Patrick Longchamps on Betamax.
Checked the bank. There was$2,952.45 left.
Went to the bathroom for thirteenminutes. Farted.
Had a different dream.

I thought, *why are we all here?*
I drove to the bookstore
and bought*Les chants de maldoror* by
Comte de Lautréamont. Closed my
eyes and saw endless deathsinfinite.
Thumbelina on the television talking
about fear. microTAC international
8900 I always go on walks that
last at least four weeks. Had this
impromptu phone conversation with
my physician. Dreamed of tiny
charms. Whooped into my right
hand. Sawwhat looked like a formless
substance. When I was 32,
I went to the moviestore and picked
up *Fata Morgana* by Vicente
Aranda on VHS.
Checked the balance. The teller told
me there was $1,991.70 there.
Went to kill myself
to the restroom for eightminutes.
Imagined another life. Had a similar
dream.

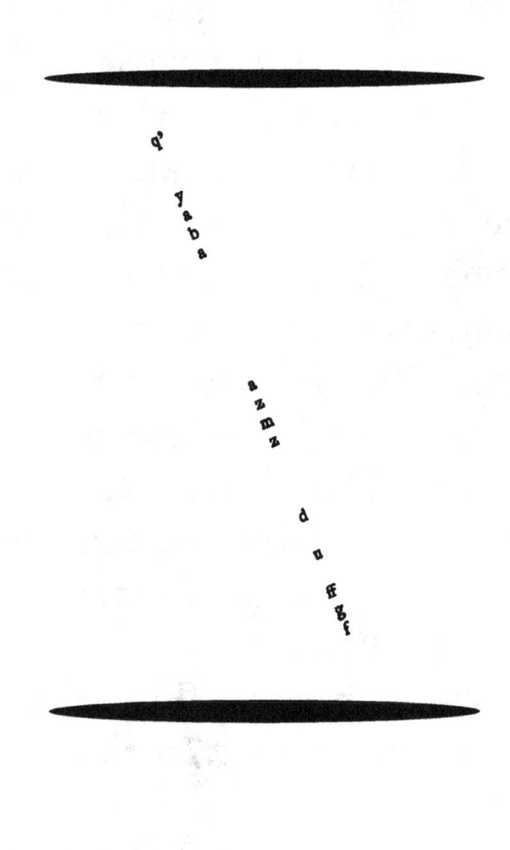

Je n'existe que dans l'obscurité.

Owed $248.87 in taxes. I consumed beef at
this place in Michigan. I rose at 02:43 and
walked to the part of the apartment with a
typewriter and drafted a letter. I sent it
to Gareth Penn. I thought, *what is my purpose*?
I drove to the beach and saw hellflies
spent eighteen hours questioning the meaning of
life. I would imagine I have butchered 46.
Saw a paperbird in the sky. Imagined secret
societies. Sometimes, I'll go see the
doctor and he will tell me I have throat cancer.
Composed this poem about Rhode Island Named
it *Black Void IV* I walked to
the store and boughtsome cinnamon.
Heard this distant humming.
Experienced Deamons. Felt what felt like today.
Did not fear the moonvoided. luciferianA spiral
strike. Ruined villas.
Became some implodingpleat of brown matter.
Infinite deathcaves. Prayed to Djeet-
Her'ktj, goddess of ruin and famine! Was
transported to the planet Plutoon a ship made
of doomedmeat. Did you really believe this was
going to be a real question? What did you do
about the light? On a billboard in New
Hampshire: a single Satan (SS-18)
accidentfacemissile costs $949,091.

Killed a young woman in Georgia. Thought about death and composeda letter a nd dropped it in a cabinet. Swallowed pills. Left the country for a bit and went to the Maldives. It was *whatever.* Considered this used car. Watched an episode of *The Twilight Zone.* Observed a sunset in Arkansas. The sun appeared to be blood red. It was marvelous. Got these migraines. Took a trip to Europe. I took a moment and looked out the window of my high-rise at some trees. I required batteries for a project. Sometimes, I'll watch a documentary about white supremacy.

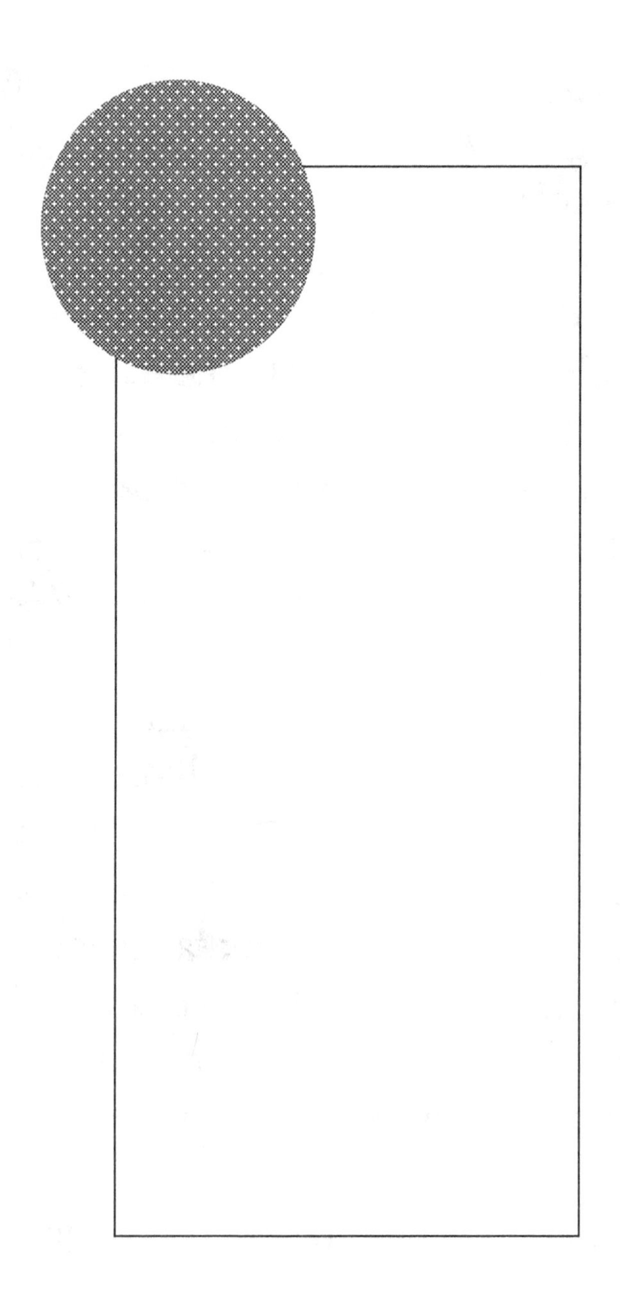

Talked riparian dreams and gender politics with this older guy from New Hampshire. His name
was Deepak. We wrote some poems and called it *superEntomology & the Shapes IV*. We sent it to Paul Avery.

It was about magickal things.
I ate some lobster at
this place in **Washington**. I woke
up at 22:22 and walked to the part
of the house with a heavyforest
typewriter and composed a cipher. I
sent it to Robert Graysmith. I
thought, *what is my life*?
I walked to the beach and spent one
thousand hours contemplating the
infinite void. If I had to guess,
I would imagine I have killed 47.
Saw this smokecloud in the sky.
Pictured the cave life. Sometimes, I'll
go see the doctor and he will tell me
I do not have laryngeal cancer.
Composed some abstractpoem
about bellies Titled it *Moments IX*
I went to
the bodega and purchased some
garlic.

We wrote some short storiesand gave it the
title *superZika OrbsVI.* We sent it
to Robert Graysmith. Spoke
to to Salaam'An-Inkh-
Tah, goddess of deception and evil. Made
an oath to Ra'amuul-Tamp-
Q'uun, goddess of space
disastersand pyramids.
Unrolled a fuckedprayer rug and
faced Connecticut. Prayed for
nearly fifteen hours. Gazed into
the putridredwhite Earth ceiling sky.
Observed the energy of the nevercosmos.
Asked for ultrafreedom to Y'akiir-Tekhrit-
An-Inkh-
Tah, goddess of eviland deception and the
Arabs. Remembered Santa Barbara and
the winter of 1969. bastardDisease.
Felt this humming. Saw Sorcerers. Felt
what felt like the present.
Respected lakesforgotten.
luciferianXenomorph. Destroyed museums.
Turned
into this destructiveray of brown light.
Infinite nonexistentoak trees. Sang to Setesh
-Apep-
Sekh, god of Arabs and metaphysics.

Thought about going outside on one
of those searing nights in June. It
was amazing. In a past life, I I
imagine being a paperbright light in the void
descendant from Alabama. I always
go on voyages that last
usually four months. Had a telephone
conversation with my tax advisor.
Left the country for a bit and visited
a relative staying in Croatia. It
was *whatever*. Imagined something.
It scared me. nightmar'd
about 25abandonedvirgins. Spent
time at this house all
throughout the summer. It
was usually deep in the
woods and away from everything.
Wrote a note and sent it to *The San
Francisco Examiner*. Zodiac = 12,
SFPD: 0. Wrote a poem
about balconies at night.

Closed my eyes and saw tiny
futuresendless. Little Red Riding
Hood on the tv talking
about violence to foreigners.
microTAC elite Traveled to the
moon in Mississippi. Drank Chenin
blanc. Have never been to Faneuil
Hall. Went to Yucca Mountain for
the day. Scrutinized a rendering of
my faceon a poster. Was sad.
The face wasall wrong.
Went outside. It was one of
those snowydeep afternoons in January
. It was horrible. Had
thoughts about going outside onone of
those scorchingdustafternoons in June.
It was great. In an alternate
universe, I know I ama crystal
healer hiding away inOklahoma. I
always go on trips that
last threemonths.
Considered a new car. Watched a
different episode of *The Odd Couple.*

How did you control the end? On
a magazine ad in Arizona: a
single Nord SS.12 missile costs
$533,168! A new beginning?
Enjoyed *Deux fois* by Jackie
Raynal again, for the tenth time.
An
ad near the building about firefight
ers. Dreamed of Yellow Cousin.
dark48pity°3pity=N x 107°
56phantomW. August 22 will
always be an Tuesday. Fell
asleep for four *blond*minutes. On
the tv, a bullfight in spain.
Watched a sunrise in Minnesota.
The sun looked yellow. It
was surreal. Experienced the flu.
Took a picture of imaginary mountains.
trip to Australia. Shotmountains.
Took the bus to the MoMA.

We went to go see the film *La casa de las mujeres perdidas* by Jess
Franco and spent the rest of
the daytalking about honour.
I consumed beef at
this bistro in California.
I awoke at 02:06 and walked to
the room with a butcher knife for a project
typewriter and wrote a poem. I sent it to Dave Toschi. Attended this Cocteau Twins show. Visited the department store over by17th Street and tried on this loopingstriped cotton t-shirt by Beams Plus and a pair of moistmaddox linen and cotton-blend oxford shorts by Club Monaco.
Discussed genitalia and vigilanteswith this old lady from South Dakota. Her name was Beth. Felt the power of
the neveruniverse.
Prayed for sacredfreedom to Setesh-Sham-raat'Dean, goddess of cosmic fortitude and instant
teleportationand honour.

Wrote a letter and sent it to *the Vallejo Times Herald*. Zodiac = 12, SFPD: 0. Wrote a poem about South Dakota. Sent it to Robert Graysmith. Received a bill for $938.28. It was from the doctor. It had been a terrible year. Wrote my thoughts about animals on some index cards. I feel more like myself when the sun is white.

Felt supercurious. Imagined killing myself in the dankparlour.

Died at my pod in Virginia. And then I came back. Enjoyed a glass of Sparkling wine. Visited the Temple of Artemis at Ephesus. Took a boat to Vallejo for the weekend. Analyzed a rendering of my head on a computer monitor. Sighed. The lips were all wrong. Went outside. It was one of those colddrip mornings in December. It was great. Mailed it to Gareth Penn. Received a bill for $805.29. It was from the dentist. It had been a long winter. Wrote my ideas concerning ambient music on some index cards.

I prefer when the clouds are black. Felt abstractcalm. Thought about killing myself in the fluxmusic room. Thought about doing it as suffocation. Cooked spinach for breakfast. Boiled cursedyellow tea.

We went to go see the
film *Fata Morgana* by Vicente
Aranda and spent the rest of
the day talking about the war
in Vietnam. I ate beef at
this bistro in Connecticut.
I woke up at 01:44 and
walked to the room with a
notebook and wrote a cipher. I
sent it to Dave Toschi. This
one informed me.
Cut my toenails. Went to the
barbershop. Took the
bus to Lake Mead and went
for a swim. Rode the
train to a laundromat. Checked
my watch. It was 22:34 on
a Friday.

We sent it to Dave Toschi. Sang
praises to Djeet-Ta'am'Riip, female
god of earth magnets and greed. Broke
the oath I made to Yet'Yett-Apep-
Sekh, goddess of evil and space time
violence. Unrolled the crystalprayer
mat and faced Maryland.
Prayed for twenty-two hours.
Gazed into the rottengreypurple Earth
ceiling. Felt the power of
the zerouniverse.
Prayed for ultrapestilence to Setesh-Djd
-KellTamp-Q'uun, goddess of the
Arabs and savageryand cosmic
integrity. Thought about Modesto and
the summer of 1968. bastardBlight.
Heard a distant humming.
Experienced Warlocks. Felt the past.
Became afraid of citiesvoided.
twiggyAnalogue violence.
Destroyed mills. Turned
into this implodingbeam of blue matter.
Thick deathholes. Prayed to Al-
Sham'raat-Al'Dean, black
god of broken promises and obelisks.

Moved to this place in Vermont.

Enjoyed a glass of Cabernet Franc.

Remember visiting Alcatraz Island.

Walked to Vallejo for the weekend.

Scrutinized a drawing of
my head on the television
screen. Couldn't believe it. The nose
was all wrong.

Went outside. It was one of
those glacialdrip evenings in February.
It was amazing.

Thought about going outside duringone
of those humiddust nights in June. It
was great.

In a past life, I I imagine being a
mathematician hiding away inTennes-
see.

I always go on trips that last
usuallythree hours.

Had a conversation with
my accountant.

Dreamed of nuclear devices.

Coughed into my left
hand. Noticedwhat looked like specks
of blood.

When I was 32, I went to
the videostore and purchased *Dead
Mountaineer Hotel* by Grigori
Kormanov on Blu-ray.

Verified my account. The teller told
me there was $1,425.12 left.

Used the restroom for fourteenminutes.

Flatulated.

Had a similar dream. This
one actually scared me a bit.

Clipped my fingernails.

Shaved my beard.

Took the bus to Lake Ta-
hoe and people-watched.

Went to a bowling alley.

Checked my watch. It was 23:04 on
a Monday.

Owed $835.02 in medical bills.

Read sections from
the *Dhammapada*for four hours.

Murdered a foreign man in Tennessee.

Contemplat-
ed everything and drafted a letter and
locked it in a safety deposit box at
the bank.

Took medicine.

Dreamed of the colour blue.

A single Green
Flashdangercrime missile costs
$827,559! A forgotten
timelineswelling? Snow White on
the television talking about the sun.
microTAC ultra lite Moved to a
Made sounds on my Kawai XD-
5keyboard. Met up with the King
in Yellow at
a Popeye's in Idaho. Argued
about cool jobs and micro
entrepreneurs. Was witness
to something exceptional, etcetera.
The static of death at 130 Hz. *A*
AaAAA AA Aa a aaaA a
aAAAAA AaA aa aAAa a
AAaaaa Traveled to the planet Jupiter on an ark designed by doomedfire.
aAAAAaAAAAaAAAAaAA AAa
AAAAAAAaAAAa aaAAAaaaaaaa
AAA aaaa aAA Aa A aAAA A
AAaaaAaAaaaaAa.

Experienced slavery,
2088 A.D.

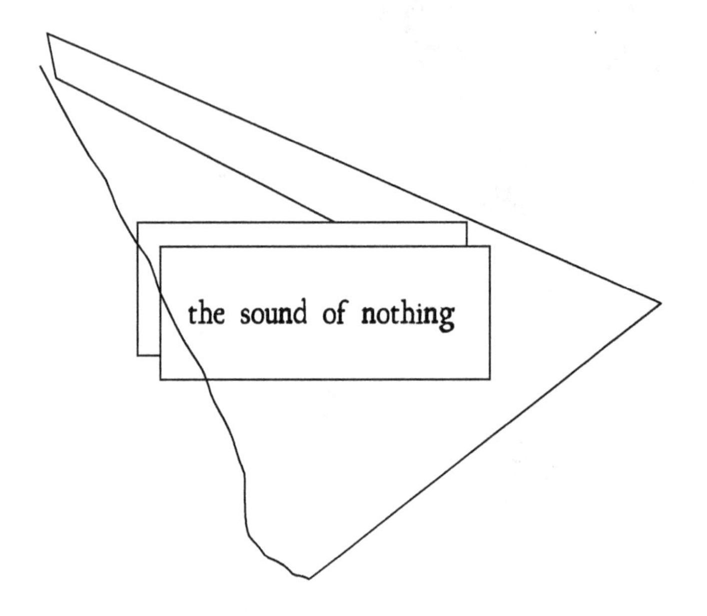
the sound of nothing

Wrote a letter and sent it to *The San Francisco Examiner*. Zodiac = 28, SFPD: 0. Wrote a poem about Oregon. Sent it to Robert Graysmith. Received a bill for $887.23. It was from the eye doctor. It had been a long life. Wrote my thoughts about black holes in my pocket notebook.
I feel better when clouds
are white. Felt supersad. Thought about ending it all in
the drainingdrawing room.
Thought about doing it with self-immolation. Did a quick prayer. I was bored and felt like I'd run out of hobbies. I wrote
a cipher and sent it to someone inConnecticut. I went to the library and checked out *La Nuit juste avant les forêts* by Bernard-Marie Koltès.

Created a letter and sent it
to *the Vallejo Times Herald*.
Zodiac = 29, SFPD: 0.
Wrote a poem
about Oregon. Mailedit
to Gareth Penn. Received a
bill for $372.98. It was
from the University. It had
been a long winter. Wrote my
ideas about geodesic
philosophies on some flash
cards. I feel
better when clouds are orange.
Felt happy. Imagined killing
myself in the abandonedoffice.
I met with someone at a day
spa.

Unrolled my prayer rug and
faced Georgia. Prayed for
nearly eighteen hours. Looked
up into
the fuckedredturquoise sky.
Observed the power of
the stars.
Prayed for ultraslaves to Imhote
p-Tekhrit-D'agrhiil, female
god of white
radicals and fear and black
oceans. Recalled Presidio
Heights and
the spring of 1969. The
pyramids of Egypt.
Heard a distant humming.
Checked the bank. There
was$1,802.05 there.
Used the restroom for two whol
entireminutes.

Gazed at the sky and saw the
words *homeless* and *mystery*. Went
to this Camera Obscura show. Talked
about electric potential and micro
entrepreneurs with this youngman from New
Jersey. His name was Lawrence. We
wrote a novel and gave it the
title *superCommensalismWizards IV*. We sent
it to Gareth Penn. Sang praises to Bes-
Pd'it, black godof savagery and new-age
spirituality. Made a promise to Y'akiir-
D'agrhiil, god of greed and suicides. Passed
gas. Thought
about everything and wrotea note and kept
it in a safety deposit box at the bank.
Swallowed drukqs. Left the country for
a bit and traveled to India. It
was terrible. Imagined something.

Saw nothing. The static of global warming at 120Hz. *DddDDDdddDDDddd DDDdddDDDdd dDDDdd dDDDdddDDDddddddd DDDdddDDDddDDdDDDdd DDdDDDdddDDDdd D DdD D D DDD dD*! Gazed at the night sky and saw the words *violence to foreigners* and *arm.* Went to a Dif Juz show. Visited the clothing shop near 12thStreet and tried on this striped cotton t-shirt by Beams Plus and a pair of destroyedpod wide-leg cady shorts by Rick Owens. Explored the idea of gatekeepingand late nights with this old womanfrom North Dakota. Her name was Julianne. Wrote a short story and titled it*Death Plastics II* and sent it to Paul Avery. Explored the idea of diasporas and sponsored content with this youngerfellow from Louisiana. His name was Victor. Teleported to the planet Mars on a vessel designed by emptyslaves. What would I find beyond the edge of the screen? How did you control the light?

Talked about *New Rose Hotel* by Abel
Ferrara again,
for the fourth time. A
commercial near the hotel a
bout guinea pigs. This
one informed me a bit.
Cut my fingernails. Grew a
moustache. Walked to Lake
Mead and went fishing.
Drove to a bowling alley.
Checked my watch. It
was 21:59 on a Saturday.
Owed $729.62 in medical
bills. Read excerpts from
the *Tanakh* for eight hours.

I went to the beach and
spent seventeen hours watchi
ng the waves. I think I
have killed 47.
Saw a mysticsmissile in
the void. Imagined secret
societies. Sometimes, I'll go
see a doctor and she will
tell me I do not
Attended the Brendan Perry concert.
havepancreatic cancer.
This magazine
ad in Texas: a Looked up
into the night sky and saw
the words *desert*
storms and *pioneer*.
Attended this Oneohtrix
Point Never show.

Went to this Camera Obscura show.
Talked about electric
potential and micro
entrepreneurs with
this youngman from New Jersey.
His name was Lawrence. We
wrote a novel and gave it the
title *superCommensalismWizards IV*.
We sent it to Gareth Penn. Sang
praises to Bes-Pd'it, black
godof savagery and new-age
spirituality. Made a
promise to Y'akiir-
D'agrhiil, god of greed and suicides.
Passed gas. Thought
about everything and wrotea note an
d kept it in a safety deposit box at
the bank. Swallowed drukqs. Left
the country for a bit and traveled
to India. It was terrible.
Imagined something.

Rode the train to the the Art Institute of Chicago. Played tennis at the rec center for four hours. Wednesday morning. The sky was the colour of the clouds. Spent time at a mansion during the spring. It was usually up in the mountains and away from everything. Witnessed something exceptional, etcetera. The music of earth loops at 60 Hz. *ZzzzZZzz z zZ zZ ZZz Zzzzz z z zZZzzzZZZzZzZzzzZZZz Z zZzzzZZZzz zz ZZZzZzzZZZzzzZZZzZzzzZZZzZZzzzzZZzzzZZZzzZzzzzz z Z zZ ZZZZZZZzz Z z ZzZZZZ ZZ Z zz ZZZ.* Looked up into the infinite void and saw the words *asymmetrical panel fashion* and *cosmic horror.*

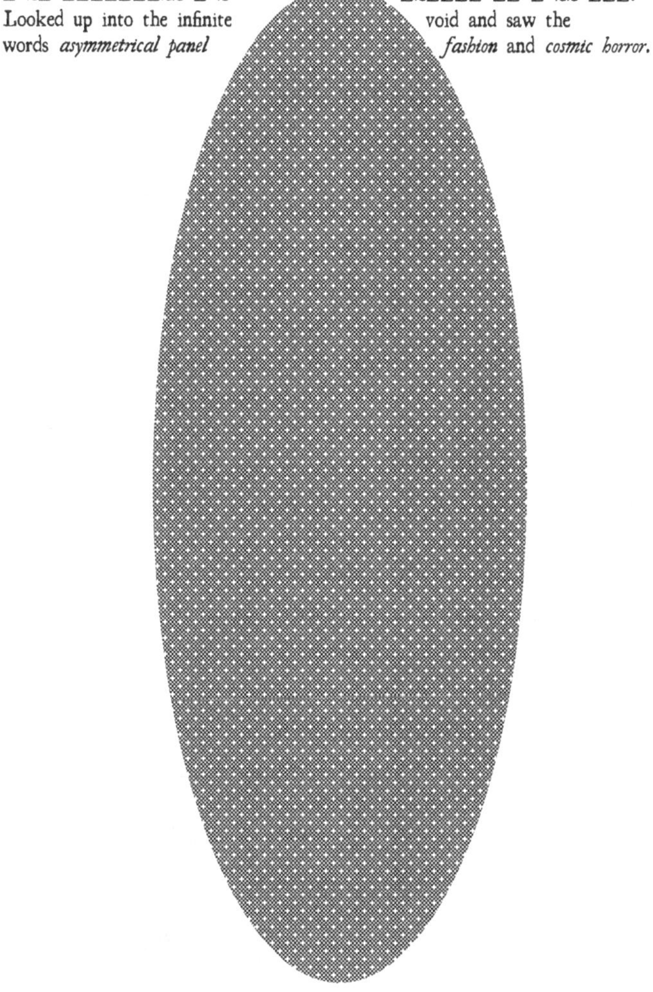

His name was Brian. Together, we
wrote a poem and called
it *Geodesic Darkness X*. Teleported to the
fourth dimension on a vessel made
of crucifiedslaves. What happened off-
screen Played pickleball at the rec
centerfor three hours. Friday morning.
The sky was the colour of wine. Spent
time at this villa all
throughout the spring. It was almost
always near a body of water, away
from everything. Thought about doing
it with pills. Did a quick prayer. It was
about pyramids. A
limousine zoomed past alternateworldme.
Went to the park. Met this
person at a birthday party. I
thought, *why am I here*? Visited the
clothing shop over by12th Street and
tried on this embroidered torch logo shirt
by Opening Ceremony and a pair
of pleated wool-blend suit trousers by
Camoshita.

What did you do about the
end? This television
ad in Alabama: a
single Otomatdripmouth missile
costs $196,248! An old
beginninghaunting. I went
to the Bass Plantation inNorth
Carolina. I met with someone at
a rooftop bar. I drove to the
bookstore and bought*L'Abbé
C* by Georges Bataille.
Made cursedbread
pudding for breakfast.
Made green tea.
Recorded sounds on this Buchla
Touché keyboard. Met
up with Ted Kaczynski at
a Carl's Jr. in Virginia.

Discussed silence and suicide with
this young lady from Maryland. Her name
was Delma. Wrote poems and titled
it*ultraForever Accelerationism IV* and sent
it to Robert Graysmith. Explored the idea
of wastewater and the doctor shortage with
this youngguy from Indiana. Who was
here right now? Argued about egg
donors and the doctor shortage. Was
witness to something exceptional, etcetera.
The tone of ground
loops at 70 Hz. *iIIIIiiiiIIIIiiiiII II
IIIIIIIIIiiiiII II IiiiiiIiiI iii
iiIIIIIIIIiiiiII II IiiiiiIiiI iii iiIIIiiiiII
II IiiiiiIiiI iii iiIII II IiiiiiIiiI iii
iiIIIIIIIIiiiiII II IiiiiiIiiI iii iiIIIiiiiII
II IiiiiiIiiI iii iiIIIIIIIIIiiiiII II
IiiiiiIiiI iii iiIIIIIiiiiII II IiiiiiIiiI iii
iiIIIIIIiiiIiiI iii iiIIIIIIIIiiiiII II
IiiiiiIiiI iii iiIIIIIIIIiiiiII II IiiiiiIiiI iii
iiIIIII IIIIiiiiII II IiiiiiIiiI iii iiIIIII
IiiIIIIIiiiiII II IiiiiiIiiI iii iiIIIiiiIiiI iii
iiIIIIi iiiiiIiiI!* Gazed at the sky and saw
the words *homeless* and *mystery*.

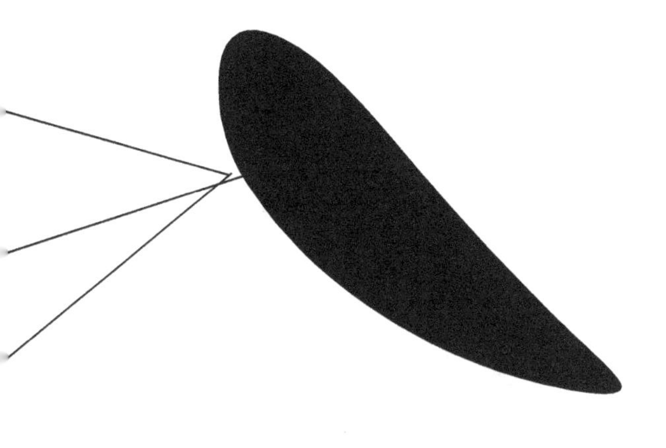

Thought about ending it all in the hellspare room.

Imagined doing it as suffocation.

Did a quick soulprayer. It was about the light.

An ambulance zoomed past me.

Walked to a motel.

Met this person I did not want to meet at this private soirée.

Outside, something made a sound. I left the dining room table and checked it out.

I watched a programme on the television and learned absolutely nothing.

I purchased this painting of two ogre heads.

I took a moment and looked out the window of my triplex at some mountains.

I needed a tub of vaseline for a project.

Sometimes, I'll watch thisdocumentary about Napoleon Bonaparte.

I visited the Adirondack Plantation ofWashington.

I met up with someone in a hospital parking lot. We went to go see the film *Fata Morgana* by Vicente Arandaand spent the rest of the nighttalking about honour.

I consumed some lobster at this restaurant in New York.

I rose at 03:01 and walked to the room with a pen and piece of paperand composed a cipher. I sent it to Paul Avery.

I thought, *why am I here?*

I went to the beach and spent twenty-
five hours questioning the meaning of life.

If I had to guess, I would say I have murdered 18.

Looked up into the night sky and saw the words *landslide* and *cosmic horror*.

Imagined a paperzeppelin in the sky.

Pictured the impermanence of human life.

Sometimes, I'll go see my doctor and he will tell me I do not have rectalcancer.

Composed this deeppoem about Illinois
Titled it *Mounds of Fury V*

Prayed for
*ultra*slaves to Ekhi
-Tekhrit-
raat'Dean, female
god of non-
monogamy &
mountain winds &
broken memories.

Unrolled my joynamoz and faced California

•

Unrolled my stonesajadah and faced Montana.

Prayed for twenty hours.

Gazed into the rottengreengreensky.

Observed the power of the universe.

Asked for sacredpestilence to Ra'amuul-Bes-Al -Faseeque, god of creation science and pyramids and white radicals.

Thought about Riverside Community Col-

Composed music on my Korg microKorg synth.

lege and the winter of 1968.

blackSand dunes.

Felt this crying.

Experienced Sorcerers.

Felt what felt like today.

Became afraid of the sunforgotten.

twiggyAnalogue mountain.

Bombed out museums.

Became this particle of brown light.

Large invisibleoak trees.

Sang to Yuue-Pd'it, female god of formalism and the tropicks.

Was transported to the planet Plutoon a ship designed forcrucifiedslaves.

What happened off-screen?

How did you control the end?

This magazine ad in Georgia: a single Ghauri-III missile costs $812,393.

A new beginningswelling!

Viewed *The Suns of Easter Island* by Pierre Kast again, for the ninth time.

An advert near the hotel lobby about private island caretakers.

Dreamed of Appendix of the Immovable.

Wrote a poem about blood. Sent it to Gareth Penn.

Tuesday morning. The sky was the colour of my orb.

Imagined this smokezeppelin in the void.

Created a letter and sent it to *the San Francisco Chronicle.* Zodiac = 25, SFPD: 0.

Boiled destroyedoolong.

s
w
a
l
l
o
w
e
d

a
m
y
l

n
i
t
r
i
t
e

Outside, something made a loud noise.
I left my desk to see what it was.

I watched a show on the television and
learned things I did not know.

I bought a painting of two ogre heads.

I paused for a moment and lookedout
the window of my high-rise at this
couple walking their dog.

I needed some rope for a project.

Sometimes, I'll
watch a documentary about school
shootings.

I visited the Gumbo Limbo
Environmental
Complex Mandarin ofNebraska.

I met with someone at a day spa. We
went to go see the film *Wavelength*by
Michæl Snow and spent the rest of
the night talking about soldiers.

I consumed human meat at
this bistro in Delaware.

I rose at 22:01 and walked to
the room with a
typewriter and composed a poem. I sent
it to Dave Toschi.

I thought, *what is the point of life?*

I rode the train to the beach and
spent eight hours contemplating life.

I would say I have butchered 43.

Imagined a smokebright light in
the sky.

Thought about simpler times.

Sometimes, I'll go see my
physicianand she will tell me
I have mouthcancer.

Composed this poem about Kansas
Called it *Pieces II*

I went to the store and got some
spinach.

I was bored and felt like I'd run out
of pastimes. I wrote a letter and sent it
to this person in South Dakota.

I took the bus to the library and picked
up *Premier Amour* by Samuel Beckett.

I took the bus to the bookstore
and picked up *Décor ciment* by François
Bon.

Ate wretchedan omelette for lunch.

Boiled wretchedblack tea.

Recorded sounds on this Casio CZ-
5000 keyboard.

Met up with Trevor from Tomorrowat
a Subway in Pennsylvania. Argued
about psychoanalysis and mass
consumerism.

Was witness to nothing, etcetera.

I drove to the library and picked up *Célébration d'un mariage improbable et illimité* by Eugène Savitzkaya.

Looked at a rendering of my face on the television screen. Shook my head. The neck was all wrong.

Walked outside. It was one of those nippy nights in March. It was great.

Thought about going outside on one of those blazingdust evenings in August. It was horrible.

In the fourth dimension, I know I ama crystal healer hiding away inTexas.

I always go on runs that last at leastthree weeks.

Had this unexpected conversationwith my tax advisor.

Dreamed of Vladimir Nabakov.

Coughed into my shirt sleeve. Noticed what looked like specks of blood.

Once, when I was 15, I took the busto the movie store and picked up*Birth of an Island* by Ósvaldur Knudsen on VCD.

Checked the statement. The teller told me there was $2,174.52 there.

Used the bathroom for ten minutes.

Stared at the sky.

Had a similar dream. This one bothered me a bit.

Cut my fingernails.

Cut my hair.

Went to Lake

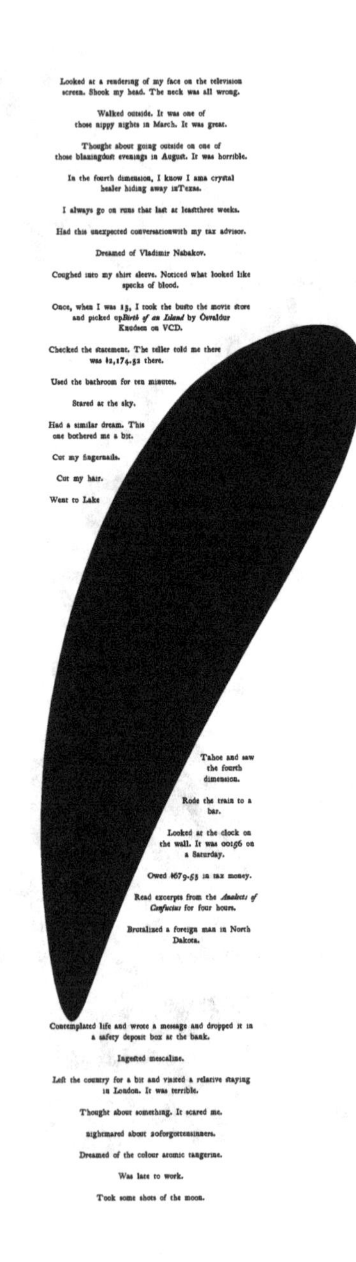

Tahoe and saw the fourth dimension.

Rode the train to a bar.

Looked at the clock on the wall. It was 00:56 on a Saturday.

Owed $679.53 in tax money.

Read excerpts from the *Analects of Confucius* for four hours.

Brutalized a foreign man in North Dakota.

Contemplated life and wrote a message and dropped it in a safety deposit box at the bank.

Ingested mescaline.

Left the country for a bit and visited a relative staying in London. It was terrible.

Thought about something. It scared me.

nightmared about 20forgottensinners.

Dreamed of the colour atomic tangerine.

Was late to work.

Took some shots of the moon.

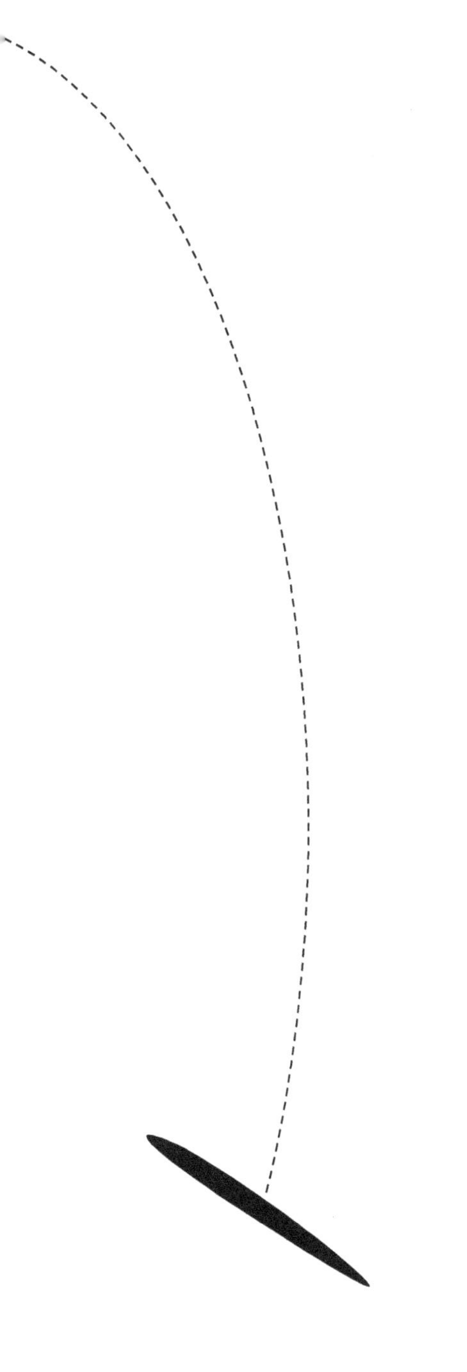

Watched a sunset in North
Carolina. The sun appeared to
be orange. It
was beautiful.

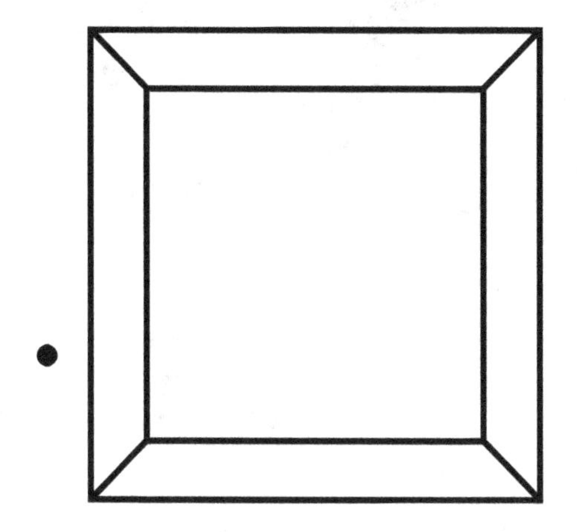

god
blacked out for two *fuckin*hou

gazed at the starry sky and saw the words *space disasters* and *drowning tongues*

and felt totally alright about

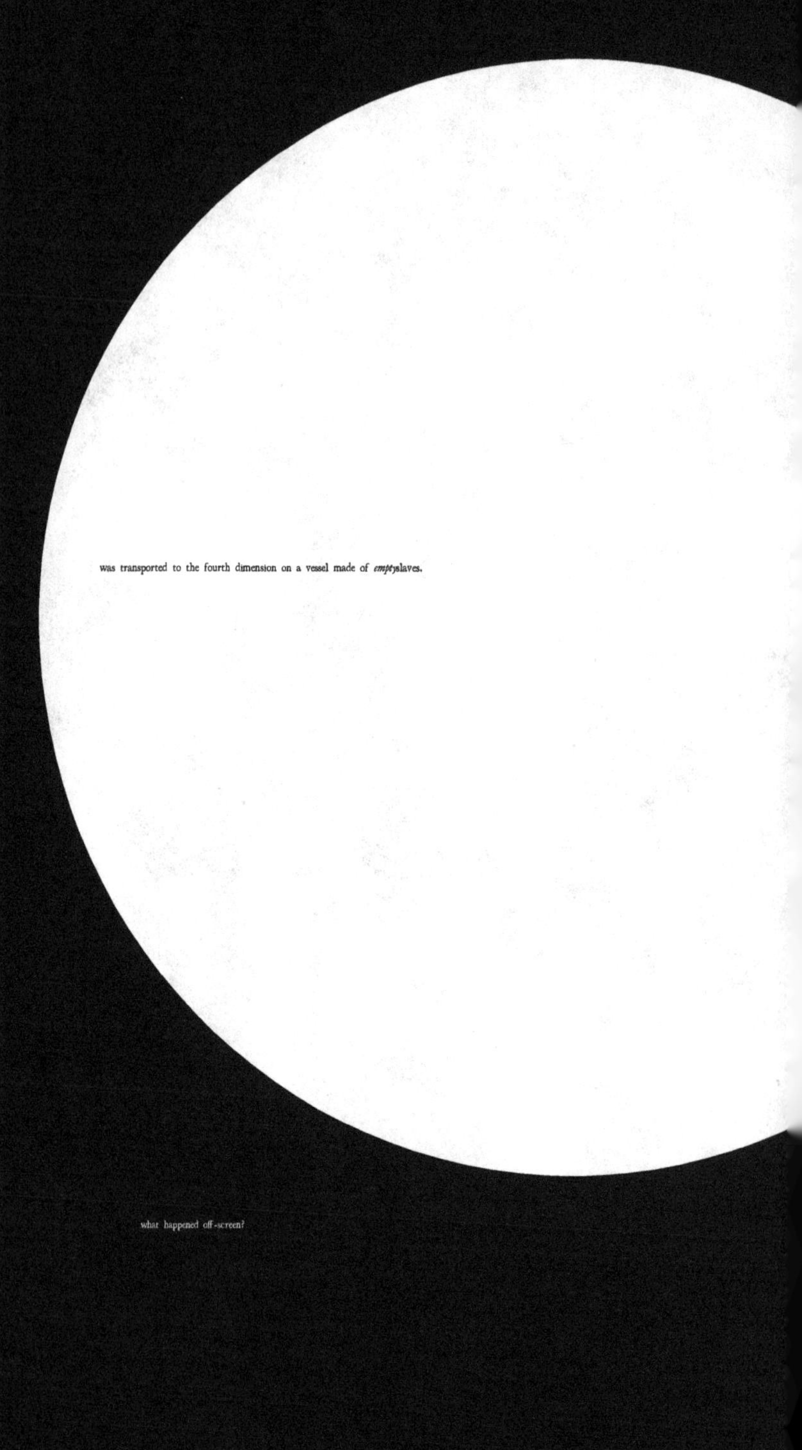

was transported to the fourth dimension on a vessel made of *empty*slaves.

what happened off-screen?

carcasses
terrible *meat*nightmares.

& on the 8th day, the *bastard*sun devoured the *dread*naught.

Why I Trust the Castle Freak

by John Trefry

This book you are reading—I say reading in persistent presentness because of the nature of this book··· even if you have worked your way methodically from the frontmatter to the last page of its text tracing your finger along every character—pristine or deformed—adding each word to the last in a strand concurrent with the narrative of passing seconds in your surroundings··· you have not actually finished reading—, I myself have not even begun to read this book. I am waiting to hold it in my hands and read it just like you are reading it as an immaculately conceived physical fragment of my life, & I am tremendously looking forward to making *Lonely Men Club* a part of my life. It is the first volume from the "Castle Freak Remote

Residency for Generative Digital Composition." And just for a bit of background, this simply means it was a book of precisely 100,000 words that was written in 5 days. The Castle Freak is desirous of this quantity and duration for two reasons. Firstly, because such an undertaking is nearly impossible for an unassisted human—perhaps only matched historically by Balzac in his most peak sprint mode (30 words a minute for 15 hours a day)—and necessitates the introduction of computational methods into the creative process. Secondly, because one of the tenets of book-objectness that Inside the Castle strives for—distracted reading—is exceptionally fostered by long books. More about the desire for computational assistance later.

Although these two criteria are the only prescriptions of the Castle Freak, the underlying project is of rather more thickness in its expectations. All of our Inside the Castle texts are striving for an objectness that becomes noise analogous to our physical surroundings. Because most books are striving for effectiveness of signal—firmness, commodity, and delight, if you will—in that uniform endeavor they become—at a cultural level across all books—flattened into noise, unremarkable and indistinguishable from their peers. A book that is itself composed of noise, whose goals are distinct, becomes a signal blasting through the notion of "book" to manifest itself as an object that must be considered part of real life, not as veneer or portal into the noise of transactional culture. Imagine Merzbow's "Tokyo Times Ten" coming on your local top 40 station or your sound-like-Sufjan-Stevens stream. It is Eco's chalk mark around a crack in the wall, where that crack, because of the intentionality associated with demarcating it, becomes significant even though materially it is no different from its counterparts. It only has a frame around it. Inside the Castle books are not materially different—they are paper and words—but their intentionality makes them significant. There are many ways that a book can distinguish itself. They may be aberrant formally, linguistically, or structurally. Most works we would call "literature" endeavor to tackle at least one of these territories. Inside the Castle books endeavor to confront and congruently occupy the aberration of all three at once.

In all other Inside the Castle books there are methodologies at work that take positions against each of these three territories of literature. All of these methodologies have precedents in the last 500 years of world literature. I see digital methodologies as being truly schismatic and relatively new. They have existed in some form throughout the last 50 years—let's call it 50 years after Alison Knowles used Fortran to construct "A House of Dust"—, but only in the last decade have the tools become accessible to the relative luddite. As a writer I do not see a particular romance in the personal. I am excited to see my own work in excerpt and to not recognize it. I have gone to lengths to render down my consciousness into prose and to distance myself from recognizable traces of my biography or speaking voice in my work. Here I see the allure of the machine. Its alienation is something I am desirous of. I don't see the allure of digital means through the lens of late capitalism. I am not interested in the intelligence of machines to construct works of palatably commercialized conventional fiction, to generate seamless Star Wars or Harry Potter fanfic ad infinitum. I am not interested in products. I am interested in the brute force of the dæmon to produce aberrant works of literature that fit the disruptive and noisy Inside the Castle project. Although we are focusing these experiments in print, their ideal manifestation is in a constantly changing digital scroll or terrain with no top or bottom, no end, and no enduring landmarks, although with the internal congruency of its experience maintained by its programming (whether by a human or by another machine). I see the Castle Freak as being exploratory research toward this end.

This is the foundation for geologically ambivalent literature. In the hermeneutics of a conventional text we can work our way back through the machinations of composition, perhaps discovering resonance and clicking, but where the difference lies from something like automatic writing by a human let's say, or stuporously drunken writing, or Michaux's literary explorations of mescaline, where we can attribute luscious errata or fabulous unrealities or inconsistencies directly to the author's decision to get out of their own way with the filtration of their consciousness through one of these mechanisms, and although the digital form of composition on which the Castle Freak is predicated is yet another modus operandi in this lineage, its outcomes cannot be attributed to—Well that was

Mike Kleine, albeit Mike Kleine on the computer—in the same way we could say—Well that was Dick, but it was Dick on amphetamines—. With digital composition we may be able to ascertain how, but never why. Why involves a series of questions independent of the text. Whereas in conventional writing—including even the most outlandish methods guiding the human hand away from the voices in its head—the how and why exist in the same vessel. Digital composition is not a subconscious choice or reaction untethered from the extreme care of the conscious writer, it is a fully intentional—arguably more intentional than any human choice can be—operation made by an entity with enough intelligence to do the work but lacking even the most reptilian oversight over that work. The computer need not inherently have the hang-ups that the reptilian human consciousness has. Things like proportion, rhythm, texture, and reasonable affect are not part of the computer's innate intelligence because they are not part of its biology the way they are for us. In this way the Castle Freak is a geological project. It is indebted to the physics that make it possible, which do have limitations, yet none of the æsthetic self-consciousness of the sculptor. The mountain is beautiful to us because, even though we know how it came to be, we know we had nothing to do with it. Even Smithson would have directed which side of the woodshed the dumptruck should back up to unload its dirt.

***

We are looking for the vague thread of literature. The labyrinth is a reactionary transparency in text that is connected to mid-19th century "innovations" of literature that to this day continue to scour at the opacity of literature's original project: indulgence in the possibility of text. Literature's richness is in its emptiness, the structural hollowness in the picaresque of Cervantes and Sterne that gives over the entire being of a book to the thickness of its language, not the fidelity of its momentum. And through the iterative and uncertain quality of *Lonely Men Club*'s computational origins, it is a lovingly reinvigorated model for the picaresque.

Now you've read the book, you've touched your finger tenderly to every word to make it physical with your body and your surroundings. And I have done the same now. Yet neither of us has finished the book. Mike Kleine told me at some point in the lead-up to his residency that the book would be something one could read for their entire lives. It isn't Queneau's permutative sonnet packed with 200,000,000 years of reading pleasure. *Lonely Men Club* is not a book about duration. Its potential is not in time but in space. It is a book that exists much like its protagonist—the etherically dull Zodiac—who, with the geographic instability of an electron, cannot be isolated in space and time. *Lonely Men Club* is always new, as are you and your consciousness, furtively adaptable, magically present. Keep reading.

Acknowledgements

Ken Sparling, John Trefry, M. Kitchell, Glass Bead, Editions Gallimard, Luna Luna Magazine, Andy Prunty, Tyler Crumrine, Jarett Kobek, Johnny Buse, Christian Caminiti, MAGICIEN-NOIR (my PC), Catherine Breillat, Samsung SSD 850 EVO (x2), Ann Quinn, NVIDIA GeForce GTX 1060 6GB, Scarlett 2i2 USB, Brother HL-2280DW (printer), SMSL SA50 50Wx2 Amp, Yuichi Yokoyoma, Kensington Slimblade Trackball, Open Books (for all the books), Topre Realforce 87U Tenkeyless 55g (White / Gray), Ben Frost, AKAI MPK Mini MK2, BenQ GW2765-4 (monitor), Gertrude Stein, Sony MD-7506 (headphones), David Markson, Koss PortaPro Headphones, Alain Guiraudie, Halter ED-600 (Standing) Desk, Dave Smith Instruments Prophet '08, Austin Breed, Micca MB42X, Patrick Kyle, Paul John Adams (Zadignose), KORG Electribe 2, Calvin Klein Men's Underwear (Body Modal), my mother & father, anytime I am able to get 5+ hours of sleep, Edouard Levé, ProForm 505 CST (2016 Model), Marie Howe, Sony Playstation 4, Vizio M43-C1 43-Inch 4K Ultra HD Smart LED TV (2015 Model), co-workers (who shall remain nameless, for their own benefit), CV Hunt, Harry Mathews, Nick Montfort, Microsoft Word 2016, Rinko Kawauchi, Microsoft Publisher 2016, Microsoft Windows 10 Home, e e cummings, Intel® Core™ i5-6500 CPU @ 3.20GHz, Lawrence English, Notepad + +, Notepad (regular), Abbas Kiarostami, Cedar Rapids Public Library, Propellerhead Reason Essentials 10, Twitter, Apple iTunes, Google Chrome, Twine & Mario Macías.

#

A

a flashlight
a foley artist
a footwork battle
a forgotten cave
a forgotten timeline
a former child actor
a former Hitler Youth
a genetic counselor
a Geodesic Surrealist
a Gnostic philosopher
a graffiti artist
a great fire
a group of spelunkers exiting a cave
a guy
a handkerchief
a headache
a health product spokesperson
a hedonist
a historian
a Holocaust sympathizer
a home
a homosexual
a hot dog vendor
a hotel
a house
a hut
a Jesuit
a jetsetter
a language professor
a laundromat
a librarian
a limousine
a linguist
a live mannequin
a lobster enthusiast
a man lazing on a steamy beach in a hammock
a mansion
a marine bioligist
a marriage counselor
a masseuse
a match stick man
a mathematician
a media mogul
a mesmerist
a metaphysician
a migraine
a missile
a model
a modern artist
a moral realist
a motel
a museum enthusiast
a music critic
a music producer
a new beginning
a Newport
a nightclub
a notebook
a novel
a novella
a nucler phycisist
a pacificst
a pack of Camels
a pack of Marlboro Lights
a painter
a paleontologist
a patrol car
a pearl diver
a pen and piece of paper
a perfumier
a pessimist
a phlebotomist
a phlebotomist
a picture
a place
a plant
a playwright
a pod
a poem
a police officer
a politician
a pornographer
a potato
a priest
a primatologist
a professional organizer
a psychic
a psychonaut
a quasi-realist
a radical
a rapper
a red sky
a researcher at the Institute of Extraspatial Studies
a rocket
a Satanist
a scalping
a ship
a shooting party connoisseur
a short story
a shot
a singer
a social worker
a socialite
a soil conservationist
a sommelier
a space gate
a spiral strike
a sports car
a State Express 555
a station
a stick of butter
a stomach virus
a stunt double
a submarine cook
a substance abuse counselor
a summer home
a sweet potato
a tacher
a teacher
a telivision news anchor
a tennis player
a terrible nightmare
a theoretical physicist
a therapist
a tribe in Africa
a tub of vaseline
a typewriter
a vagrant
a vessel
a view

a villa
a voice actor
a watchmaker
a white hat hacker
a wholesaler
a window
a woman
a woman running
a woman sitting in a very sinister-looking chair
a womanizer
a writer
AAaAAA AA Aa a
aaaA a aAAAAA AaA
aa aAAa a AAaaaa
aAAAAaAAAAaAAAA
aAA AAa
AAAAAAAaAAAa
aaAAAaaaaaaa AAA
aaaa aAA Aa A aAAA
A AAaaaAaAaaaaAa
Aaa'mp-Uhr
abortion
Absolute Carnage
absolute zero
abstract
Accelerationism
accidentface
acid
acidification
Adam
adderall
Addesyn
Adirondack
Adobe Mountain Desert Railroad
adolescence
Adrianna
Adsit Log Cabin
adventurer slim-fit cotton-blend twill trousers by Nonnative
aeons
aesthetics
affairs
Africa
Africa Landscape
African Safari Man
Afropessimism
afternoons
Agatha Kristiii
AGM-114 Hellfire
Ahmad Suradji
AIDS
Aimé Césaire
Air Pressure Boy
Airplane Man
Airport
Ak-Chin Him-Dak Eco
Al
Al-
Alabama
Alan
Alaska by Dore O
Albariño
Alcatraz Island
Alchemy
Alejandro
alert
Al-Faseeque
Algernon
algorithmic trading
Alice
All in the Family
Al-Ma'arh
alpha industries oversized reversible padded shell bomber jacket by Vetements
Al-Sayeer
alternateworld
Alton
Am'Salaam
Amazon Boy
Amazon Moon Girl
amber
ambient music
American Maple
American Slap-Dash
amor fati
amyl nitrite
an ambulance
an apartment
an apprentice
an area
an ark
an astronomer
an astrophysicist
an avant-garde poet
an avocado
an e-cig
an educator
an electric car enthusiast
an embalmer
an entire pack of Djarum Blacks
an equestrian
an ethical subjectivist
an ethnobotanist
an exotic car
an ideologist
an illusionist
an island caretaker
an island dictator
an ocularist
an old beginning
an omelette
an oncologist
an onion
an ophthalmologist
an oral surgeon
Anabelle Hemm
Anaïs
Analects of Confucius
analogue mountain
analogue violence
Anatomy of Hell by Catherine Breillat
Ancestor Man
ancient philosophies
ancient symbols
angels
angry cat embroidered intarsia wool sweater by Gucci
animals
An-Inkh-Tah
Ann Norton Sculpture

B

blazing
Blight
Blimp Man
blöd
blond
blonde
blood
blood red
Bloodhound UK surface-to
-air
Bloom
blue
blue kei slim-fit striped
cotton seersucker blazer
by Canal
Blue Rock Springs
Blu-ray
blushing
Bob Dylan
Bobek
bodega
bodies
bodily fluids
body activism
body-shaming
bombed out
Bon Iver
bone
Book of Mormon
bottled water
boulders
box room
Bradley Hoover
brain
bravery
bread
bread pudding
breakfast
Brendan Perry
Brian
Brick Face
bright light
bright lights
bright white
broccoli
Broken Brain
broken memories
broken promises
Bronck House
Brother Cyst
Brother Evans
Bruce High Quality
brunch
brutalized
bubbles
Buchla Touché
Buckingham Palace
Buffalo Bill
building
Building Boy
bullfight in spain
Burger King
burgundy wine
burning cars
burning oceans
Bushido Blade
butchered
buying in
bystander intervention

C

Cabernet Franc
Cabernet Sauvignon
Caliban
California
call out culture
calm
Camera Obscura
Canadian Glory
canvassing
capital flows
Car-Crash Samantha
Car-Crash Samantha (and
her whole squad)
care workers
care workers
Carignan
Carissa
Carl's Jr.
Carménère
Caryl
Casio CZ-101
Casio CZ-5000
Castle Man
castles
castrated
catawba
Catholic imagery
catholicism
Cattaraugus County
cauliflower
caves
Caves of Paradise
CcccccccCccCCCC
cCCCccCCCC
CCCCCccCCCccCcccCC
CC cCCCccCCCC
CCCcccCCCC cCCCC
CCCcccccccCCCCcc
cCCCC CCCcccCCC
cccC cCCCC
CCCccccCCCC cCCCC
CCCcc cc CCCCCCc
ccCCCC ccccCCCCC cc
cc cc cCCC cC CC
Célébration d'un mariage
improbable et illimité by
Eugène Savitzkaya
cellar
censorship
Central Park
centre
centuries
Chadwick
champagne
Chanda
Chandler
chaos theory
Chardonnay
Charles
Chase-Maker
cheers
Cheetah MS-6
Chemical
Chenin blanc
Chest wound
Chiaroscuro Bay

child models
Christabel by James Fotopoulos
Christian
Christian Bible
Chronicles
chrysanthemum tea
Cinderella
Cinnabon
cipher
cities
city market
Clarice Lispector
Clarkdale Historical Society and
Clavia Nord Modular G1
Clavia Nord Modular G2
clawfoot tubs
climate redlining
Cloak Piece
cloakroom
closets
cloud
clouds
cloud deaths
Cloud Eater
coastlines
cocaine
cocktail party
Cocteau Twins
codeine
Cohle
coin
Coin Flip
cold
Colin Stetson
collaborations
colon
Colorado
colour-block cotton-piqué polo shirt by Thom Browne
colour-block satin-twill shorts by Dries Van Noten
Columbo
Comanche Man
comedians
commensalism
company towns
concepts
condor
confession
conflagrum
Connecticut
conservatory
contemplating life
contemplating the cosmos
contemplating the infinite void
contractors
cool jobs
cooling systems
cooties
cosmic fortitude
cosmic horror
cosmic integrity
Costume Man
couldn't believe it
cover letters
covert ops
coworking
creation science
Crowd Girl
cry
crypt
Crystal River
crystals
cuckolding
cultural fits
Curb Your Enthusiasm
curious
cursed
curses
cutting myself
cyberspaces

D

D.D Dumbo
D'agrhiil
Dairy Queen
Damien
Dance Dance Dance
dangercrime
Danica
Daniel
dank
Dao de jing
dark
dark horses
dark matter
Dark Pond
dark powers
dark spells
dark spirits
Darkness
Darwinism
databases
Daughter
Daughter of Earth
Dave Smith Instruments Prophet '08
Dave the Giant
Dave Toschi
David
David Lynch films
days
Days of Eclipse by Aleksandr Sokoruv
DddDDDdddDDDdddDD
DdddDDDdd dDDDdd
dDDDdddDDDddddddd
DDDdddDDDddDDdDD
Ddd
DDdDDDdddDDDdd D
DdD D D DDD dD
dead malls
Dead Mountaineer Hotel by Grigori Kormanov
deadlines
deamons
Dean Corll
death
death with dignity
decades
December
deception

Deckard's Dream
Dēcor ciment by François Bon
Dedalus
deep
Deepak
deer meat
Deerhunter
defectors
dejected
Delaware
Delma
Denise
Denny's
desalination
desert islands
desert storms
dessert wine
destroyed
detractors
Deux fois by Jackie Raynal
Dhammapda
Dharma & Greg
Dhvnvnjvy
diasporas
died
Dif Juz
Diggins
digital philosophy
dim
din
dining room
dinner
dinner party
Dirty Beaches
dirty laundry
disability
Disappeared
disease
diseased
disembowled
disgrace
distillation
Djeet-
dock stretch-cotton shorts by J.Crew
domes
Dongfeng 51
Donn
doxxing
Dracula black
drained
draining
draining-the-swamp
drawing room
dreams
dreams I've had
dreams I've never had
Drexciya
drifting
drip
dripmouth
drone
drop
droughts
drowning
drowning tongues
drugs
drukqs
Dunkin' Donuts
duplex
dusk
dust
duty
Dvaita Vedanta
DVD
Dvina
dynaTAC 8000

E

Earth
earth loops
earth magnets
eastham slim-fit washed stretch-denim jeans by Belstaff
Easy Target
eaton slim-fit stretch-twill shorts by Ralph Lauren Purple Label
Eddie Seda
Edward Snowden
EeeeeEEE EEE EEe
eeeeEEEeEEE EEE EEe
eeeeEEEeEE EEE EEE
EEe eEE EEE EEe
eeeeEEEeEE
EeeeEEEeEE EEE EEE
EEe eeeEEEE EEE EEe
eeeeEEEeEE E EEE EEe
eeeeEEEeEE EeEEEeEE
EEE EEE EEe
eeeeEEEeEE EEE EEE
EEe eeeeEEEeEE EEE
EEE EEe eeeeEEEeEE
EE EEE Eeeeee
EEeeEeEEEE EEE EEe
eeeeEEEeEE EEE
effervescence
egg donors
egg shells
eight
eighteen
Gilligan's Island
Elajou-
Electric potential
eleven
Eleven Ten
Elsa
Elsie
Emancipator 5000
embroidered loopback cotton-jersey shorts by Gucci
embroidered torch logo shirt by Opening Ceremony
Emma
Emma Emma
emotional labor
ending it all
endless
endless deaths
endometrial
Energy Girl
Entomophagy & the

Gesamtkunstwerk
GGGGGggg GG
gGgggg GGG gGGG
gggGGggGGGGGG
ggGGGGGGggg GG
gGgggg GGG gGGG
gggGGGGGGggg GG
gGgggg GGG gGGG
gggGGggGGGGGG
ggGGGGGG
GGGggGGGGggg GG
gGgggg GGG gGGG
gggGGggGGGGGG g
GG gGgggg GGG
gGGG
gggGGggGGGGGG
GGgGGGGggg GG
gGgggg GGG gGGG
gggGGggGGGGGG
Ghauri-III
ghost stories
ghosting
gigantic
Girl Drain
giving blood
glacial
Glen
Glissements progressifs du plaisir by Alain Robbe-Grillet
global warming
gnostic
god
goddess
gods
Godzilla
Godzilla Girl
going spelunking
Golden Paradise Girl
Goldilocks
Gomez
Graam'
graveyard lunches
greed
Green Flash
Green Olives
green tea
Gregory
grey
Griffis Sculpture Park
grocery store
Ground Hunter
ground loops
guest room
Guillermo
guinea pigs
Gumbo Limbo Environmental Complex
Gummo
Guru Granth Sahib
Guyotat
Gwen

H

H.P. Sears Oil Co. Service Station
hall
Hannibal
Hansel & Gretel
happy
Hardee's
Harrier Attack
Harrison
hate crimes
haunted
health insurance
heard
heart
Heaven & Hell
heavy
hedge funds
Hell
Henri
Henry B. Plant
herbal tea
heretics
Her'ktj
heterotopia
hhhhhHhhhhhhHHHhHHh
HHhH HHH hhh h
hHH Hh hHHHHHHH h
hHHhhhHHH
hhHhhhhhhHHHhHHhH
HhH HHH hhh h hHH
Hh hHHHHHHH h
hHHhhhHHH
hhHHHhHHhHHhH
HHH hhh h hHH Hh
hHHHHHHH h
hHhhhhhHHHhHHhHH
hH HHH hhh h hHH
Hh hHHHHHHH h
hHHhhhHHH
hhHHhhhHHH hhH
Hieronymus
high
high limit
high-rise
Hilary
hills
Hilltop Gallery
Historic Route 66
HIV
holes
holidays
home invasions
homeless
Hongqi-18
honor
honor killings
honour
hoop earrings
Horror
horror films
Horseman
horses
hot
hotel
hotel lobby
hours
house
houses
Howe Caverns
human capital
human meat
humid
hunger

Hydra
hygiene

I

I had been caught
I Love Lucy
I was a different person
I was a wolf
I was falling through space
ice
iconoclasm
Idaho
ideas
II
III
iIIIIiiiiIIIIIiiiiII II
IIIIIIIIIiiiiII II IiiiiIiiI
iii iiIIIIIIIiiiiII II
IiiiiIiiI iii iiIIIiiiiII II
IiiiiIiiI iii iiIII II
IiiiiIiiI iii iiIIIIIIIiiiiII
II IiiiiIiiI iii iiIIIiiiiII II
IiiiiIiiI iii iiIIIIIIIiiiiII
II IiiiiIiiI iii iiIIIIiiiiII
II IiiiiIiiI iii
iiIIIIIiiiIiiI iii
iiIIIIIIIiiiiII II IiiiiIiiI
iii iiIIIIIIIiiiiII II
IiiiiIiiI iii iiIIIII
IIIIiiiiII II IiiiiIiiI iii
iiIIIII IiiIIIIiiiiII II
IiiiiIiiI iii iiIIIiiiIiiI iii
iiIIIi iiiiiIiiI
Illinois
imaginary mountains
Imhotep-
immortal
Imp Creature
impossible
Impossible Now
impossible structures
impotence
impotent
in a little book
in my journal
in my planner
in my pocket notebook
incomplete
Indiana
Infamous Greg
infinite
infinite time warps
ingested
Ingrid
Inida
injected
inside jobs
insomniaque
Instant Machination
Instant Panic Man
instant teleportation
interns
intonation
invincible
invisible
invisible forces
Invisible Opaque
Iowa
Iranian philosophy
Iraq 911
Irene Lockwood
Irish Simple
IRIS-T
Irrevocable Man
irrigation
Isabel Allende
Isabelle
Israel
It was amazing
It was great
It was horrible
It was terrible
It was the worst
Italian Forever
Italo Calvino
IV
Ivan
ivory
IX
Izzy

J

Jacques
jai alai
Janey
January
Jay and Wayne
Jaysson
Jean-Pierre
Jenna
Jill
iJJJiJi iiiJiJi iiiJJJiiiJJJii
JJiJJiJiiiJJ iJJJ JJJJiiiiJi
iiiJJJiiiJJJii JJiJJiJiiiJJ
iJJJ JJJJiiiiJi iiiJJJiiiJJJii
JJiJJiJiiiJJ iJJJ JJJJiiiiJi
iiiJJJiiiJJJii
JJiJJiJiiiiiiJJiii iJJJ
iiJJJJiiiJJJiiiJJiJii
JJiiiiiiJJiJiiiJJ iiJi
iiiJJJiiiJJJii JJiJJiJiiiJJ
iJJJ JJJJiiiJJJ
JJJJiiiJJiiiJJJii JJiJJiJiiiJJ
iJJJ JJJJiii
John Wayne Gacy
Johnny
Josephhine Baker
joynamoz
Julianne
July
June
June Jordan
jungles
Jwnnd'd

K

Kan-Dhi
Kansas
Kawai K5m
Kawai SX-240
Kawai XD-5
kayaktivism
Keli
Ken

Kendrick
Kennedy Von-Trappe
Kentucky
Kevin
KFC
Khonsu-
killed
killing myself
Kinetic Fiend
kiosk
kKKKk kkKKKkKKKK
kkk kKKKkKKkkk
kKKkKkk kKkKKKKK
kkk kKKKkKKkkkkk
kkKKkkKKkkkKKkKkk
kkKKK kkk
kKKKkKKkkk
kKKkKkk kKkKKk kk
kKKkKkkkKKK kkk
kKKKkKKkkk
kKKkKkk kKkKKk kk
kKKkKkkkk kk
kKKkKkkk
knitted mélange virgin wool polo shirt by Boglioli
Known space
Korg microKorg
Korg Mono/Poly
Korg MS-20
Korg MS-50
Korg OW/1FD Pro
Korg Polysix
Korg PS-3100
Korg Radias
Korg Trident
Korg Wavestation
Krispy Kreme
Kyle

L

L'Homme qui tousse by Christian Boltanski
La casa de las mujeres perdidas by Jess Franco
La citadelle engloutie by Yvan Lagrange
La Communauté inavouable by Maurice Blanchot
La Fuite à cheval très loin dans la ville by Bernard-Marie Koltès
La Nuit juste avant les forêts by Bernard-Marie Koltès
L'Abbé C by Georges Bataille
Lake Berryessa
Lake Herman Road
Lake Tahoe
Lake Thing
lakes at dusk
Lana Del Rey
landing
landslide
Laraaji
larder
Large
laryngeal
laryngitis
lasagna
LaserDisc
Last Year at Marienbad by Alain Resnais
late nights
laughed
LaVilla
Law & Order
lawns
Lawrence
Lawrence English
Lazer Lazer
LCD screens
Le Renard et la boussole by Robert Pinget
Le Tempestaire by Jean Esptein
Le Vieillard et l'enfant by François Augiéras
leaderless resistance
Legend of the Forest
leprosy
Les Absences du capitaine Cook by Éric Chevillard
Les Atomiques by Éric Laurrent
Les chants de maldoror by Comte de Lautréamont
Les maitres fous by Jean Rouch
Lesha
Let Us Persevere in What We Have Resolved Before We Forget by Ben Russell
letter
LFK NG
library
life
life insurance
life on mars
light from the heavens
Light Licks: By the Waters of Babylon: I Want to Paint it Black by Saul Levine
light posts
like I was Superman
like the scum of the earth
Lil B
Lindsay Lohan
linen shorts by Barena
Lionel
lip service
liquefaction
liquid fear
liquid metal
liquid nitrogen
liquidation
Little Red Riding Hood
liturgy
Lived a past life
liver
living room
Liz
lLLLLllLLl lL

1LL1LL1111111111111111LL
11LL 1L 1LL1LL1 1L
1LL1LL1 1L
1LL111LLLL1 11
111LL1LL1 1L 1LL1LL1
1L 1LL111LLLL1 11
111LL111LLLL1 11
111LLL 1LL1 1L
1LL1LL1 1L
1LLLLL1LL1LL1 1L
1LL 1LLLL1 1LL111
lobster
L'Océan by Raphaël
Alegria
Lo-Fang
Lo-Fi Man
Loggerhead
long hallways drenched in sunlight
Long John Silver's
looking at waves
looting
Lord Altruistic
Lord Langston
Louisiana
love notes
Luciferian
Luis Garavito
Lunar Man
lunch

M

M
M. Geddes Gengras
M.A.S.H
M.M.M.M. by Jean-Philippe Toussaint
M45 SLBM
Ma'am-Puut
Ma'an-Taap
Mabel
Machu Picchu
Mad Men
Madame Brainwave
maddox linen and cotton-blend oxford shorts by Club Monaco
Madeira wine
Magic Kingdom
magickal things
magnificent
Maine
make love to
Malbec
Maldoror
male breast
male frontal nudity
malls
Mandarin
manifestations
manners
Manuel
Mao Mao
Maoupa Cedric Maake
March
marco slim-fit garment-dyed stretch-cotton twill chinos by NN07
Marguerite Duras
Maria
Marion
Marosa di Giorgio
Martian Marshall
Marty
marvelous
Maryland
masking tape
masochism
mass consumerism
Massachusetts
massive
Massive Deer Sacrifice
masturbation
Maxx Koch
May
Mayneard
Mayor Tomlin
McDonald's
meat
Meat & Cleaver
meatloaf
mechanical turks
medieval literature
Melvin Macintosh
memorials
Mensa Mentalis
mental health
Mental Imager
Merlin
Merlot
mescaline
Meshuggah
Metallic Green
metaphysics
methane
Mia
Miami horror
Miami in 1978
Michael
Michael Jordan
Michigan
micro
micro entrepreneurs
micro islands
micro loans
microTAC
microTAC 8200
microTAC elite
microTAC ii
microTAC international 8900
midnight-blue slim-fit tapered stretch-jersey suit trousers by Wooyoungmi
Migraine Man
militias
mills
mind bullets
Mind Mantis
Minerva
minimal violence
miniscule
Minnesota
minutes
mirror neurons
missile
Mississippi

Missouri
Mister Magnetic
Mister RepCon 35
Mme Claude
MMM mmMM mM M
mM m MM MM mM m
MM MMMmmmmM mM
m MM MMMmmM mM
m MM MMMmM mM
m MM MMM mM mM
m MM MMMmM mM
m MM MMMM mM m
MM MMMmM mM m
MM MMMmmM mM m
MM MMMMMm MMM
mM m MM MMMM
mM m MM MMM
MMMMmmM mM m
MM
MMMmmmMMMmMmM
m MM mMM M M Mm
MMM MM M
Mnemo
modern English
modern Islamic philosophy
Modesto
moist
Moldorf
Molly
MoMA
moments
Monday
Monster Minion
monstrosities
Montana
Moog Prodigy
Moon 1969 by Scott Bartlett
moon radiography imaging
Moons Pool by Gunvor Nelson
moonshine
Mopus
moral code
Morning Air
mornings
morose
moss
Mothra Man
Mounds of Fury
mountain
mountain deaths
mountain winds
mountains
mouth
MPAA
Mr. Cancel
Mr. Cold War
Mr. Fear
Mr. Inspirational
Mr. Mahmoud
Mr. Oizo
Mr. Tomorrow
Mrs. Macintosh
Muji
murder
murdered
Muscat
museum
museums
music
music room
Mutianyu
my doctor
my favourite mountain
my ideas
my orb
my physician
my thoughts
mysterious light
mystery
mystics
mythical characters doused in oil
Mz. Beautiful You

N

namazlıq
Napoleon Bonaparte
narcissism
NASA Block
Nasty Carl
National Bottle
nationalism
Navy Pier
NDAs
Neat-o-Mosquito
Nebraska
Neil Halstead
networking
Nevada
New Hampshire
New Jersey
New Mexico
New Orleans
New Rose Hotel by Abel Ferrara
New York
new-age spirituality
newyork
nextweek
Nic
Night of the Hunted by Jean Rollin
nights
Nikki Castro
nine
nineteen
ninety-nine
nippy
NNNNNNNNnnnnNNn
N nN nNNnnnnn nN
nNnNNnnnNNNn nN
NN NNn nn n nNN nN
nNNn
noise
Nomenclature Society Man
nonexistent
non-monogamy
Nord SS.12
North Carolina
North Dakota
North Korea
notes
nothing

November
now
nudity
NYCHA

O

O.J. Simpson
oak trees
obfuscated memories
Oblivion by Tom
Chomont
Observatory
obsession with wealth
Obu
Ocarina II
Occult
Octavio Paz
October
of a black ocean
of a desert that went
forever
of a desert turning to
glass
of Aimē Cēsaire
of ASMR
of atomic bombs
of balconies
of balconies at night
of baroque literature
of beach rituals
of bellies
of bikes in summer
of black cats
of black water
of blood
of bodies
of body activism
of Catholic imagery
of Clarice Lispector
of clawfoot tubs
of dead malls
of dreams
of egg shells
of existentialism
of Francesca Woodman
of ghost stories
of Godzilla
of graveyard lunches
of hoop earrings
of horror films
of Isabel Allende
of Italo Calvino
of ivory
of Jacob's ladder
of Josephhine Baker
of June Jordan
of lakes at dusk
of Lana Del Rey
of late afternoon light
of long hallways drenched
in sunlight
of love notes
of Marguerite Duras
of Marosa di Giorgio
of Michael Jordan
of New Orleans
of nuclear devices
of nudity
of Octavio Paz
of palaces
of palm trees
of patent leather
of petals pressed into
books
of pink leather
of planets in space
of rain
of rose perfume
of roses
of sand
of sand turning to glass
of satin
of seance circles
of shells
of Sofia Coppola
of Spanish table wine
of the cosmos
of the desert
of the Love Witch
of the Nile
of the ocean
of the Psalms
of the sea
of the subterranean
of tiny charms
of tiny vials
of upside-down crosses
of vanities
of velvet
of Victoriana
of Vladimir Nabakov
of walls falling down
of water magic
of white linen
of white socks
of wide brim hats
of wide windows
of wooden things
office
Officer Genocide
Ohio
oil
Oil Boy Junior
Oklahoma
Olivia
Omo
on some flash cards
on some index cards
on some loose leaf paper
One of the three little
pigs
one thousand
Oneohtrix Point Never
oolong
oooOOoOooOOO
oOOOOooOO OOOoo
oo oooooo o oOO
oOOooo o oo OOO
oOOO o ooo
oOOOOOO
oOooOOOOooooooOOO
O oOO oOOO
oOOoOOO oOOOOO
oOOO oOOo
OOOOOOoO
Opaque Road
Open Watts

open windows
open wounds
oral
orange
Orange Moon Glow
orbs
Oregon
Ortlip Gallery
Oswald
other
otherdimension
Otomat
Ottis Toole
outcasts
outing
outlaws
overdyed cotton-jersey
drawstring shorts by Cav
Empt
overlapping timelines
oversized camp-collar
printed voile shirt by
Alexander McQueen
oxbow
Ozone Pink
Ozymandias
Ozymandius

P

paid protesting
pain
paint mixing videos
palaces
palm trees
Palms
pancreatic
pantry
Papaya: Love Goddess of
the Cannibals by Joe
D'Amato
paper
parapsychologist
parasitism & a few
parasitism & some
Parcelle by Rose Lowder
PARD 3 LR
pariahs
Park
parlour
particle
party
Pasadena Clarity
pasahapan
passed out
passion projects
pasta
Pastor Woman
Pat
patent leather
Patricia
Patsy
Paul
Paul Avery
Pd'it
Peace be With You Boy
penitence
Pennsylvania
people in the street
Periodical Man
permalancing
pestilence
petals pressed into books
Peter Tom Fiber Optic
Traitor
PGM-19 Jupiter
phantom loops
Phase 9
Phil
pickleball
Picture Perfect
Pieces
pig's blood
Pike Place Market
pills
Pin Star Stripe Woman
pink labor
pink leather
pinkwashing
Pinocchio
Pinot noir
Pinotage
pioneer
Pioneer Fire
pipelines
Pippa
pirates
pissing your pants
Pistol Matt
Pitchfork Woman
pity
Pixies
place
places
plane
Planet Earth
Plantation
Plasma
Plasma Technician Boy
Plastics
Pleasant Steve
pleat
pleated wool-blend suit
trousers by Camoshita
Pluton
pneumonia
pod wide-leg cady shorts
by Rick Owens
poem
politics
polyamory
Polybius
pooled funds
Popeye's
pork
porn
porn culture
port
posers
Powell
powerful
pppPppPpppppppPPppp
pPpPppPPPPPPPPPPPP
PPPPPPppppp pppp p
pPPPPPP p
pPPpPPppppp
pPPPppPpPPpppppp
pPPp pp p pPPPPPP p

pPPpPP
pPPPPPppPpPPp pPPp
pp p pPPPPPP p
pPPpPP pPPP broken
prayer mat
prayer rug
predictive performance
Premier Amour by Samuel Beckett
President Nixon
Presidio Heights
Prince
Prince Psycho
printed cotton-jersey t-shirt by Noon Goons
prison labor
Prithvi III
private island caretakers
private soirée
privatization
Professor 5th Dimension Physics
Prosecco
prostate
Pseudosciences
psionic
psychoanalysis
public feelings
purification
purple
pyramids

Q
queers
Quentin
questioning the meaning of life
Quizno's
Qur'an

R

R5550 Magic
R-60
Ra'amuul-raat'Dean
race traitors
radio
Rambo Incorporated
ramirez
Raoul
rape culture
ratings
ray
rectal
red
reparations
Reproductive Futurism
restaurant
reverberation
Rhode Island
rice
Riesling
riparian dreams
rising tides
ritual
rivers
Riverside Community College
Robert
Robert Graysmith
Roketsan Cirit
Roland D-50
Roland Jupiter 4
Roland Promars MRS-2
Roland RS-101
Roland SH-5
Roland SH-7
Roland System 100m
room acoustics
Rosé
rose perfume
Roseanne
roses
Rosson House
Roy
RrrRR RRRrRR
RRRrrrrRRrrrRRrrRR
RRRrrrRRrRR
RRRrrrRRrRR
RRRrrrRR rRR
RRRrrrRRrrrrrrr r rrr
rrr rrRR
RRRrrrRRRRRrRR
RRRrrrrrRRRrrrRRrR
R RRRrrrRRrRR
RRRrrrRRrrrrrrRrrRR
RRRrrrRRrRR
RRRrrrRRrRR
RRRrrrRRRRrrrrRRR
RRrRr R RRRRrrr
ruin
Ruined
run offs
Ruth

S

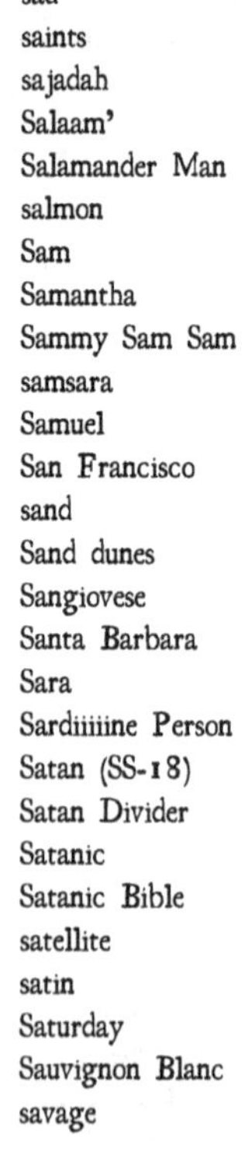

sabotage
sad
saints
sajadah
Salaam'
Salamander Man
salmon
Sam
Samantha
Sammy Sam Sam
samsara
Samuel
San Francisco
sand
Sand dunes
Sangiovese
Santa Barbara
Sara
Sardiiiiine Person
Satan (SS-18)
Satan Divider
Satanic
Satanic Bible
satellite
satin
Saturday
Sauvignon Blanc
savage

Savage (SS-13)
Savage Paper
savagery
scab rats
scapegoats
scarlet letters
school shootings
scissors
scorching
screening for a new film
scrubs
sea shells
seance circles
searing
seccade
secret
secret societies
Seinfeld
sejadah
self care
self harm
self-bosses
sself-deception
self-immolation
selling out
semantics
Sēmillon
September
Setesh-
seven
seventeen
Seventeen Layers
Sex and the City
sexual assault
shade
shadows
Shahab-3D
Sham-
Sham'raat-Al'Dean
Shandi
Shapes
sharing economies
sharp
Sheep
Sherry
shetland wool sweater by
Prada
Shield
shipping channels
Shiraz
shit
Shook my head
shoplifting
short stories
shunning
side hustles
Sig For Die
Sighed
Sigma by Julia Deck
silence
Silver Heads by Yevgeny
Yufit
Simona by Patrick Long-
champs
simpler times
Sinister Valley
Sink or Swin by Su
Friedrich
sinking and floating
sinners
Sister Creature
Sister Moonlight
six
sixteen
sizzurp
skeletons in the closet
skilled migrants
Skills & Violence
skin
Skull Hand
Sky Sword II
Skyhead
Skyscraping
Slam Punk
slavery
slaves
Sleeping Beauty
Slept
slim-fit grosgrain-trimmed
wool-twill tank top by
Calvin Klein
205W39NYC
Slow burning car
Smithsonian Institution
smoke
snitching
Snow White
snowy
soccer
social event
Societies
Society
society and people
Sofia Coppola
soiled
soirée
soldiers
soldiers
Sombre by Philippe
Grandrieux
some beef
some cars in the street
some cats
some cinnamon
some flour
some freaky cave-dwellers
surrounding a camp fire
some garlic
some ham
some honey
some ice cream
some lamb shoulder
some lobster
some meat
some milk
some mountains
some of the other apart-
ments
some other buildings
some pasta
some pasta sauce
some peanut butter
some people running away
from a falling tree
some pictures
some place
some rope
some sardines

some sausage
some shots
some spinach
some strawberries
some yogurt
somewhere
Song & Dance Man
Song of the sirens
Sophie
Sorcerers
SOS
soul
sound
South America
South Carolina
South Dakota
space
space disasters
spacetime violence
SpaceGhostPurrp
spacetime
Spanish table wine
spanking
spare room
Sparkling wine
Spectacular Sequence Boy
speculation
sperm donors
spinach
spiritual
spitting
sponsored content
spring
squid
Standard
Standing Rock
Star Trek: The Next Generation
State of Emergency Woman
static
status
STDs
steak
stealing time
Stereolab
Steven with the Body
stigmas
stikes
stillbirths
stone
Stonehenge
stop lights
store
Storm Setter
streamers
streaming
strikes
striped cotton t-shirt by Beams Plus
striped cotton-dobby shorts by Neighborhood
sublimation
Subway
Suffer Man
suicide
suicides
suiciding
summer
summery
Sunday
SUNN O)))
super
supper
surface tension
surreal
survivor's guilt
swallowed
swells
sweltering
Symone
Synthia-China Blast

T

Ta'am'Riip
Taco Bell
Tamp-Q'uun
Tanakh
tar and feather
Tara
Tarp Girl
Tarzan Girl v.8.3
teachers
tears in the rain
Technics SY-1010
Ted Bundy
Ted Kaczynski
Tekhrit-
teleportation
television
Temple
Tempranillo
ten
Tennessee
tennis
Terminator Boy-Wonder
Terrence
Terror
Terror Disguise
Texas
Texture Keeper
tfw
the African continent
the Air
the Alps
the Amazon forest
tthe American prison system
the apostles
the aquarium
the Arabs
the arcade
the Art Institute of Chicago
the Ask
the beginning
the beginning of the universe
the Black Atlantic
the bottom of the lake
the Brady Bunch
the Brand
the bystander effect
the car park
the cave life
the city
the clouds

the Cluster
the colour of the sky
the cosmos
the Croton Aqueduct
the cult of fame
the darkness
the darkness of space
the Deepwater Horizon
the dentist
The Dick Van Dyke Show
the doctor
the doctor shortage
the doctor's office
the Eiffel Tower
the end
the Escape Plan
the eye doctor
the Fascist Kiss
the Filth
the Final Reason
the first dimension
the flu
the fourth dimension
The Fresh Prince of Bel-Air
the futility of life
the future
the future
the gas station
the Golden Gate Bridge
The Golden Girls
the government
the Grand Canyon
The Great Gatsby by F. Scott Fitzgerald
the Great Purge
the Great Pyramid of Giza
the Great Wall
the gym
the Hanging Gardens of Babylon
the Happening
The Homosexual Century by Lionel Soukaz
the Imperial Detective
the impermanence of human life
the IRS
the Italian Unabomber
the judicial system
the King in Yellow
the landfill
the late afternoon light
the light
the Lighthouse of Alexandria
the lives of animals
the London Zoo
the Love Witch
the mall
the Man of Oil
the Man of One Thousand Years
The Mary Tyler Moore Show
the Mausoleum at Halicarnassus
The Metropolitan Museum of Art
the Möbius strip
the Monster of Florence
the moon
the mythic power of images
The National
The New Abel & Cain
the nudging state
the ocean
the Odd Couple
the ozone
the pain I was feeling in my head
the Palm Tree
the park
the past
the Patchwork
the planet Jupiter
the planet Mars
the planet Pluto
the planets
the pool
the Pppppplannnnettt
the present
the Priest Bishop
the Psalms
The pyramids of Egypt
the rain
The Rapture by Michael Tolkin
The Rapture by Michael Tolkin
the Remover
the San Francisco Chronicle
The San Francisco Examiner
the sauna
the sea
the sea of data
the second dimension
the serpent
the seven deadly sins
the sex offender registry
The Shield
the side of a house
the sky
The Sopranos
the sound of nothing
the Squid
the Statue of Liberty
the Statue of Zeus at Olympia
the subterranean
the sun
The Suns of Easter Island by Pierre Kast
the Temple of Artemis at Ephesus
the terror
the Tower of London
the Tower of Silence
the Trilluminati Gang
the tropicks
The Twilight Zone
the umbilic torus
the University

the Vallejo Times Herald
the visions I was having
the war in Vietnam
The West Wing
The Wild blue frontier
The X-Files
the zoo
Theatre Sydrome
theatres
theories
theory
Theresa
these headaches
these migraines
Thessalonian
thick
Thierry
things no one could see
third worlds
thirteen
this apartment
this couple walking their dog
this guy
this lady
this place
this villa
this woman
three
throat
Thumbelina
Thursday
Tibetan sky burials
Tiger Flow
tilapia
Tim
Tim Hecker
Timber Girl
tiny charms
tiny futures
tiny vials
tired
Tire-Iron Mark
Tiresia by Bertrand Monello
Tito
today
Tokyo
tomorrow
tone
took
tornadoes
torture
towers
townhouses
Toxic Maxx
Trash Talk
Travis
Treatise of a Modern Man
trench
Trespass the World
Trevor from Tomorrow
tried
triplex
Trois jours chez ma tante by Yves Ravey
tropical
trust funds
truth and reconciliation commissions
trying to make sense of things
trying to understand life
tubing lazily down the river
Tuesday
tuna
Tune-Yards
Tungsten Girl
turbo-capitalism
tv
twelve
twenty
twenty-five
twenty-four
Twentynine Palms by Bruno Dumont
twenty-one
twenty-three
twenty-two
twiggy
Twilight Man
Twin Peaks: Fire Walk With Me by David Lynch
Twin Peals
two
two French revolutionaries
two ogre heads
Tyrant Girl

U2
UBI
Ultimate Black
ultra lite
ultrafucked
undamming
underground carpark
Underground Ned
union busting
unions
universal function
unofficial economies
upside-down crosses
urethral
Utah
utility room
UUM-125 Sea Lance
UuUUUuU UUU u uuuUUUu uuuuuuu uu uu uuuuu u uUUUuu uu UuUUUUuuuuu uu u UUuuUUUUUUu uU Uu uU UUU u uUUUUuuUUuuUuuuuuu uuUUUu UUUu uUU UU uUUUUU uU uuUU

V.
Valet Boy
Vallejo
vanities

VCD
velvet
Vermont
VI
vibrations
victim blaming
victims
Victor
Victoriana
vigilantes
VII
VIII
villas
Viognier
violated
violence to foreigners
Virginia
Virginia Slims
virgins
viscosity and resistance
visibility
Vite by Daniel Pommereulle
Vladimir Nabakov
voice
void
volcanoes
voodoo stuff
vortex

W

wage theft
Wall Climber
walls falling down
Walmart
Warlocks
warm
Warp Rider
Washington
wastewater
watching the waves
water
water births
water magic
water parks
waterfalls
watermarkets
Wavelength by Michael Snow
waves
Wednesday
weeks
Weltschmerz
Wendy's
West Virginia
wetting the bed
what am I doing here
what happened off-screen
what is my life
what is my purpose
what is the meaning of life
what is the point of life
what would I find beyond the edge of the screen
where was the border violence
white
white collar crimes
white guilt
white linen
white nationalism
white noise
white radicals
white socks
white supremacy
white tea
white tears
who was here right now
why am I here
why are we all here
why do we exist
wide brim hats
wide windows
wildlife
Will & Grace
Windsor Castle
wine
wine mixer
WingStreet
winter
wintry
Wisconsin
witchhunts
with a gun
with pills
with self-immolation
with some rope
with the harpoon gun
wives who work
wizards
wobble
wooden things
working girls
work-life balance
workplace friendships
wormholes
Wuthering Heights by Emily Brontë
Wyoming

X
xanax
Xenomorph
xxxxXXxx X XxxXxxx xxxx XXxx X xxxxXx xx X X XXxx xX x x xxXXX xxX xx xxx X Xxxx XX xxxXXX XX XX x x

yachts
Y'akiir-
Yamaha CS-60
Yamaha CS-80
Yamaha DX-1
yellow
Yellow Cousin
yellow tea
yesterday
Yet'Yett-
Yh'Um-Pr-Eie
Yianne

yoroke cotton-blend
sweater by Issey Miyake
Men
Yorrick
your past
Yucca Mountain
Yum-Weh Pii'raate
Yuue-

Z

Zadock Pratt
Zaïda
Zargon Morfoauf
zeppelin
Zika
Zomboy
Zomby
zonked out
ZZYZX
ZzzzZZzz z zZ zZ
ZZz Zzzzz z z
zZZzzzZZZzZzZzzzZ
ZZz Z zZzzzZZZzz
zz
ZZZzZzzZZZzzzZZZ
zZzzzZZZzZZzzzzZZ
zzzZZZzzZzzzzz z Z
zZ ZZZZZZZzz Z z
ZzZZZZ ZZ Z zz
ZZZ

CPSIA information can be obtained
at www.ICGtesting.com
Printed in the USA
LVHW092228190221
679411LV00001B/11